MUSHROOMS

Text by Mirko Svrček

BLITZ EDITIONS

Text by Mirko Svrček
Translated by Daniela Coxon and Marie Hejlová
Photographs by Ladislav a Zdeněk Drahokoupil (294), Ladislav Hagara (124),
Jiří Baier (29), Jaroslav Klán (4)
Line drawings by Bohumil Vančura

Designed and produced by Aventinum Publishing House, Prague, Czech Republic
This English edition published 1999 by Blitz Editions,
an imprint of Bookmart Ltd.
Registered Number 2372865
Trading as Bookmart Limited
Desford Road, Enderby, Leicester LE9 5AD

ISBN 1-85605-445-4
Printed in the Czech Republic by Polygrafia, a.s., Prague
3/07/21/51-02

CONTENTS

THE MORPHOLOGY OF FUNGI

Fungi are thallophytes that have no green-plant pigment (chlorophyll), their cells possess a true nucleus, and they reproduce by spores. Being incapable of the photosynthetic assimilation usual in green plants, they derive organic substances from the bodies of other organisms, living or dead; this way of obtaining nourishment is described as heterotrophic. The fungal body (thallus) is either a single cell or a threadlike structure (hypha). A large number of branching hyphae together constitute the mycelium which gives rise to usually multiform spore-producing cells. Spores are either uni- or multicellular. In most types of fungi, spore-producing cells (basidia, asci, conidiophores) form a part of a special structure made up of hyphal tissue and called the fruit body (sporocarp). Although the fruit bodies are given to extraordinary variation in shape, size and colouring, these do remain fairly constant in individual fungus groups, and so are useful distinguishing characteristics. The same applies to spores. It is exactly the internal and external morphology of fruit bodies, the morphology of spores and the way in which the latter are reproduced that provide the principles underlying the systematic classification of fungi. In this book fungus fruit bodies are classified according to their similarities as well as according to features considered as a manifestation of their affinity.

The simplest types of fungi possess a unicellular, filamentous, branching thallus whose cytoplasm contains a great number of nuclei with no partitions (septa) to divide them; this is the type of thallus encountered in true molds (Phycomycetes). Characteristic of more developed fungi is the presence of septa dividing the mycelial hyphae into a multitude of segments.

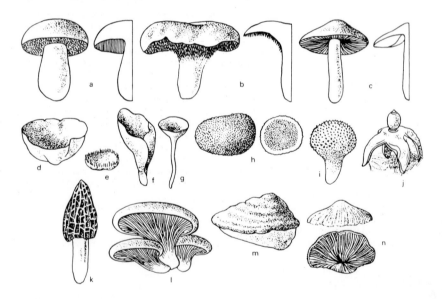

1) Various shapes of fruit bodies: **a** – fruit body of Boletaceae differentiated into a cap and a stipe; **b** – fruit body of Hydnaceae with a spiny hymenophore on the underside of the cap; **c** – fruit body of gill fungi with gills on the underside of the cap; **d** – patelliform fruit body (apothecium) of *Peziza*; **e** – patelliform fruit body ciliate (hirsute) in the margin and on the outer surface (genus *Scutellinia*); **f** – upright apothecium in *Otidea*, open on one side; **g** – cup-shaped apothecium of *Microstoma* possessing a long stem; **h** – tuberous fruit body of *Elaphomyces*, its cross section on the right; **i** – fruit body of a puffball (*Lycoperdon*); **j** – fruit body of an earthstar (*Geastrum*); **k** – fruit body of a morel (*Morchella*); **l** – fruit body of a still fungus with a lateral stipe (*Pleurotus*); **m** – fruit body of a stipeless polypore, laterally attached to the substrate; **n** – cap-shaped, stipeless fruit body with a gilled hymenophore (*Schizophyllum*), viewed from above and from bellow.

Under specific conditions the fungi produce sporiferous cells. In primitive types these sporiferous cells may arise directly from the mycelium. In other fungi, fruit bodies are the first to develop and subsequently to originate spore-bearing cells.

The fruit body is an extraordinarily multiform structure in its dimensions (ranging from microscopic sizes up to the size of several tens of centimetres) and also in its shape and colouring. The fruit body of simpler forms may be nothing but a little ball of hyphae entwining the asci. In Ascomycetes the fruit body is either globular, permanently closed (in which case it is known as the cleistothecium – e.g. in mildew, Erysiphales), or it opens either through a regular pore (as does the perithecium of flask fungi – Deuteromycetes) or irregularly. Finally the apothecium, the fruit body characteristic of the Discomycetes, is a more or less open, cup-shaped or discoid fruit body.

In view of the aim and limited scope of this book we shall deal only with the morphology of fruit bodies of higher fungi (Macromycetes). Here we meet with two basic fruit-body types determined by the location of the spore-bearing tissue. In the first case the spore-bearing tissue is situated inside the fruit body which is often globular in shape, as for example in the stomach fungi (Gasteromycetes); such a fruit body is described as being angiocarpous. In the second case the sporiferous part of the fruit body is laid out either over its entire surface or only over a limited part of it; this is a gymnocarpous fruit body encountered in all the other Basidiomycetes. In gill fungi (Agaricales) and boleti (Boletales), as well as in non-gilled fungi (Aphyllophorales) and some disc fungi (Discomycetes) we may come across two types of gymnocarpous fruit bodies:

1. Resupinate fruit bodies are produced, for example, by *Tomentella* and numerous non-gilled fungi, such as *Peniophora*. They form more or less conspicuous layers with either indistinct or sharply delimited margins, of various consistency (floccose, felted, cobwebby, membranous, coriaceous), usually very thin but in some cases several millimetres thick. Basidia, as a rule, are arranged into a hymenium covering the entire upper surface of the fruit body; on the substrate it is often turned downwards, to the ground. Resupinate fruit bodies may be found on the underside of dropped branches and uprooted trunks. Sometimes a tendency to produce lateral caps or forms with a partially recurved or elevated margin can be observed.

2. Upright fruit bodies occur both in the Basidiomycetes and in some Discomycetes. The hymenium covers either the entire external surface or only its upper part (for example in the Clavariaceae). The most developed type is a fruit body differentiated into a stem or stipe (stipes) and a cap (pileus). Most gill fungi and boleti, as well as some tooth-fungi belong to this group. The hymenophore, i.e. the part of the fruit body bearing the hymenium, is usually confined to the underside of the cap. Stipeless fruit bodies, attached to the substrate either dorsally or laterally, occur in some genera of gill fungi (for example *Crepidotus*) and in a great many polypore species (Polyporaceae, Poriaceae).

The hymenophore takes different forms: it is either completely smooth or variously corrugated (veined, wrinkled), or assumes the shape of spines, gills or tubes. All of these forms occur in all the types of fruit bodies referred to above.

The cap and the stipe are also multiform. The cap often changes its shape in the course of the gradual development of the fruit body from youth to old age, and is, moreover, subjected to intraspecific variability, i.e. the caps of single fungi belonging to the same species are not exactly the same. Gills (lamellae) play an important part in classifying and identifying fungi. The manner of their attachment

2) **a** – Septate hyphae without clamp connections, **b** – hyphae with clamp connections, **c** – part of fruit-body tissue from the stipe surface of a russula; clavate dermatocystidia in the upper part, globose spherocystidia lower down, lactifers scattered among normal cylindrical hyphae are dark-coloured, **d** – sclerotium of *Claviceps purpurea*, giving rise to pedicellate stromata. Perithecia protruding above the surface only by their verruciform ostioles are embedded in their stilbeous terminal part.

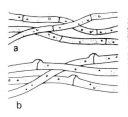

3) Various forms of the hymenophore: **a** – smooth (resupinate); **b** – irregularly reticulate, lacunar to faveolate; **c** – spiniform; **d** – gilled (attachment of gills to the stipe); **e** – tubiform (view of tube pores in the vicinity of the stipe); **f** – in the form of irregular, wavy, richly anastomosed gill folds.

to the stipe is of importance. This characteristic appears most clearly in the longitudinal section through the fresh fruit body, preferably a young and undamaged one – in older specimens it is not always possible to discover how the gills are attached. Of no less significance is the colouring of the gills which changes with the aging of the fruit body. As it matures the fruit body's colouring is affected by the colour of the spores ripening on the basidia which are sometimes produced in quantities so large that they cover the entire gill surface as a white or variously coloured powder. The same applies to the tubes of Boletales and to hymenophores of other fungi. Although nowadays the colouring of the spore print is no longer considered a principal classification criterium of higher fungi, it continues to be of major importance in determining the species.

The cap cuticle provides a great number of important and constant characteristics. Its properties: separability, sliminess, viscosity, dryness, fibrousness, scaliness, etc. are determined by its microscopic structure. More detailed information is given in the chapter dealing with fungi under the microscope. The most conspicuous feature is the colouring of the cuticle – it is the first to attract attention. However, the specification of colours is a highly subjective matter. A certain degree of objectivity may be reached by comparing the colours of the fruit body with printed colour tables (known as chromotaxes) where the colours are arranged according to a certain system and numbered, and eventually named. Several such chromotaxes have been worked out – most of them, however, are inaccessible to non-specialists.

4) Various shapes of the cap: **a** – slightly convex; **b** – flatly expanded (applanate); **c** – obtusely umbonate at the centre; **d** – acutely mucronate (tipped with a sharp wart); **e** – depressed; **f** – deeply infundibuliform; **g** – conical; **h** – campanulate (bell-shaped), radially striate up to the centre; **i** – laterally attached polypore cap in cross-section; **j** – section through a semiresupinate cap (in some polypores).

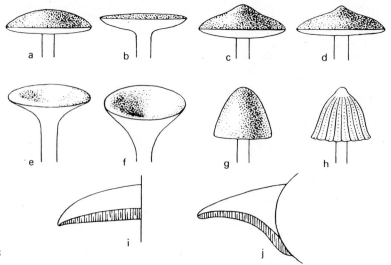

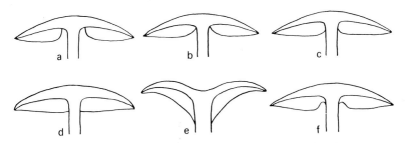

5) Attachment of gills to the stipe in gill-bearing fungi (schematic sections through the cap):
a – remote; **b** – free; **c** – adnexed; **d** – adnate; **e** – deeply decurrent or arcuate-decurrent; **f** – sinuate and attached by a tooth (or decurrent by a tooth).

For example, one of the most accomplished ones, repeatedly cited in all fundamental mycological works, is Ridgeway R., *Colour Standards and Colour Nomenclature*, published in 1912. In other chromotaxes exactly those hues are often lacking which most frequently appear on fungus fruit bodies, i.e. brown, yellow and red. In most cases, the colour table attached to Moser's key *Die Röhrlinge und Blätterpilze*, 1978, may adequately be used, though to a limited extent.

In gill fungi and boleti, quite young fruit bodies are often enclosed in a cover called a velum. This cover is of two types: the universal veil (*velum universale* or *velum generale*), and the partial veil (cobwebby veil or cortina – *velum partiale*). The former deposits scabby remains on the surface of the cap and a volva on the stipe base of a fully developed fruit body, while the latter connects the cap margin with the stipe and its remnants may be found both in the marginal zone of the cap and in the basal portion of the stipe; also the ring encircling the upper part of the stipe belongs to them. The heterogeneous character of the velum, ranging from fine filaments to a hard membranous cover, makes it essential to examine both quite young and fully developed fruit bodies in identifying some genera (for example *Cortinarius*).

The flesh is of various consistency – it may be very friable, pomaceously brittle, fleshy, watery, succulent, dry, fribrillose, coriaceous, tough or woody. When cut or broken, a number of significant features may be seen of which the most relevant is the colour change which may sometimes be different in the cap and in the stipe, while in the stipe differences may in turn prevail in the colouring of the basal portion and of the other parts. Sometimes the context exudes latex, a colourless or milky liquid whose colouring is either persistent or changes on exposure to air. No less important is the taste of the context (tasting belongs to the indispensable diagnostic procedures in identifying fungi). A discussion of smells and odours emitted by fruit bodies could fill a chapter by itself. There are many of them, and they are often compared to the well-known, as well as to the less usual, smells characteristic of other organisms, plants, animals, or chemical compounds. Their evaluation is often largely subjective, yet the

6) Various shapes of the basal part of the stipe in gill fungi: **a** – bearing annular stripes; **b** – with a ring in the upper part of the bulbous basal portion; **c** – with a fusoid extension radicating in the ground; **d** – globularly enlarged; **e** – thickened and tapering to a beet-like extension; **f** – with a high coriaceous or membranous sheath; **g** – with a circumscissile or marginate-depressed bulb.

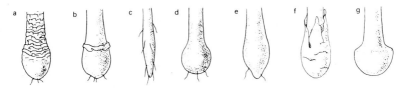

smells are so specific in the individual species that a good expert is in a position to identify a fungus even from small fragments of the fruit body on the basis of their characteristic smell only. Some fungi (e.g. the tooth fungi) maintain their specific smell even as exsiccations (dried specimens).

FUNGI UNDER THE MICROSCOPE

In identifying and studying fungi we cannot do without a high-quality microscope equipped with an immersion lens. Of course we can distinguish several hundred fungus species by the naked eye, but this has its limitations and in a great many cases the identification remains questionable without confirmation by microscopic analysis. Consequently, the confirmed enthusiast should consider whether to invest time and money in the use of a microscope. If so, the fascinating world of the microcosm, lavishly abounding in extraordinary and aesthetically impressive forms, opens before us. As well as the current set of eyepieces and lenses, an ocular micrometer is also indispensable for measuring the size of spores, hyphae, hymenial and other elements.

The mycelium (the actual fungus body) is a relatively uniform structure composed of long cylindrical, septate, colourless or coloured hyphae, sometimes provided with clamp connections. The hyphal walls are smooth, and may be thin or thick, and sometimes encrusted.

The differentiation of individual organs of the fungus body becomes plain only in fruit bodies. The most important organ is the hymenophore, whose internal structure remains constant in the individual genera. It is best observed on the tangential section across the gills, obtained manually with the help of a razor blade. With a little feeling and patience we are sure to succeed in selecting from among a larger number of available sections at least one sufficiently thin to enable us to observe the structure of the trama in a microscopic mount. The trama assumes four basic forms: regular, irregular, bilateral and inverse. The details clearly appear in Fig. 8.

The hymenium is a spore-producing layer composed either of fertile basidia only, or of basidia and sterile, multiform cells. These are cystidia of various types which are longer than basidia, of various shapes, with a bare or encrusted surface, thin- or thick-walled, often growing out of the deeper layers of the gill tissue. The cystidia situated on the gill edge, the so-called cheilocystidia, are frequently arranged into continuous rows, sometimes different in colour from the gill face; such an edge, if observed with a lens, is finely lacerate or ciliate. In some cases the cheilocystidia are filled with coloured pigment. The cystidia present at the gill face are termed pleurocystidia and may be different from cheilocystidia in shape. Gloeocystidia (occurring more frequently in Aphyllophorales) are characterized by a granular or light-refracting content, somewhat oily in appearance. Basidíoles (sterile cells similar to basidia in both shape and size) are sometimes present among them; if their shape is different, they are termed cystidioles. While in Agaricales and Boletales the shape of the basidia is, in the main, uniform (usually clavate), in Aphyllophorales it is considerably diversified and plays an important part in their taxanomic classification.

7) Veils of gill-fungi fruit bodies: **a** – development of the sheath and warts from the universal veil (*velum universale*) and of the ring on the stipe from the partial veil (*velum partiale*) in amanitas (two young fruit bodies, one mature fruit body; **b** – one young and one mature fruit body with a developed partial veil leaving a ring on the stipe; **c** – partial veil developed only as a fibrous cobweb (*cortina*); in the youngest fruit bodies it connects the cap margin with the stipe surface and covers the gills, later on it remains in the upper part of the stipe as a fibrous ring or as single filaments.

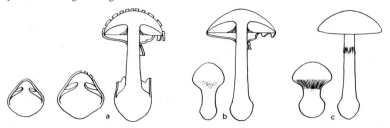

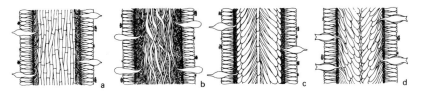

8) Gill-trama types (tangential section): **a** – regular; **b** – irregular; **c** – bilateral; **d** – inverse; the layer of smaller cells bellow the basidia (forming a continuous layer – the hymenium) is termed subhymenium; cystidia are protruding among the basidia.

At the basidial apex there are usually four apicules (sterigmata) each of which bears a single spore; basidia with two sterigmata are relatively common, while those having only one or alternatively having more than four sterigmata are rather rare. Developmentally lower types of Basidiomycetes have septate basidia (divided either by transverse walls or lengthwise, by two walls perpendicular to each other), or basidia separating into two branches. Siderophilous basidia are typical of some genera of Tricholomataceae – *Lyophyllum*, *Tephrocybe*, etc.; their plasma contains granules staining black when exposed to ferric acetocarmine.

Trama in the broader sense of the word is the tissue of the entire fruit body, whereas in the narrower sense it implies the gills, cap and stipe but excluding the surface tissues. The context itself, the fruit-body trama, is formed by a system of hyphae of the following three types: generative, binding and skeletal. Most common are fruit bodies consisting of generative (so-called basic) hyphae only; they are ramified, septate, and with or without clamp connections – this is known as the monomitic system. If, besides these, another type of hyphae is present – either binding hyphae (which are more or less thick-walled, strongly fruticose, aseptate and lacking clamp connections), or skeletal hyphae (these are thick-walled, unbranched, long, aseptate) – this is known as the dimitic system. If all the three hyphal types are present in the tissue, they constitute the trimitic system. The fruit-body tissue of some fungus genera contains lactiferous tubes. These are very long, sinuous, usually aseptate hyphae filled with thick plasma of a frequently lacteal character, such as latex in the *Lactarius* species.

The context of fungi of the genera *Lactarius* and *Russula* contains – besides threadlike filaments and lactiferous tubes – clusters of globular cells, the so-called spherocystidia, conditioning the peculiar pomaceous brittleness of the flesh of these fungi. Of particular importance among the surface tissues is the cap cuticle which consists of one or more layers. The outermost layer of a multistratous cuticle is the epicutis, the layer between the epicutis and the cap context is known as the hypoderm or subcutis. If the cuticle is made up of clavate to globose cells, it is known as the hymeniform cuticle.

9) Tangential section through a part of gills in a russula: the hymenium contains infertile clavate basidia (basidioles) on the one hand, fertile basidia with four sterigmata and warty spores at their apices on the other hand, and, moreover, cystidia exceeding the basidia in length. The gill tissue is composed of relatively large subglobose cells (spherocystidia), cylindrical hyphae and densely granular, long lactifers extending in some places as far as the hymenium.

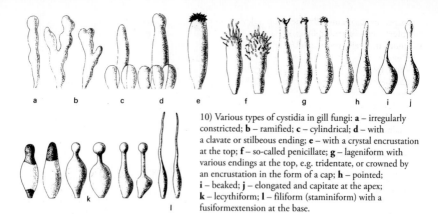

10) Various types of cystidia in gill fungi: **a** – irregularly constricted; **b** – ramified; **c** – cylindrical; **d** – with a clavate or stilbeous ending; **e** – with a crystal encrustation at the top; **f** – so-called penicillate; **g** – lageniform with various endings at the top, e.g. tridentate, or crowned by an encrustation in the form of a cap; **h** – pointed; **i** – beaked; **j** – elongated and capitate at the apex; **k** – lecythiform; **l** – filiform (staminiform) with a fusiformextension at the base.

The colouring of fruit bodies depends upon physical processes taking place within the fruit bodies on the one hand, and upon the presence of pigments (whose distribution also has taxonomic significance) on the other. Intracellular pigments are present either in the plasma or in vacuoles, pigments are also in hyphal walls and in intercellular spaces. The white colour is caused by the air filling intercellular spaces; if these are filled with water, the white colour becomes glassy and colourless (hyaline).

11) Various types of spores and ornamentation: **a** – globose; **b** – subglobose, obliquely extending into an apiculus at the base; **c** – ellipsoid; **d** – cylindrical; **e** – fusiform; **f** – angular; **g** – echinulate; **h** – verrucose; **i** – with a pectinate ornamentation; **j** – with a reticulate ornamentation; **k** – tuberculate; **l** – ovoid without an apiculum; **m** – obtusely fusiform; **n** – cylindrical; **o** – divided by transverse and longitudinal septa (so called muriform); **p** – allantoid; **r** – filiform with transverse septa.

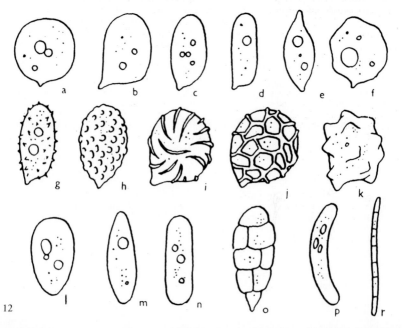

Spores are taxonomically the most relevant and constant characteristics. They are extremely multiform, uni- or multicellular, colourless or exhibiting a whole scale of colours, up to black. To be examined in detail, spores should always be observed under an immersion lens, at first in a colourless medium in water, in a 10-per cent solution of potash lye (KOH), in ammonia, etc.; another mount is coloured by Melzer's reagent, cotton blue, or another colouring matter. Details not always clearly discernible in a cursory inspection of a microscopic mount are subjected to thorough examination: spore-wall thickness, presence of the apicule, shape and size of the germ pore, ornamentation of the spore wall, presence of the suprahilar disc or depression. One of the most significant discoveries that helped clarify the inter-relationships among gill fungi as well as among other fungus groups was the ascertainment of spore-wall amyloidity. Amyloidity is determined by Melzer's reagent with the aid of which the walls of spores or hyphae change either to some shade of blue (amyloid reaction), or to yellow-brown, red-brown or purple-brown hues (dextrinoid reaction). A more recent discovery is cyanophilia: here the spore or hyphal walls turn blue when touched with cotton-blue solution.

Only a brief mention will be made here of the disc fungi, whose larger representatives can often be come across by a mushroom-picker. The spore-bearing layer of their fruit body (apothecium) is composed of asci and paraphyses. The asci are cylindrical or clavate in shape and, as a rule, contain eight spores (ascospores) which are released either through a pore in the tip of the ascus, or by the opening of a lid. In some genera the ascus walls are amyloid. Paraphyses, i.e. sterile filaments occurring among the asci, are often pigmented and consequently affect the colouring of the thecium (hymenium). In general, what has been said about spores of the basidiomycetes applies also to ascospores. The context of the apothecium – which is either directly attached to the substrate or seated on a sterile stem or stipe – has a relatively simple structure and its external layer bears various growths, such as bristles or hairs.

REPRODUCTION OF FUNGI

Fungi reproduce in two ways: sexually and asexually. Both of them are commonly encountered. Sexual reproduction is generally regarded as a union of two sexually differentiated nuclei, e.g. in spores. The germinating spores from a unisexual mycelium (primary mycelium), consisting of hyphae with uninucleate cells. Each of these cells contains a nucleus with a certain number of chromosomes. The primary mycelium may go on growing for a very long time without forming any sex organs. If two uninucleate, sexually differentiated mycelia meet, the plasmas of the conjugating cells unite into a single binucleate cell – the dicaryon. The dicaryon grows into hyphae made up of binucleate cells, into the secondary mycelium. Even this mycelium can take a very long time to grow; under suitable external conditions, however, it gives rise to fruit bodies. Hence it follows that fruit bodies are composed of hyphae with binucleate cells.

12) Various types of basidia: **a** – unicellular basidium (holobasidium) with four sterigmata at the apex; **b** – basidium with three transverse septa (phragmobasidium), a single sterigma grows out at the side of each of its cells; **c** – basidium forked at the top into two branches terminating in a sterigma; **d** – basidium divided by four longitudinal walls down to the base (side and top views); **e** – bisporous holobasidium with two sterigmata; **f** – a section of the hymenium with basidia and a cystidium; **g** – ascus with spores and paraphysis.

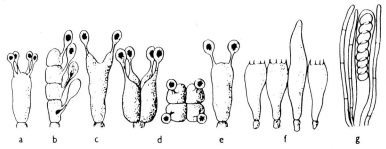

a   b   c   d   e   f   g

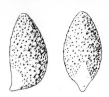

13) A spore of *Galerina* with a verrucose ornamentation and a suprahilar plage in the vicinity of the apiculus; on the left, the side view of the spore (with a discernible depression just above the hilar appendage), and its front view.

The fusion of the two dicaryotic nuclei takes place only at the hyphal end, in terminal cells transformed into basidia or asci. The single nucleus arisen through the association of two dicaryotic nuclei has a double number of chromosomes (2n), that is, a double amount of nuclear matter and thus of hereditary information. It is only through the subsequent reduction division that the number of chromosomes is lowered to the original state (n). These nuclei give rise to spores – basidiospores on basidia, ascospores in asci. Even though, of course, there are exceptions to this scheme, it is sufficient for a basic understanding of the principle of sexual reproduction in fungi.

Asexual reproduction is never preceded by a fusion of the nuclei of two cells. Its simplest form involves the decomposition of the mycelium into simple fragments termed arthrospores. Another form is the abstriction of independent germ spores (conidia) from specialized hyphae (conidiophores). The conidia vary in shape, size and colouring; they may be unicellular or multicellular. Chlamydospores are thick-walled spores developed from mycelial cells. Their function is that of resting cells capable of surviving long-lasting unfavourable living conditions. Cells giving rise to asexual spores are generally designated as conidiogenous. In classifying the conidial stages of fungi, a great many of which occur independently and are included in the subsidiary class of imperfect fungi (Deuteromycetes, formerly also *Fungi imperfecti*), particular importance is attributed to the manner in which asexual spores are formed.

Spores originating in any of these ways are produced by fungi in such enormous quantities that they not only populate the whole biosphere of our planet but can be found even in the atmosphere. As spores the fungi are omnipresent, and most of them seem to be endowed with the capacity to withstand unfavourable influences and to remain in a latent stage without losing their viability. This overproduction of spores is a necessary precondition for the survival of the species.

SOME POINTS OF INTEREST IN THE LIFE OF FUNGI

The life of fungi belongs to the most interesting chapters of mycology. Heterotrophic nourishment, which represents the principal characteristic of this huge group of organisms nowadays considered as an independent kingdom besides green plants and animals, has called forth a number of divergent

14) Reproduction in Basidiomycetes: **A** – cross section through a tube of a bolete; **B** – formation of spores on a basidium; **C** – development of a fruit body from the mycelium; **a** – hymenium; **b** – primary mycelium; **c** – secondary mycelium; **d** – basidium; **e** – sterigma; **f** – sexually differentiated spores.

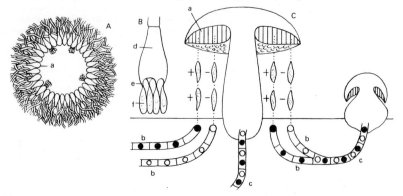

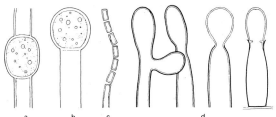

15) Development of asexual spores: **a, b** – thick-walled chlamydospores (**a** – intercalary; **b** – terminal); **c** – hypha subjected to chain-like disintegration into immobile spores; **d** – various ways of the development of conidia.

a   b   c   d

phenomena and properties. Saprophytism and parasitism, two large categories differing in their relation to the environment from which fungi obtain organic substances necessary for building up their fruit bodies, assert themselves in a characteristic manner in the development of fungi; in the remote past, they gave rise to innumerable fungus forms differing not only in shape but also physiologically and genetically. Their classification is a task to be coped with by mycological taxonomy.

Saprophytic fungi, including the greater part of the so-called large fungi (Macromycetes), as well as a good many other fungi, live in their mycelial form in an environment composed of dead plant and animal remains at different stages of decomposition. Their hyphae penetrate through the soil, humus and detritus, through the wood of decaying tree trunks, stumps and branches, or live in the network of withering leaves, needles, herb stems, grass stalks, etc. Many saprophytic fungi are bound by their way of life to a specific and often limited environment.

A generally widespread phenomenon is the symbiosis (co-existence) of fungi with the roots of higher vascular plants, less frequently with ferns and bryophytes; it is termed mycorrhiza. The mycelium either clothes the roots only externally (ectotrophic mycorrhiza), or penetrates inside the root tissue (endotrophic mycorrhiza). The ectotrophic mycorrhiza is easily discernible by the naked eye: the little roots are usually short but thick and often forked so that they may resemble corals in appearance. The mycelial hyphae envelop the roots like a continuous covering with protruding short surface excrescences. The endotrophic mycorrhiza, on the other hand, does not appear on the outside because the hyphae pervade the intercellular spaces of the root network. This type of mycorrhiza is more common than the former. The fungi living in mycorrhizal dependence upon the roots of live trees are not easily raised in pure cultures in a laboratory, and it is only rarely that they may be compelled to form fruit bodies. The cultivation of other saprophytic fungi – particularly lignicolous ones – presents no great problems.

The relationship between the two organisms, the green plant and the fungus, has been and continues to be subjected to a great many studies because of the considerable practical importance of the problem area concerned. Fungi of most various systematic groups live in mycorrhizal association. Mycorrhiza is particularly frequent in Basidiomycetes, but also exists in other groups (e.g. in moulds and ascomycetes). A single tree may be found to live in this kind of symbiotic relationship with several fungus species simultaneously – as a rule, however, only one of them produces fruit bodies (often only after the tree has attained a certain age). This gives rise to the heterogeneity and variegation of the mycoflora of forest growths, whose specific structure changes with the age of the forest. Mycorrhizal fungi are indispensable for the life of some plants, e.g. for the seedlings of numerous orchids growing in free nature.

Another remarkable phenomenon is the symbiosis of fungi with animals. Termites (Isoptera) establish and grow in their nests cultures of fungi whose mycelium produces spherical bodies serving the termites as food. Various termite species grow various species of fungi as, for instance, fungi of the genus *Termitomyces* belonging to the Trichomataceae family, whose large fruit bodies growing out of termite nests are collected by the local inhabitants for culinary purposes. Microscopic fungi are cultivated as foodstuffs by ants inhabiting trunks and stumps; the same is done by bark-beetle larvae (Ipidae) growing the mycelium of the so-called ambrosial fungi in their galleries. An independent group of the

16) Fruticose and bulbous mycorrhiza on a pine-tree root.

15

microscopic fungi Laboulbeniomycetes lives on the body surface of most various beetles, especially of those inhabiting a relatively damp environment. They do not seem to do any harm to their hosts.

In the remote past, a close co-existence of fungal hyphae and algae gave rise to complex organisms called lichens (Lichenes). Owing to the fact that the fungal component of the lichenous thallus is most frequently represented by an ascomycete, this group of lichens is called Ascolichenes (also lichenized Ascomycetes); as fruit bodies they developed apothecia or perithecia. A much smaller part of the hyphae involved here belongs to the Basidiomycetes – this group of lichens is called Basidiolichenes (or lichenized Basidiomycetes). Some mycologists now regard various gill-fungi species as lichenized Basidiomycetes, although their fruit bodies differ from those of other gill fungi in nothing but the presence of algae in the tissue of some part of the thallus.

After exhausting the nutritional substances in one place, the mycelium of some fungi starts spreading in stripes or in more or less regular circles into the neighbourhood, and its growth in a particular direction manifests itself also by the development of fruit bodies. This is most conspicuous in the so-called 'fairy rings' formed by fungi of the genera *Ramaria, Hydnum, Clitocybe, Tricholoma, Marasmius*. The shape of the rings depends not only on the nutrient content of the soil but also on the layout of tree roots, and it may also be affected by the pattern of water dropping from tree crowns. The radial growth of the mycelium can also be seen in the fungi raised in pure cultures on agar soils.

To a considerable extent, saprophytic fungi participate in the decomposition of cellulose in the wood pervaded by the mycelium which not infrequently causes its characteristic disintegration (for example, cubiform red rot, fibrous white rot, etc.). Some saprophytic wood-destroying fungi also pass over to weakened but still living trees, speeding up their death; consequently they appear as occasional facultative parasites and are called saproparasites. They enter the trunks either through frost cracks or through scars left by broken-off branches, eventually by injuries connected with wood production. The wood infested with fungi sometimes acquires a specific colour. For example, the beautifully green-coloured wood of beeches or other deciduous trees is pervaded by the mycelium of the minute disc fungus *Chlorosplenium aeruginosum* secreting xylochloric acid insoluble in water. Another well-known feature is the phosphorescence of wood created – besides by bacteria – by the mycelium of the Honey Fungus (*Armillaria mellea*). Fungi whose fruit bodies give off a bluish sheen visible by night are widespread in the tropics. The species *Omphalotus olearius* with fluorescent gills, growing in southern Europe, belongs to this group.

Other saprophytic fungi have become specialized on ecologically narrowly confined environments and are never found elsewhere. Anthracophilous fungi live exclusively on burned-over soils or in old fireplaces, in fact wherever wood was burned and where, for some time at least, a suitable microclimate (soil humidity, shade) exists. In such an environment, the gradual succession of individual species can best be examined. As a rule, one of the pioneer species is the disc fungus *Pyronema confluens*, which is minute but still conspicuous due to its proliferation; it may often be seen covering the burned soil with extensive, pink-red layers of its innumerable apothecia. Somewhat later it is replaced by other representatives of disc fungi (*Geopyxis carbonaria*) and various cup fungi (*Peziza subviolacea, P. echinospora*). The last ones to grow here, when the burned-over areas are already overgrowing with mosses or liverworts, are the gill fungi *Pholiota carbonaria, Tephrocybe carbonaria*, and others.

A characteristic fungus community grows on excrements of various animals. These fungi, termed coprophilous, occur in great abundance and probably come from all fungus groups. The most conspicuous among them are members of the genus *Coprinus* whose short-lived, quickly developing fruit bodies are very common indeed. Coprophilous fungi can be successfully cultivated and studied in laboratory conditions on excrements collected in nature and kept in a moist but airy environment. They are therefore often raised as models for physiological and genetic experiments.

Some fungi are parasites, obtaining their nourishment from the bodies of other living organisms, while the host upon which they live is at a disadvantage, being more or less damaged or gradually completely destroyed by the fungus. Most of them are microscopic fungi surpassing the saprophytes in the number of species. Rusts (Uredinales) and smuts (Ustilaginales) are large groups of exclusively parasitic fungi; their economic relevance is due to the serious damage many of them cause in the tissues of cultivated plants. Rusts either develop on a single host, or change their hosts in which they successively produce various stages. Other fungi live inside their host's tissue as endoparasites, while ectoparasites live on its surface, sending within only their mycelium. There are many parasites among the

Ascomycetes (e.g. mildew – Erysiphales) and Pyrenomycetes. The proportion of parasites among higher fungi is sunstantially lower, but cases of a large fungus parasitizing another large fungus are known. By way of example let us mention *Xerocomus parasiticus* living on *Scleroderma citrinum*, or *Volvariella surrecta* parasitizing the fruit bodies of *Lepista nebularis*. Species belonging to the genus *Nyctalis* are commonly found growing on *Russula; Cordyceps ophioglossoides* lives on the subterranean fruit bodies of *Elaphomyces*. Other numerous representatives of the genus *Cordyceps* are widespread, especially in the tropics, and parasitize insects.

There also exist huge numbers of microscopic fungi parasitizing other fungi. In autumn the fruit bodies of some boleti are covered with conspicuous golden-yellow, farinaceous layers of the hyphomycete *Sepedonium chrysospermum*: this is the conidial stage of *Apiocrea chrysosperma*. Fine moulds of the genus *Spinellus* often live as parasites on the caps of fungi of the genus *Mycena*, and brown, matted-tomentose covers of the mould *Sporodinia* occur on the caps of various other gill fungi. However, parasites also have their parasites – for example, the rust *Puccinia* is attacked by the coelymacete *Darluca filum*.

An ecologically specific group are fungi confined to an aquatic environment. Most abundant are the representatives of water moulds (Blastocladiales, Saprolegniales, etc.) living on decaying organic matter submerged in water. Some of them even parasitize aquatic animals. Still smaller aquatic moulds live as parasites on pollen grains fallen into the water, or within the cells of water algae. Rotten leaves lying in shallow and clear water currents are inhabited by a whole community of microscopic Hyphomycetes producing conidia of extraordinary shapes. Larger fungi growing on decaying wood logs and branches submerged in water include representatives of Pyrenomycetes as well as some Discomycetes. A quite specialized group consists of some Pyrenomycetes growing on wood submerged in sea water.

Both parasitic and saprophytic fungi trigger off various chemical changes in the substrate or in their host's body through the operation of their enzymes (ferments). The most important of these, which are most utilized by man, are enzymes evoking alcoholic fermentation. Also amylolytic (disstatic) ferments transforming starch into sugar are generally applied.

Developmentally a very old group of organisms, fungi are at home almost all over the Earth, and their spores are practically omnipresent in the atmosphere. This of course does not imply that the distribution of all the species is worldwide (cosmopolitan). Many species of fungi have an extensive range of distribution, but far more species are confined to specific, often considerably restricted, localities. The occurrence of such fungi is conditioned not only by the presence of an adequate substrate or host, but also by climatic factors, by the underlying geological stratum and its chemical composition, etc. Furthermore, the structure of the mycoflora of each region is the result of a long-lasting developmental process. While the genera and species of fungi growing in many European countries are almost the same, in North America, where the number of species is considerably higher, only about one third of the total corresponds to European species. One reason for this is the specific abundance of woody plants and herbs in North America which have affected the structure of fungus species in the course of their long-term development. While the temperate belts of both hemispheres are characterized by a predominance of saprophytic fungi, in the tropical regions there is an exceeding abundance of microscopic parasitic fungi. It should be emphasized that not all the parasites closely dependent on their host are present in every locality inhabited by that host: their occurence is often substantially restricted, or they are known from isolated finds only; they may also pass over to substitute hosts. As regards the elevation above the sea level, in comparison with other vascular plants no striking differences appear in the fungi; yet a great many species occur exclusively in high mountains (even above the timberline), others again grow at lower elevations only.

Adventive fungus species are brought from their original homes to remote regions, e.g. by the action of man. A classical example is the transfer of some stinkhorns (Phallaceae) from North America and Australia to Europe.

THE IMPORTANCE OF FUNGI FOR MAN AND THE LIVING ENVIRONMENT

In nature we come across fungi at every step, without being aware of it. They are omnipresent just like bacteria or viruses, but are usually invisible since the spores, wherein genetic information specific for every species is coded, do not exceed microscopic dimensions. They move about in the atmosphere just like the other aeroplankton, being particularly abundant in its low-lying strata and in environments where, under certain conditions, they are capable of reproducing and renewing their vitality. Most people are acquainted with fungi only in the form of their fruit bodies which have always aroused interest of the observers of nature by their general appearance, so different from other plants. Yet these conspicuous fruit bodies are formed only by a small proportion of fungi. The other fungi are too minute in size to be discernible without an optical instrument. In nature, both large and microscopic fungi occupy a significant position irreplaceable by any other organisms. An evaluation based on human criteria primarily on sanitary and economic grounds, shows them to include organisms either useful or detrimental to man. The first group comprises fungi of practical use in food industries – for example, the entire fermenting industry depends on the capacity of yeast to transform sugar into alcohol and carbon dioxide. Yeast is used not only in the production of alcoholic beverages but also in the brewing, baking and dairy industries. Cultivated strains not only of yeast but also of other fungi (e.g. species of the genus *Penicillium* in cheese production) have many valuable uses. The discovery of substances with an antibiotic effect resulted in a breakthrough in the therapy of a number of diseases of both man and animals – let us only mention penicillin, a product of one strain of the mould *Penicillium notatum*. In the course of the last decades, numerous other fungi have been subjected to research and further antibiotics have successfully been isolated from some of them.

The tradition of mushroom picking, i.e. of collecting large mushrooms for table use, has developed in many countries of the world. This collector's relation to fungi has given rise to a sporting hobby which brings people into the wood for a certain purpose, and consequently has a recreational significance. A drawback of this hobby, however, is the risk to one's life as shown by the growing number of cases of poisoning by toxic fungus species in connection with the increasing popularization of the collection of edible mushrooms. In some countries, the rising demand for mushrooms is compensated, to a certain extent, by an intensive hotbed production of cultivated Common Field Agarics, as well as by the search for other cultivable species, of which particularly the Oyster Fungus (*Pleurotus ostreatus*) and *Stropharia rugosoannulata* seem to be promising.

Fungi are of invaluable help to anyone capable of benefiting from their biological properties. On the other hand, some of them present themselves as enemies: they infest living organisms, plants, animals, and even Man himself. Fungi parasitizing the human body give rise to mycoses, i.e. often chronic and dangerous diseases of the skin, hair, but also of the whole body. These are usually caused by hyphomycetes, yeast fungi and true moulds. Mycoses show a rising tendency in the recent past, and a long-termed application of antibiotics to combat them leads in turn to the danger of yeast infections. Also the spores of some Hyphomycetes can occasionally penetrate into the respiratory organs and cause health troubles.

A whole plant-protection branch – phytopathology – is concerned with diseases caused by parasitic fungi attacking cultivated vegetables, flowers and crops, as well as fruit-bearing, ornamental and forest trees and shrubs. Let us mention, by way of example, rusts and smuts parasitizing corn, *Phytophthora infestans* causing potato murrain, *Synchytrium endobioticum* causing potato cancer, *Plasmodiophora brassicae* living on the roots of brassicas, mildews *Plasmopara vitticola* and *Sphaerotheca humuli*, and also polyporoses, i.e. diseases in wood caused by pore fungi. In some regions, considerable stretches of forest growths are infested by *Heterobasidion annosus* and by the Honey Fungus (*Armillaria mellea*); the Dry Rot Fungus (*Serpula lacrymans*) can destroy everything made of wood inside houses.

However, the basic importance of fungi rests in their intensive participation in all decomposing processes and other chemical reactions. The decay and putrefaction of organic substances, which are in fact the most important agents in maintaining the natural balance, ensue from the cooperation of bacteria and particularly fungi which, as reductants, turn the accumulated organic compounds into newly utilizable inorganic compounds. Fungi play a role of major importance in the soil. Their mycelium and spores permeate the forest humus, while mycorrhiza often enables woody plants to grow in places where, without the fungi, they could not vegetate. Fungi are present in all ecosystems, both within and outside the forests. They are enormously old organisms that were in existence – together with *Cyanophyta* and algae – as early as the Precambrian era hundreds of millions of years ago. In the course of this tremendously long period they have undergone an unimaginable development about which the recent fungus species, being the last link of a long chain, present an often complexly enciphered evidence. Mycologists, who make painstaking efforts to decode them, observe with anxiety the phenomenon which, in our time, is assuming an almost catastrophic form: the extinction of organisms due to the tempestuous development of industrialization and unmerciful destruction of nature in the name of civilization. Whatever holds for the ever-increasing speed with plant and animal species are nearing their exinction, applies in the same measure to fungi. The number of hithero recognized and described species is estimated to exceed 100,000; according to recent opinion, however, the number of actually existing species is probably 250,000 to 300,000, i.e. approximately the same as that of seed plants. If 40–50 per cent of seed-plant species are to die out by the end of the 20th century, as some scientists assume, it is highly probable that the same number of fungus species will simultaneously disappear from the surface of this planet for ever, since most of them are dependent on the endangered plants. They will disappear – many of them without ever having been discovered, identified, and perhaps also utilized for the benefit of mankind. Thus a deep contradiction has arisen between the law of ethics and the coarsely exploiting interests of Man. A change should be brought about while there is still some grounds for hope.

POISONOUS FUNGI AND THE SYMPTOMS OF POISONING

Numerous fungus species contain substances detrimental to human beings. In the past most fungi were considered poisonous or at least viewed with suspicion, and people preferred to shun them without thinking of using them for food. Later on, however, hand in hand with a more thorough acquaintance with species and progressing mycological knowledge, the assortment of edible and consumable species started to expand. Mushrooming was ardently indulged in several European countries. The popularization of mushrooming was sometimes so inordinate that almost all fungi were declared edible. It was only the growing incidence of cases of poisoning, which frequently proved fatal, that provided a warning signal and again called for increased caution. Nowadays a responsible evaluation of the edibility or toxicity of many fungus species is often problematic, since it comes to light that species formerly currently collected and eaten are less innocent than was previously assumed. Involved here are not only the toxic principles representing the direct cause of poisoning, but also other, largely still unknown toxins which can accumulate in the human body after repeated ingestion of some mushrooms and unfavourably interfere with the activity of various organs, mainly of those belonging to the digestive system.

According to the symptoms or types of toxins concerned, poisoning can roughly be divided into several categories. In each of these we shall confine ourselves to those species of poisonous fungi which come into account as the most frequent cause of poisoning.

1. **Poisoning that damages the liver** is also termed phalloid poisoning. This name is derived from the specific name of the Death Cap – *Amanita phalloides* – which is the most frequent cause of this type of poisoning. The fruit body of the Death Cap contains two groups of poisonous substances (toxins) present in high concentration, namely amatoxins and phallotoxins. Both groups of toxins are also present in the closely related species od the so-called poisonous white amanitas, in *A. verna* and *A. virosa* (Destroying Angel), in concentrations still higher than in the Death Cap. Moreover, they were found in some small *Lepiota* species (*L. helveola, L. scobinella*) as well as in some species of *Galerina*. Phallotoxins are rensponsible for 80–95 per cent of cases of fatal mushroom poisoning and belong to the most insidious poisons as the first symptoms of poisoning appear after a long lapse of time.

Anybody intending to collect edible mushrooms and not willing to confine himself to gathering boleti and chanterelles must inevitably be acquainted with the Death Cap. Although the Death Cap is greatly variable in colour, some of its characteristics are so conspicuous that it can readily be recognized even in case of an atypical colouring. Its toxicity manifests itself after the ingestion of quite a small amount of food prepared of it. One fully developed fruit body was found capable of causing the death of two persons. The first symptoms appear after a relatively long interval (the so-called period of latency), six hours after the ingestion at the earliest (earlier after consuming a raw toadstool), usually in 8–24 hours; sometimes the period of latency is still longer. The first symptoms of poisoning appear as an irritation of the digestive system – intensive vomiting and diarrhoea. These symptoms may last for 48 hours in the course of which the patient suffers great losses of body fluids and mineral substances followed by extreme exhaustion. Cramps in the legs subsequently set in, accompanied by urination disorders which may result in a total stoppage of urine secretion and general apathy, since the organism suffers from poisoning by waste materials it fails to get rid of. The disappearance of diarrhoea and vomiting signals the onset of a short but extremely dangerous period of alleviation which, however, only precedes a further phase characterized by liver-tissue impairment. This period is critical. If sufficiently effective help has not been secured in time, or if the afflicted person has eaten a greater number of fruit bodies, he becomes unconscious and dies on the fifth or sixth day with symptoms of liver failure and sometimes of brain tumescence.

Thirty years ago, up to 80 per cent of those poisoned died after having eaten the Death Cap. Nowadays, when new therapeutic methods are continuously being applied in departmens of intensive care, the death rate has considerably falen and does not exceed 15 per cent. At any rate, phalloid poisoning always seriously endangers life. The therapeutic success attained is due to all who have ventured the long way leading to the identification of toxins contained in the Death Cap and to the discovery and enforcement of new therapeutic procedures.

The first experiments with the Death Cap were carried out as early as 1793 on dogs, but it was not before the 19th century that it was found to contain substances with a hemolytic effect (i.e. causing the lysis of red blood cells), also other toxins were discovered in it later on. Thus both the principal toxis, amanitin and phalloidin, were distinguished. In the thirties of the 20th century, further relevant knowledge was obtained with the aid of chromatographic methods. The formula of phalloidin was published in 1940, the formula of amanitin one year later. Further partial compounds were discoverend in the course of the following years. At present two toxin complexes are distinguished: phallotoxins and amatoxins, differing in chemical composition. Phallotoxins include phalloidin, phalloin, phallisin, phallacin and phallacidin. Amatoxins are marked with Greek letters from alpha to omega; also amanin and the ineffective amanulin belong to them. Most of these substances have also been artificially prepared and some of them are produced synthetically for experiments with laboratory animals. During the experiments a substance was discovered which was called antamanid and is capable of neuralizing the effect of amanitins. 100 g of fresh fungus were found to contain, on the average, 10 mg phalloidin, 8 mg of alpha-amanitin and 5 mg of beta-amanitin, 0.5 mg of gamma-amanitin; all the other toxins and antamanid are present in traces only.

The treatment of poisoning caused by the Death Cap is aimed at the quickest possible elimination of poisonous substances from the blood (still present the 24-36 hours after the ingestion); first of all, however, a stomach rinse is necessary, as well as repeated rinses of intestines, in order to eleminate the extremely toxic spores from the flods of mucous membranes. Then the fluids and mineral substances missing from the patient's body should be supplied, eventually an infusion of sorbite solutions containing large doses of vitamins B and C. In accordance with the values obtained from laboratory tests, large doses of tioctic acid (300, 500 mg or even more per day) are supplied by continuous infusions. In cases of more serious poisoning, when the patient lapses into insensibility or when the poisoning has been diagnosed too late, further treatment in the intensive-care department of the nearest hospital is absolutely essential.

It is often difficult to tell with certainty that the poisoning has actually been caused by the Death Cap; such a diagnosis is conclusive only when fruit-body remnants are found in the organism. Sometimes also the pieces of mushrooms not used in preparing the meal may be helpful. According to T. Wieland and Palysa, the presence of amanitins in any fungus can be ascertained in the following way: a drop of juice is pressed out of the fresh fruit body on a piece of newspaper or on sawdust, or the fungus is cut apart and the section is applied to a piece of paper so that the juice is sucked in. After the spot has been left to dry, hydrochloric acid is dropped on it. If it turns blue, the fungus contains amanitins and hence is deadly poisonous.

Anyone suspected of being poisoned by the Death Cap or other related species must be taken to hospital as quickly as possible – at best to a large hospital equipped with resuscitative aids. Any delay is dangerous. If vomiting, the patient must be given large quantities of liquids to drink (no alcohol or milk!) the best being unsweetened mineral or other water.

Phalloid poisoning may also be caused by some small *Lepiota* species related to *L. helveola* whose toxins are identical to those of the Death Cap. The course of poisoning and its treatment are also the same. (This concerns thermophilic *Lepiota* species which appear more commonly only in some central European regions and in southern Europe.)

Poisoning caused by some *Galerina* species was neglected for a long time, although the first cases were reported as early as 1912 from North America, after the ingestion of *G. autumnalis*. Later on, this and several other – mostly North American – species were found to contain amanitin, but it was not until the early 1960s that conslusive evidence of poisoning by the European species *G. marginata* was reported from Russia. Chemical analysis revealed the presence of alpha-amanitin amounting to about 40 per cent of its content in the Death Cap. The cause of poisoning is ignorance resulting in the confusion of *G. marginata* with the similar but edible *Kuehneromyces mutabilis*. It is therefore necessary to beware of gathering not only *G. marginata* but also all other similar lignicolous *Galerina* species – the short-stipitate *G. badipes* and the unicolorous *G. unicolor*. Amanitin was also discovered in several other species of *Galerina*, mostly in those growing in moss.

In its clinical course, paraphalloid poisoning resembles phalloid poisoning, though the presence of phallotoxins has not been proved. It involves rare cases of poisoning after the ingestion of larger cup fungi, usully *Gyromitra esculenta,* and occasionally also the Sulphur Tuft (*Hypholoma fasciculare*). Poisoning caused by *G. esculenta* is rather puzzling, as many people gather and eat this fungus without any negative consequences whatsoever. Nausea, headache and abdominal pain appear in 5–10 hours after the ingestion, together with repeated vomiting which does not last so long as in phalloid poisoning. Often blood-circulation failure and brain tumescence set in, regularly accompanied by jaundice. The patient may sometimes succumb to a hepatic coma. This poisoning has long been attributed to the effects of helvellic acid; only recently have scientists proved the non-existence of such an acid, pointing out that a mixture of several non-toxic substances is involved. Simultaneously, however, a new effective principle was isolated and called gyromitrin, which quickly decomposes into the strongly poisonous methylhydrazine. However, both the mentioned substances are extremely volatile and disappear almost completely after 10 minutes' cooking. After a normal heat-preparation of fresh *G. esculenta* for table use, neither gyromitrin, nor methylhydrazine can be regarded as the cause of poisoning. In this fungus further four substances related to gyromitrin have been discovered; of these, hemolysin initiating the lysis of red blood cells is also destroyed by cooking. The most plausible explanation is that some old and infected fruit bodies of *G. exculenta* become poisonous only secondarily.

Occasional cases of poisoning after eating some other larger Discomycetes – *Gyromitra gigas, G. infula, Sarcosphaera crassa,* etc. – take the same course as poisoning by *G. esculenta*. Both gyromitrin and methylhydrazine were found in some of them.

Cases of poisoning by the Sulphur Tuft have repeatedly been reported from Russia as well as from some central and southern European countries. Their course was typically phalloid. Japanese mycological literature states that the Sulphur Tuft belongs to poisonous fungi responsible for the greatest amount of poisoning in Japan. This is almost incomprehensible in wiew of the fact that the Sulphur Tuft has an offensively bitter taste which remains unaffected by cooking.

2. **Muscarine poisoning.** Its name is derived from the specific name of the Fly Agaric – *Amanita muscaria*. In the past, fruit bodies of the Fly Agaric were steeped in milk used for poisoning flies. It has been discovered only in the 20th century that both the Fly Agaric and the Panther Cap (*A. pantherina*) contain but a small amount of muscarine, and that their toxicity is due to another toxic principle. On the other hand, muscarine was found in large quantities in other species, particularly in those of the genus *Inocybe* and in some white species of *Clitocybe*.

Muscarine poisoning sometimes manifests itself while the meal is still being eaten – as a rule, however, within two hours after it. The symptoms are conspicuous perspiration, salivation, lacrimation, vomiting and diarrhoea, fall of blood pressure, slowing down of the pulse and shivering. A remarkable symptom is the contracton of pupils accompanied by sight disorders. A reliable antidote is atropine; this, however, must not be applied in poisoning caused by the Fly Agaric and Panther Cap. In the whole of Europe, muscarine poisoning is mostly caused by *Inocybe patouillardii* containing approximately 500 times more muscarine than the Fly Agaric. A fatal dose is contained in 100–150 g of a fresh fungus. Also other

Inocybe species contain relatively large quantities of muscarine – e.g. *I.lacera, I.geophylla, I.argillacea,* and it is only in some species of this genus that no presence of muscarine has been proved (e.g. in *I.jurana*). Also several white *Clitocybe* species contain large quantities of muscarine – namely *C. dealbata* and the closely related (or perhaps identical) *C. rivulosa, C. phyllophila,* and *C. cerussata.* A small amount of muscarine was discovered in some *Hebeloma* species, e.g. in *H. crustuliniforme* and *H. sinapizans,* but also in *Armillaria mellea* and *Omphalotus olearius.* Slight symptoms of muscarine poisoning appear after their ingestion. Moreover, *O. olearius,* abundant in southern Europe, causes symptoms showing the presence of another content principle, hitherto unknown. According to some authors the true *O. olearius* occurs only in southernmost Europe, while the fungus growing further northwards (e.g. in the Czech Republic belongs to a different species, probably related to some poisonous *Omphalotus* species from North America, containing the toxins illudin S and M. Also the type of poisoning caused by *Mycena rosea* bears some resemblance to muscarine poisoning; its content principle has not yet been discovered.

3. **Psychotropic poisoning** involves serious cases characterized by the irritation of brain tissue. For a long time the intoxication caused by the Fly Agaric was the only form of mushroom poisoning accompanied by psychic disturbances. It was not before the 1950s that other so-called cult fungi, formerly used in religious ceremonies and rites, were identified; their ingestion leads to different manifestations of psychic disturbance. Two types of psychotropic poisoning are distinguished: psychotonic poisoning caused by the so-called mycoatropine, and psychodysleptic poisoning caused by psilocybine.

In Europe, poisoning by mycoatropine is caused by three *Amanita* species. Most common are cases of poisoning after eating the Panther Cap, less frequent are those caused by the Fly Agaric, and practically unknown is poisoning by *A. regalis.* The poisonous content principles of these amanitas have not yet been exactly identified, and this is why the designation 'mycoatropine poisoning', though inadequate, is still used nowadays.

The course of poisoning caused by all the three species is substantially the same: nausea is experienced between half an hour and three hours after consumption, accompanied by vomiting, headache, quickened heartbeat, and a persistent dilatation of pupils occasionally leading to vision disturbances. Often the condition of the affected person resembles alcoholic intoxication: the patient becomes talkative, shouts obscenities, sometimes laughs or weeps, strikes himself and keeps on runing to and fro. These states of excitement may be dangerous for the sick person and must therefore be mitigated. Subsequently the patient faints, recovers from time to time, hallucinates, screams, defends himself against invisible danger, etc. but finally falls into a profound sleep from which he usually awakens into a normal state, without remembering his previous behaviour. This poisoning comes to its fortunate end on the second or third day. First aid consists in the stimulation of vomiting and in taking the patient to hospital; he must be given neither milk nor alcohol. The treatment starts with a stomach rinse, the excitement is controlled by remedies of the chlorpromazine type, physostigmine (never atropine!) is administred as an antidote against mycoatropine.

Psilocybine poisoning occurs after consuming some species of the genus *Psilocybe,* or fungi belonging to related genera about which, nowadays, abundant literature is availabe. These fungi are distributed mostly in Mexico and in some Central American countries. They contain so-called hallucinogenic subtances thanks to which they had long been used in religious rituals and were kept secret until the twentieth century. Their research is due to the efforts of the American ethnographers Mr. and Mrs. Wasson who succeeded in acquiring hallucinogenous fungi, which they studied and identified with the help of mycologists. Chemical analyses of these fungi were carried out, and it was even possible to cultivate some of them. The effective substance was finally produced artificially, whereby its experimental testing on volunteers and its application for therapeutic purposes was made possible.

Fungi containing hallucinogenic substances generally produce small, inconspisuous fruit bodies growing on dung or excrements. They belong to the genera *Psilocybe, Panaeolus, Panaeolina* and *Stropharia.* The amount of effective substances in the fruit bodies is variable, particulary in the European representatives of the mentioned genera whose effect is substantially smaller in comparsion with the Mexican species.

The psychic symptoms following the ingestion of halluciogenic fungi are extremely varied. In some individuals they manifest themselves as euphoria, in others as sight disorders and hallucinations;

sometimes they assume the from of the kaleidoscopic effect involving the duplication of objects in inappropriate colours; still other persons, on the contrary, feel anxiety and fear, suffer from terrifying delusions, and these states may lead to delirium and suicide attempts. Thanks to a lower content of effective substances, the European fungi evoke much milder symptoms.

Hallucinogenic fungi contain four active substances; psilocybine, psilocine, baeocystine, and norbaeocystine. Psilocine is considered the main bearer of hallucinogenic properties. However, poisoning by these fungi is exceptional, and there is no danger of misusing European hallucinogenic fungi for intentional intoxication.

4. **Orellanin poisoning caused by _Cortinarius_.** The first mass poisoning by _Cortinarius orellanus_, reported from Poland in 1962, attracted the attention of all mycologists. Since that time, powerful toxic substances have been proved to exist in a number of _Cortinarius_ species originally considered harmless, and evidence of their presence in other species is recorded annually.

A characteristic of orellanin poisoning is the relatively long time interval between the ingestion of fruit bodies and the first symptoms of poisoning. It is the longest latency period in mushroom poisoning which may take up to 17 days; hence it follows that, as a rule, the first symptoms of poisoning are not at first connected with the consumed food. This type of poisoning manifests itself as acute or chronic kidney damage: urine secretion is overabundant at first, but slows down later and ultimately stops altogether; stomach pains appear, accompanied by vomiting, a feeling of dryness in the mouth, and thirst. The sick person dies, showing symptoms of kidney failure.

The toxin – which is the effective substance here – is called orellanin and was first isolated from _C. orellanus_. It is more powerful than the toxins present in the Death Cap. A mixture of about ten compounds is involved here, the most important of which is grzymalin (named after the author of the discovery). The treatment of orellanin poisoning is possible only in specilized large-hospital departments where the patient may be supplied with an artificial kidney. Similar poisoning was observed after the ingestion of _C. speciosissimus_ and _C. gentilis_; the opinion is justified that other _Cortinarius_ species of this group are equally poisonous; this applies e.g. to _C.phoeniceus, C.turmalis_ and _C.bolaris_. Therefore, mushroom pickers should avoid collecting absolutely any member of the genus _Cortinarius_.

5. **Poisoning called forth by the ingestion of various other fungi.** We shall confine ourselves to several common species about which the reader should be informed. Of particular interest is _Paxillus involutus_ which, until recently, had been considered edible. Up to now it has not been found to contain any toxins. The poisoning involved assumes the from of allergy: in individuals who have been eating this mushroom for years without any difficulties whatsoever, its further ingestion may cause nausea, abdominal pains, diarrhoea, sometimes very high temperatures, red urine, and an acute kidney insufficiency. The symptoms may set in gradually the kidney damage may turn chronic. It is nowadays considered poisonous and to be avoided.

Characteristic of southern Europe is the occasional incidence of poisoning by _Tricholoma pardinum_ manifesting itself half an hour to two hours after ingestion by vomiting and diarrhoea (i.e. loss of fluids and mineral substances), possibly resulting in kidney damage. The same symptoms may be observed in poisoning by _Entoloma lividum_, eventually by other poisonous _Entoloma_ species, such as _E. rhodopolium_ and _E. nidorosum_. Poisoning caused by _Nolanea verna_ is accompanied by an intensive diarrhoea lasting for several days and by the consequent exhaustion of the organism. Here the first symptoms of poisoning appear in 2–4 hours, maybe also in 24 hours. In some countries there have been cases of poisoning by _Agaricus xanthoderma_, because of its confusion with edible agarics of a similar appearance. It is only after eating a large amount of fruit bodies that this type of poisoning manifests itself by persistent vomiting which may last for several hours. Also after consuming large amounts of fruit bodies of fungi sometimes used as spices, digestion disorders may turn up – for example in case of _Lactarius helvus, Collybia fusipes, Scleroderma citrinum_ and _S.verrucosum_. In the case of _S. verrucosum_ symptoms of poisoning appear very quickly after eating this mushroom fried on fat.

In specilized literature, data concerning the edibility or inedibility of many fungus species are often contradictory. In general, increasing knowledge tends to increase the number of species considered inedible or poisonous, rather than the other way round. Hence is urgently recommended that the collection of mushrooms for table use should be confined to the narrower assortment of well-tried species to avoid running any risk. The rule of distinguishing edible species of _Russula_ and _Lactarius_ according to the taste of the flesh of fresh fruit bodies helps to exclude all the hot-tasting fungi belonging to these genera as inedible, although some of them are suitable for eating if subjected to a special preparation (this actually happens in some countries). Hot-tasting *Russula* and *Lactarius* species (e.g. *Lactarius turpis* and *L. torminosus*) may cause poisoning which manifests itself by stomach and intestinal troubles. This is caused by substances of a still unknown chemical composition characterized by thermolability. This is why in some countries, particulary in the north, these mushrooms are collected, cooked and preserved in salt or fermented. However, in southern and central Europe the very same species are considered inedible or poisonous.

In conclusion let us briefly refer to mushrooms currently collected as edible whose ingestion, however, sometimes calls forth unpleasant troubles or individual intolerance. Cases of this kind have so far not been explained, and naturally the content principles causing them are still unknown. For example, poisoning by the Honey Fungus whose symptoms appear after eating not only raw or inadequately prepared mushrooms but also well-prepared ones is completely unaccountable. It is assumed that a poisonous species may exist as one of the complex of so-called microspecies (the Honey Fungus represents exactly such a complex) which have not yet been satisfactorily distinguished. Also the brown-coloured *Tricholoma* species, especially those growing in coniferous forests (mostly under pine trees) on the lower slopes of mountains, include suspect species calling forth symptoms of poisoning. Some yellow or greenish species of *Tricholoma*, often bitterish to burning in taste, are mistaken for *T. flavovirens* and cause gastric troubles. The separate species of the genus *Ramaria,* abundantly collected in many regions, are not distinguished by practical mushroom gatherers; they contain the laxative emodin, concentrated in the branch tips of their fruit bodies. It is therefore necessary to use them with care. Allergenic properties may be observed in many dozens of other fungus species described in books as being edible and are mostly eaten without ill-effects.

It is a generally known fact that no alcoholic drinks must be taken after eating meals prepared with certain mushroom species, otherwise symptoms of poisoing might appear. Best known in this respect is *Coprinus atramentarius*. In most cases, poisoning makes itself felt soon after ingestion; its symptoms include reddening of the skin, intense heart palpitation, asthmatic troubles, vomiting, diarrhoea and feelings of anxiety. They disappear wihin two hours but can re-emerge after drinking some more alcohol. The same holds for some other mushrooms as well.

EDIBLE MUSHROOMS

The definition of 'edible mushroom' is extremely difficult. The findings obtained in the course of the last decades reveal the necessity to be reserved and evaluate individual fungus species on the basis of much stricter criteria. In the present conception, a fungus species is considered edible if eating it causes no health disorders, provided it has been properly cooked (boiling, frying, baking). The basic amount is a 100–200 g portion of mushrooms prepared. It is recommended to refrain from eating any raw fungi whatsoever. The ingestion of even small portions of raw fruit bodies of certain current mushroom species, which may be eaten quite safely after cooking, can cause grave nausea (e.g. the Honey Fungus). The time needed for cooking varies from species to species, since it depends on the consistency of the flesh: in fruit bodies with soft flesh it takes about 10 minutes, for tougher flesh at least 20 minutes are necessary. Only faultless, young or recently developed fruit bodies should be gathered for the table; they must be neither overripe and flaccid, nor infested with microorganisms, mould or insect larvae. Fruit bodies covered with a slimy and viscid cuticle, such as is usual e.g. in the *Suillus* species, must be cleaned and deprived of their pellicle in the very place where they have been found: this saves us a lot of extra work when cleaning them at home. It is also advisable to avoid collecting flabby, large caps of some *Leccinum* species unable to withstand transport. The collected mushrooms are put into a wicker basket. Plastic bags are absolutely inappropriate for the purpose, as the fruit bodies deposited therein get crushed and overheated. At home it is best to keep the mushrooms in a refrigerator at a temperature of 5–8 °C; here they remain in a good condition for 24 hours, but desiccate more rapidly.

The dish prepared with mushrooms should be eaten at once if possible, its further preservation (in the refrigerator of course) and reheating reduces its goodness and substantially affects its edibility. Mushrooms should be prepared for the table according to well-tried recipes, or it is possible to enrich the diet by using some species to prepare special dishes accentuating their taste qualities. For example, Saffron Milk Cap (*Lactarius deliciosus*) is best when pickled in vinegar, prepared as goulash or roasted on butter; puffballs are appetizing in soups; caps of *Lactarius volemus* and of the Parasol Mushroom taste excellently when roasted on fat, etc.

If we refuse to risk poisoning and the often ensuing serious damage to health, we must observe the basic rule – namely, that only the species we are quite reliably acquainted with should be collected. If, in spite of everything, we are keen on enlarging our assortment and knowledge by further species, it is best to contact some specialist who will identify the mushrooms for us or confirm the correctness of our identification. It is also expedient to visit mycological advice bureaus functioning in certain cities, or else it is possible to attend special lectures and courses organized by mycological associations or clubs. The identification based exclusively on comparison with coloured plates is often rather unreliable (in view of the great colour and shape variability characterizing many species, of a possibly inaccurate reproduction of colours, etc.). It is always only a detailed, exhaustive description that can be conclusive and decisive.

The digestibility of mushrooms is directly related to the cellular structure of their bodies. Mushrooms are less digestible than other plants due to the fact that their cell walls are largely composed of the polysaccharide chitin resistant to the action of digestive fluids in the human organisms. The cellular plasma contains 70–95 per cent of water and only a negligible amount of sugars and fats which represent the substantial proportion of nutritional substances. The mushroom flesh contains about 3–9 per cent of proteins, their compounds being amino acids and peptides. Altogether, about 20 various amino acids were found in mushrooms; their content varies even in individual specimens of the same species. Sugars represent 1–6 per cent of the content, for the most part in the form of polymers, but there is also glycogen, mannitol, traces of sorbitol, arabitol, and others. Mushrooms further include 0.5–3.5 per cent of fats, mostly glycerides and glycolipides, less frequently phospholipides (e.g. lecithin), often in the form of oil droplets within spores or in the tissue. Also vitamins are present in mushrooms, especially the provitamin carotene, vitamins of the vitamin-B group, vitamin D, E and K in small quantities, and traces of vitamin C. Mushrooms also contain various enzymes and substances with antibiotic effects. The mineral substances contained in mushrooms are first of all potassium (K), phosphorus (P), calcium (C) and iron (Fe). The capacity of fungi to accumulate from the soil these mineral substances (trace elements), which are so important for the enzymatic processes taking place in the human organism, presumably exceeds that of green plants. The concentration of trace elements in fungus fruit bodies depends on the habitat.

Recommendations as to which edible mushrooms should be collected are always a problematic matter, connected with various circumstances among which tradition, conservatism, individual taste, etc. play a major role. In general it can be said that in countries where wild edible mushrooms are not habitually collected, preference is given to artificially produced field agarics. Among the mushrooms gathered in their natural state, high value is attached to those belonging to the Boletaceae family: in most cases they are easily recognized and endowed with a pleasant smell, taste and consistency. The most popular and generally known bolete is of course the Edible Boletus or Cèpe (*Boletus edulis*). Otherwise it is recommended to eat mushrooms in mixtures in which the specific taste qualities, consistency and smell of the single species come to the fore. Species with a less distinct taste are added to strongly aromatic or more acridly tasting species. An adequate preparation in the kitchen renders the mushrooms more palatable and more digestible. Tougher species are cut into thin slices, dried mushrooms ground into powder can be used as spices, many species can be preserved in salt or pickled in various solutions. The trimmings added to mushroom dishes should be easily digestible – e.g. potatoes and vegetable salads. Special literature brings a great number of recipes for everybody to choose according to his individual taste.

In popular mushroom manuals and mycological exhibitions, the described, illustrated and exhibited species are usually divided into poisonous, edible and inedible ones. The category of inedible fungi is one which is most problematic and most difficult to define. For the most part, this designation covers fungi which are neither edible nor poisonous, or whose edibility is still open to doubt due to a lack of exact information. As a rule, they possess qualities making them unsuitable for table use: too small fruit bodies, unpleasant smell and taste, excessively tough flesh, and sometimes they inspire distaste by their appearance or place of occurence (e.g. coprophilic fungi). Most of these features, however, can be purely subjective. With the spreading of knowledge of individual fungus species, some of them are gradually being reclassed from the category of inedible fungi into that of poisonous fungi. In future it might be expedient to omit the category of inedible fungi altogether, and to distinguish only mushroons suitable for table use and safely verified as regards their harmlessness to health, and fungi detrimental to the human organism – i.e. poisonous.

WHERE AND WHEN TO GO MUSHROOMING

There is a difference between those who gather mushrooms exclusively for practical purposes, i.e. for enriching their diet, and those who regard fungi as an object of scientific interest. However, both kinds of mushrooming can be pursued as a hobby.

The practical mushroom picker's attention is usually focussed on a limited number of fungus species which he can safely recognize and which he prefers. Only if he fails to find his favourite species, or on the recommendation of other collector, will he also take other edible mushrooms. The mushroom picker's actual season is relatively short: in European conditions, it is concentrated at the end of summer and the beginning of autumn, i.e. from August to October, when mushrooms grow most abundantly. It is also necessary to take account of the weather, as the most favourable conditions for mushrooming arive after heavy rainfalls followed by warm weather. Mushrooms like neither wind nor excessive temperature variations. However, edible mushrooms may be found even in spring, if the weather is both moist and warm. This is the time when large-sized spring Discomycetes appear – morels (*Morchella*) and members of the genera *Discina* and *Gyromitra*; of the gill fungi it is *Hygrophorus marzuolus*, *Strobilurus* species growing on cones, later on St. George's Mushroom (*Calocybe gambosa*) and *Entoloma clypeatum*. Mushroom pickers prefer sunny places sheltered from wind, such as southward-facing woodland margins, laws (even in city park), gardens, forest clearings, etc. It is advisable to look for light deciduous or mixed forests, while in extensive, monotonous conifer forests no mushrooms are usually found in springtime. In summer, if the weather is exceedingly dry, situations on shady slopes facing northwards or in river an brook valleys should be looked for.

Some edible mushrooms may be gathered from spring till autumn on tree stumps or trunks, e.g. *Kuehneromyces mutabilis*. In the period of the most intensive vegetation of fungi we may find mushrooms almost in every forest, but not all forest growths are equally rich in mushrooms. Sometimes you will roam large spaces without success before striking on a woodland locality where a numbers of species grow side by side. There are mushroom pickers who mark the trees in whose vicinity they have found, for example, various boleti. Such a place often remains fertile for a number of years, since these mushrooms live in mycorrhizal dependence on a particular woody plant and regularly form fruit bodies there at a certain time. A knowledge of woody plants helps in the search for mycorrhizal mushrooms (a number of boleti grow exclusively under aspens, birchers and poplars). Wherever the countryside is richer in its natural aspect, particularly as concerns the structure and specific variety of woody plants, its mycoflora also displays a greater abundance of species. Geophilous fungi growing in the humus, fallen foliage or needles prefer forests without any herbal or shrubby undergrowth. Where the wood is excessively overgrown with grass and a buoyant, dense herbal vegetation, or where the soil is covered with a continuous layer of branches left behind after wood sifting or wood production, geophilous fungi are usually scarce.

Edible mushrooms are also gathered outside the wood, e.g. in meadows, fields and pastures. Whole swarms of champignons (*Agaricus*) often appear there after summer rainfalls. After the height of the season, which is usually in September, several lignicolous species may be found growing on stumps and decaying tree trunks in the cool season – perhaps also during a mild winter. This applies to the Winter Fungus or Velvet Shank (*Flammulina velutipes*) and the Oyster Fungus (*Pleurotus ostreatus*).

Anybody whose concern for fungi is primarily based on his scientific interest can pursue his hobby on a substantially larger scale: he may collect and study fungi almost all the year round, depending only on the group he selects. Leaving aside all the microscopic fungi wherein scarcely any amateur mycologist takes interest nowadays, there still remains a number of interesting and often little-known species (sometimes even unknown ones, hitherto not described) whose seeking in nature, microscopic examination and identification yield much satisfaction to anybody whose attention they have aroused by their various shapes and way of life. They can be collected from spring to winter in most various habitats within and outside the forest. During our excursion we proceed as slowly as possible, focussing our attention both on the ground and on stumps, dead branches either scattered about or jutting out, trunks of uprooted trees, but also on the remnants of herbs and grasses, decaying leaves, needles, animal excrements, burned-over areas, roadside edges overgrown with low moss, and ditch banks or old walls. Good results follow from a systematic inspection of some selected small ecotypes (e.g. areas around springs, alder coppices), examined in regular intervals throughout the year or for several years, while all findings are recorded and documented and a detailed description of the ecology of individual species is supplied. A mycological herbarium composed of exsiccati (dried fungi) is an inseparable part of descriptions and notes made in connection with these observations: it serves not only as a documentary material but also as a valuable comparative material for further study.

HOW TO COLLECT AND IDENTIFY FUNGI

With regard to the aim of this book, the present chapter will again deal exclusively with higher fungi which are the most conspicuous ones in nature, and consequently are the first to attract attention. The major part of the higher fungi consists of so-called pileate fungi, whose fruit bodies are usually differentiated into a stipe and a cap. The pileate fungi moreover include fruit bodies of stomach fungi (Gasteromycetes) – puffbals (*Lycoperdon*), members of the genera *Bovista* and *Scleroderma*, but also other species whose fruit bodies are conspicuous in shape, e.g. stinkhorns (*Phallus*) and earth stars (*Geastrum*). Some species of larger cup fungi (Discomycetes), flask fungi (Pyrenomycetes) and nongilled fungi (Aphyllophorales) belong here as well. The fungi included here predominantly belong to the Basidiomycetes, while the representation of the Ascomycetes is relatively small.

All the fungi whose bodies are collected in the open air for the purposes of study and identification should immediately be deposited with care, one by one, in metal or plastic boxes of various size. Non-gilled lignicolous fungi are cut off together with a part of the substrate and wrapped into a piece of newspaper or put into a paper bag. We must not forget to put down the name of the host or, rather better, to enclose a fragment of the plant whereon the fungus has been found; in lignicolous fungi either a fresh or a dry leaf of the woody plant in question will do. It has proved useful to add to the fresh small and fragile gill-fungi fruit bodies a fresh leaf of any green plant which, by evaporating water, keeps the air in the box humid and thus prevents the fungus from desiccating. After our return from the expedition, we put down on the margin of the paper in which the separate finds are wrapped the data concerning the locality, habitat or substrate, and the date of collection. After processing the material the notes are clipped out and deposited together with the collected specimens first into the drier and then into a herbarium envelope. They are crucial for writing the herbarium label. In lignicolous fungi, particularly in those having resupinate fruit bodies, the quickest possible desiccation of the collected material is necessary: only in this way is it possible perfectly to preserve on the exsiccations the qualities of the hymenium (especially the shape of basidia) which are of primary importance for the identification.

The present classification of gill fungi is predominantly based on microcharacteristics observable only under the microscope (shape, size, ornamentation of spores, fruit-body tissue, structure of the gill trama, cuticle of the cap and stipe, etc.). Notwithstanding, it is of extraordinary importance to work out a detailed description, or at least notes, concerning all the perceivable characteristics involved (colour, taste, smell, chemical reaction of the context): these characteristics usually disappear in the desiccated fruit body, or change so much that they can no more be reliably ascertained. The spores and the fruit-body structure can of course be most easily studied on fresh fruit bodies, yet they can also be examined

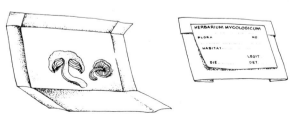

17) A herbarium envelope of strong paper for keeping exsiccations and a label containing the necessary data (the name of the identified fungus, its locality, habitat, substrate, the date of the find, the name of the collector and that of the identifier) to be glued on the herbarium envelope.

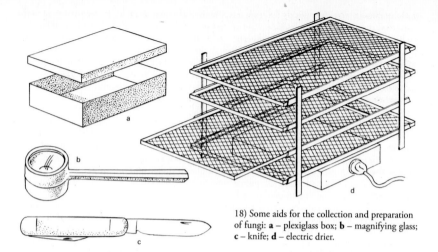

18) Some aids for the collection and preparation of fungi: **a** – plexiglass box; **b** – magnifying glass; **c** – knife; **d** – electric drier.

on well dried exsiccations at any later time. Fruit bodies are usually dried as a whole, only large specimens are cut lengthwise into two or more parts. They are dried in moderate (40–60 °C) but permanent temperatures, without interruption, until they become bone-hard or fragile. Then they are placed for a few hours into a plastic bag containing a piece of paper or cotton wool dipped in water. The fruit bodies absorb a small amount of moisture, which makes them pliable. Only then do we put them into herbarium envelopes of tough, strong paper, and slightly press them by hand. This will prevent the fruit body from breaking when further handled. The collection of exsiccati must be kept dry and disinfected at least once a year (carbondisulphide fumes being the best disinfectant), and protected against insects by chemical agents.

An important distinguishing feature of fungi is the colour of the spore print. The spore print is obtained by cutting off the cap of a fresh, ripe fruit body from the stipe and placing it flat, gills downwards, on a piece of white paper (eventually on a black one, if a white spore print is expected). The cap together with the paper are either inserted into a plastic bag, enclosed in a tin or covered with a bowl. As a rule, the spore print appears on the paper in a few hours. When using a microscope, we jot down and draw the shape and size of spores (these are measured, just like other micro-elements, by an ocular micrometer), as well as the ornamentation of the spore wall, ascertained with the aid of an oil immersion lens after applying Melzer's reagent or cotton blue to obtain the required colour reaction. Further, sections are cut through the gills and the cuticle of both the cap and the stipe. Minute parts of tissue from the fruit-body surface are cut off with a razor blade and turned into so-called crush mounts; these are far less elaborate and usually prove sufficient for identification. A tiny piece of tissue, perhaps a fraction of a gill, is mounted in a droplet of water on a microscope slide, and a small glass cover slip is placed over and slightly pressed. Microscopic mounts of fresh fruit bodies are prepared in water, those of exsiccations in an aquaeous ammonia solution, in a 10-per cent potassium hydroxide (KOH) or lactophenol.

Every observation is recorded and sketched on a separate sheet of paper. On principle, each finding and herbarium item is kept separately. This method has turned out to be the best: it allows an easy manipulation and a large number of descriptions can easily be classified according to a certain system,

19) The spore print of gill fungi is obtained by cutting off the cap and placing it on a piece of white (eventually black) paper.

or alphabetically, and can quickly be looked up again. Descriptions may be complemented with coloured sketches or photographs. Everybody who takes a serious interest in mycology must become acquainted with the fundamentals of working with a microscope, for nowadays it has become absolutely impossible to do without a good microscope in pursuing this branch of study. Anybody who can draw well is on the winning side, because no microphotograph, and frequently not even a macrophotograph, good as it may be, can fully replace an exact and readily made sketch of the fruit bodies under examination.

Today the identification of fungi is aided by an extensive literature – from general keys up to monographic elaborations of genera or whole families. It is advisable to use the most modern versions and continuously to compare them with older works. The best solution for a beginner is to contact a specialist in the respective fungus group who will help him to overcome the first and most difficult obstacles.

Steps in the Description of Macro- and Microcharacteristic of Gill Fungi

Mode of developement

Cap: size, shape (in youth, at maturity, in old age), margin, centre, cuticle and its colouring, presence or absence of the velum, consistency.

Stipe: size (length and thickness), shape, attachment to the cap, surface, mycelium at the base, presence or absence of the velum, consistency, properties of the context in the longitudinal section.

Gills: attachment to the stipe, distance, breadth, colouring, edge, surface, colour change on injury.

Tissue: original colouring and eventual changes on the cut, presence or absence of latex (and its changes), smell, taste, consistency.

Spore print: colouring.

Microchemical reactions (on the cap cuticle, stipe surface, gills, context where broken): the most frequently used media are green-vitriol solutions, phenol, sulphovanillin, guaic tincture, ammonia, potash and soda lye, phormol, hydrochloric, nitric and sulphuric acid, argent nitrate, sulphorormol, benzidine.

Microcharacteristics: basidia, cystidia and other hymenial elements, spores (size, shape, apiculus, germ pore, wall-thickness, ornamentation, colouring, amyloidity, cyanophilia), trama; structure of the cap and stipe cuticle, mycelium at the stipe base; hyphae in the fruit body (presence or absence of clamp connections, pigmentation, etc.)

Ecological data about the habitat

Locality

Date of collection

Total amount of fruit bodies used for the description

Illustration of the material described (drawing, photograph)

Registration of the exsiccatus (number in the herbarium, in the list of finds)

20) Examples of some Myxomycetes: **a** – *Dictydium cancellatum*; **b** – *Arcyria nutans*; **c** – *Leocarpus fragilis*; **d** – *Lycogala epidendron* (aethalia); **e** – *Perichaena chrysosperma* (capillitium); **f** – *Physarum* sp. (capillitium widened into calcareous nodules).

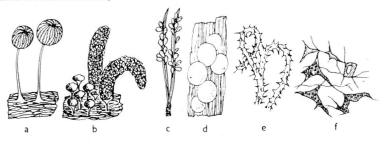

a   b   c   d   e   f

CLASSIFICATION OF FUNGI – A BRIEF SURVEY

Views about the classification of fungi are far from uniform: the evaluation and sometimes even the content of higher and lower categories differ according to individual authors. What one regards as a class represents a phylum for another, not to speak of the differences in the lower categories (orders, families, subfamilies, etc.) and their classification in the system. The present chapter has been restricted to merely a basic survey of the orders constituting the two principal groups of the so-called true fungi (Eumycophyta) – i.e. Ascomycetes and Basidiomycetes. Within each order, the families included in this book are referred to and, for the most part, briefly described. This will enable the reader to acquire a good picture of the systematic classification of the fungus species presented here. Mycetozoans (Myxomycota), nowadays generally regarded as fungi, and also moulds (Phycomycetes) remain outside the sphere of your interest. Imperfect fungi (Deuteromycetes) are briefly referred to, owing to their relevance in studying 'large' fungi (Macromycetes).

FUNGI

Phylum: true fungi – Eumycophyta
  Class: Ascomycetes
    Subclass: Protoascomycetidae
      Order: Eurotiales
      Order: Microascales
      Order: Onygenales
      Order: Laboulbeniales
    Subclass: Ascohymenomycetidae
      Order: Erysiphales
      Order: Pezizales
      Order: Tuberales
      Order: Helotiales
      Order: Phacidiales
      Order: Xylariales
      Order: Hypocreales
    Subclass: Ascoloculomycetidae

  Class: Basidiomycetes
    Subclass: Heterobasidiomycetidae
      Order: Protoclavariales
      Order: Auriculariales
      Order: Tremellales
      Order: Uredinales
    Subclass: Holobasidiomycetidae
      Order: Aphyllophorales
      Order: Polyporales
      Order: Boletales
      Order: Agaricales
      Order: Russulales
  Class: Gasteromycetes
  Auxiliary class: Deuteromycetes

Ascomycetes

Ascomycetes are usually regarded – together with Basidiomycetes – as 'higher fungi'. The common feature of all Ascomycetes is the production of spores in spore sacs (asci), most often eight to an ascus. The mycelium is always septate, and the septa are furnished with a simple minute opening facilitating the passage of plasma and nuclei. The principal constituent of mycelial walls, as well as of all hyphal walls in the fruit body, is chitin. The greater part of Ascomycetes produce fruit bodies on their mycelium which basically assume two forms substantiating the division of these fungi into two main groups. In the first group the fruit body is usually globular, closed, opening at maturity either by rupture (the cleistothecium), or by a small pore at the apex (the perithecium or pseudothecium). In the second group the fruit body is freely open, either from the very beginning or at least in the later stages (the apothecium). Together with the asci, sterile filaments (paraphyses) also develop within the fruit body. Many species also form asexual (conidial) stages to which the designation anamorphs is nowadays applied, while the ascus stages are termed teleomorphs.

The classification and identification of Ascomycetes is based exclusively on the ascus stage. This large group of fungi, including about 40,000 hitherto described species, is predominantly composed of inconspicuous fungi with fruit bodies usually no more than 1 mm in size, occuring in nature on most various substrates. They are commonly divided into Pyrenomycetes and Discomycetes, but in fact both these groups represent several independent developmental lines whose delimitation is not uniform. In principle, three groups exist which are attributed the value of subclasses: Protoascomycetidae, Ascohymenomycetidae and Ascoloculomycetidae.

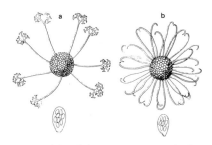

21) Examples of mildews: celistothecia with appendages, asci with spores; **a** – *Microsphaera* sp., **b** – *Uncinula* sp.

Fungi of the subclass **Protoascomycetidae** have globular asci with a thin, simple wall provided with no opening apparatus; it becomes slimy and desintegrates at maturity. Four orders of almost exclusively microscopic fungi are included here:

Fungi of the order **Eurotiales** are saprophytes currently distributed in soil and humus where they decompose organic remains. The so-called moulds of the genera *Penicillium* and *Aspergillus* belong here – of course both these names relate only to the conidial stages, valid names for the much rarer ascus stage of the genus *Penicillium* being *Talaromyces*, for *Aspergillus*, *Eurotium*. This order, however, also includes some larger fungi with globular fruit bodies up to several centimetres in size. They are represented in our forests by the genus *Elaphomyces*.

22) Examples of some moulds: **a** – *Peronospora* sp. (branched sporangiophore with sporangia); **b** – *Rhizopus nigricans* (sporangiophores with sporangia); **c** – *Spinellus fusiger* (sporangiophores on a Myxomycetes cap); **d** – *Albugo candida* (deforming *Capsella bursa-pastoris*); **e** – *Rhizophidium pollinis-pini* (sporangium with a single strand zoospore on a pollen grain of a pine tree); **f** – *Mucor mucedo* (a stalked sporangium growing out of branched mycelium); **g** – *Mucor* sp. (formation of a zygospore).

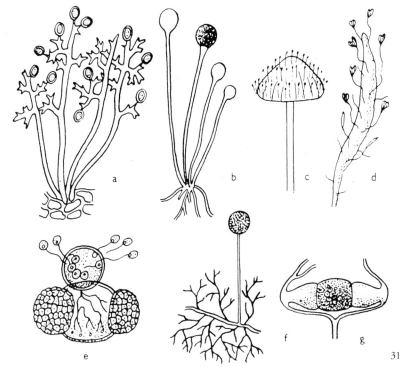

31

23) Various types of Ascomycetes fruit-bodies: **a** – apothecium in cross-section, **b** – apothecium (fullview), **c** – perithecium in cross-section, **d** – perithecium (full view); pictures **a** and **b** are greatly enlarged and schematized.

a   b   c   d

The order **Microascales** has become notorious particularly by its microscopic member *Ceratocystis ulmi* whose mass occurrence has led to the extermination of most European elms. The disease caused by this fungus is called Dutch elm disease.

Fungi of the order **Onygenales** have small, stipitate, globular fruit bodies growing on the horny tissue of claws, hoofs, horns, but also on the feathers of dead birds. These ceratophilous fungi are represented by the genus *Onygena*.

Fungi of the order **Laboulbeniales** are sometimes regarded as an independent class of Ascomycetes and their position in the system is still ambiguous. They are narrowly specialized parasites of insects (especially beetles) and spiders to which, however, they do not seem to cause much harm. Their minute, fusiform fruit bodies are fastened to the surface of the host's body by a 'foot'.

Fungi of the subclass **Ascohymenomycetidae** have asci whose length usually exceeds their breadth. Their apex is equipped with an opening apparatus or a lid for discharging ascospores. The ascus wall is thin, and does not turn slimy when mature. They are usually divided into seven orders:

The order **Erysiphales** (mildews) includes the most common and also most conspicuous parasites of vascular plants. Their surface mycelium often forms extensive coatings, particularly on the leaves, which are either white, farinaceous (family Erysiphaceae), or brown to blackish (Meliolaceae, currently distributed almost exclusively in the tropics or subtropics). Minute, globular, closed fruit bodies (cleistothecia), often provided with variously shaped filaments, appear to the naked eye as dark little dots. Numerous pests of cultivated plants belong to this group, for example *Uncinula necator*, grapevine mildew (known especially in its conidial stage as *Oidium tuckeri*), further *Podosphaera leucotricha* on apple-trees, *Microsphaera quercina* on oaks, etc. Traditionally the order Erysiphales was classed with the subclass Protoascomycetidae referred to above; at present, however, it has been reclassified as a member of the subclass Ascohymenomycetidae, with respect to its asci opening through a lid.

The following four orders are currently referred to as cup fungi (Discomycetes).

The fruit body of **Pezizales** is a typical apothecium, globularly closed only in youth; soon it opens into its definitive shape which is semiglobular, patelliform or discoid, often flatly expanded or even convex. The inner surface, known as the disc (thecium), bears asci and paraphyses arranged in palisade-like structures. Fruit bodies in the most developed forms, Helvellaceae and Morchellaceae, are differentiated into a stipe and a cap. Asci open by a lid and ascospores are shot out. In some genera the

24) Examples of apothecia in Discomycetes (cup fungi): **a** – *Orbilia*; **b** – *Hymenoscyphus*; **c** – *Ascocoryne*; **d** – *Dasyscyphus*; **e** – hysterothecia of *Lophodermium pinastri*; **f** – *Leotia lubrica*; **g** – *Geoglossum*.

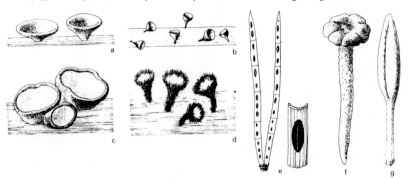

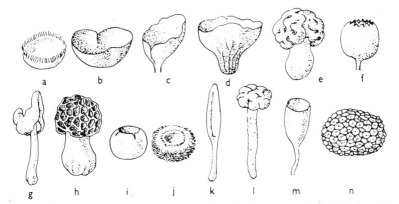

25) Examples of fruit bodies in Ascomycetes: **a** – *Scutellinia*; **b** – *Peziza*; **c** – *Otidea*; **d** – *Helvella*; **e** – *Gyromitra*; **f** – *Tarzetta*; **g** – *Helvella elastica*; **h** – *Morchella esculenta*; **i** – *Peziza vesiculosa*; **j** – *Mycolachnea hemisphaerica*; **k** – *Geoglossum*; **l** – *Leotia lubrica*; **m** – *Urnula craterium*; **n** – *Tuber aestivum*.

ascus membranes are markedly amyloid. As well as numerous representatives of minute size, Pezizales also include the largest and hence the most conspicuous species of Discomycetes. Some of them show remarkable colours, especially red, orange and yellow. They grow almost exclusively as saprophytes on bare ground, in moss, on putrescent wood or on other plant remnants, many of them on excrements, dung and on burned-over soils. They are generally divided into six families. An important identifying feature is – besides other characteristics – the ornamentation of their ascospores. This book deals with species of the families Humariaceae, Otideaceae, Pezizaceae, Helvellaceae and Morchellaceae.

The order **Tuberales** consists of hypogeous fungi. The tuberiform fruit body remains closed, the incidence of spore-bearing locules opening on its surface is rather rare. Asci usually cover the walls of galleries and cavities inside the fruit body. Spores are often large, ornamented; unlike the preceding species, they are not ejected out of the asci but get free through the decomposition of the entire fruit body. The Tuberales are mycorrhizal fungi distributed mainly in warm regions, in deciduous forests, and on calcareous soils. They include the families Tuberaceae and Terfeziaceae.

The order **Helotiales** is the largest group of cup fungi. Their lidless asci open at the apex by a ringshaped apparatus through the centre of which the spores are violently discharged. Their fruit bodies are typical apothecia, mostly minute in size (1 mm and less in diameter), sesssile or stipitate, smooth or hairy, bristly and felted, in some genera embedded in the substrate at first and pushing their way to the surface; more advanced types have upright fruit bodies with long stipes, cylindrical or pileate (e.g. in the family Geoglossaceae). They grow predominantly as saprophytes, rarely as parasites, on plant stems, leaves, wood or rind.

The fruit body of fungi belonging to the order **Phacidiales** is called the pseudoapothecium; this is embedded in the tissue of the host plant and covered with a black stromatic layer which bursts open at maturity, disclosing the disc. The disc is covered up in dry conditions. The fruit body opening through a longitudinal slit is called the hysterothecium and is characteristic of the family Hypodermataceae. This includes for example the genus *Lophodermium*; some of its species live as needle parasites, causing a disease known as needle cast. Other typical representatives of this order are the genus *Rhytisma* whose conidial stage causes black spottiness on maple leaves, and *Colpoma* with the species *C. quercinum*, commonly found on dead oak branches.

The last-named two orders have been given the common designation Pyrenomycetes (flask fungi). These include also the subclass Ascoloculomycetidae (with the exception of the order **Lecanorales**). Here the fruit body is a typical perithecium containig asci which, in the orders **Xylariales** and **Hypocreales**, are unitunicate, opening at the apex by an amyloid pore or by an opening apparatus of another kind. The globular or lageniform perithecium has its own wall made up of pseudoparenchyma, even when it is embedded in the stroma. It ordinarily opens through a minute circular opening at the apex, often terminating in a neck-like extension (ostiole) whose channel is lined with hyphae (periphyses).

The order **Xylariales** is a group extraordinarily rich in species; it is divided into a number of families sometimes considered as independent orders. They live predominantly as saprophytes on branches and trunks of trees or shrubs and on herbal stems; many species are coprophilous. Larger and more conspicuous Pyremycetes belong for the most part to the family Xylariacese; some of them are commonly found on dead wood logs, trunks and stumps.

Fungi of the order **Hypocreales** are distinguished from the preceding species by their colouring – their perithecia or stromata are mostly bright red or yellow. They include a large number of genera and species distributed predominantly in the tropics. In the north temperate zone they are represented by the genus *Nectria*. *N. cinnabarina* is a lignicolous pyrenomycete whose conidial stage, known under the name *Tubercularia vulgaris*, is one of the commonest small fungi living on dead branches of various woody plants. Also the well-known ergot belongs here; it is the sclerotium of *Claviceps purpurea*, nowadays cultivated and industrially processed for medicinal purposes.

The subclass **Ascoloculomycetidae** includes on the one hand three orders of Pyrenomycetes, and on the other hand lichenized fungi – i.e. the greater part of lichens subjected to research by an independent scientific branch, lichenology. A characteristic feature of this subclass are bitunicate asci whose walls consist of two layers. After the spores have attained maturity, the outer layer bursts open at the apex, while the inner layer juts out of the newly created opening and the ascospores are discharged. The small fruit bodies resemble the perithecium but are regarded as a special structure termed the ascocarp (also pseudothecium or ascostroma). It is in fact a stroma consisting of one or more locules with no special wall dividing them from each other. This group comprises a vast amount of genera and species of both parasites and saprophytes inhabiting most various parts of plants. No uniform classification of orders and families has so far been worked out.

Basidiomycetes

This is the developmentally most advanced class of fungi, including at least 20,000 species. The characteristic feature common to all fungi of this group lies in the origin of spores (basidiospores): they develop on specialized cells called basidia. A young basidium has two nuclei coalescing into a single nucleus. A twofold reduction division gives rise to four haploid daughter nuclei entering by apical or lateral pedicels (sterigmata) into the basidiospores borne at the tips of sterigmata. Basidiomycetes of a less advanced type usually possess divided or septate basidia. The shape of basidia remains constant and is considered of paramount taxonomic significance in determining mutual relationships. Basidiospores are unicellular and are constant in shape and size in the individual taxons. Another important distinguishing feature is their wall, often ornamented with various excrescences, and amyloid in many species or genera. Basidia are usually aggregated in a continuous layer (hymenium), wherein special sterile cells (paraphyses, cystidia) are often present. The mycelium consists of simple or branched hyphae penetrating through the substrate; sometimes they are quite conspicuous. Mycelial hyphae are septate, consisting mostly of chitin. Each septum is furnished with a 'dolipore' (an opening in the central, bilaterally thickened part of the septum covered by a semiglobular membrane). In the primitive types,

26) Examples of fruit bodies in Aphyllophorales and Tremellales: **a** – *Exidia*; **b** – *Darcymyces*; **c** – *Coltricia perennis*; **d** – *Ramaria*; **e** – *Hydnum repandum*; **f** – *Fomes*; **g** – *Hericium coralloides*.

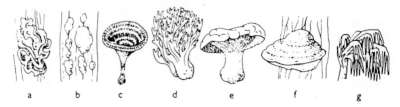

a   b   c   d   e   f   g

the fruit body itself is reduced to a layer of hyphae bearing the hymenium or single basidia only; they usually assume the form of coatings or membranes which are termed resupinate fruit bodies. More highly developed forms usually possess an upright fruit body differentiated into the pileate part (cap, pileus) and the stipitate part (stem, stipes). The hymenium, which in the simpler forms covers the entire outer surface of the fruit body, is confined in the more advanced forms to a specific, exactly delimited part, the so-called hymenophore, situated usually on the underside of the cap. The surface of the hymenophore is often enlarged by various excrescences, tubes or gills. The fruit body either has no apparent cover (a gymnocarpous fruit body) or is enclosed – at least in the initial stages of development – in a special covering (veil, velum). The spore-producing tissue sometimes develops within the fruit body, as for instance in the Gasteromycetes.

Basidiomycetes usually live as saprophytes on decaying plant remains, on the forest floor or in humus and duff; many of them form symbiotic relationships with roots of green plants (mycorrhiza). Most species are confined to the forest environment: here they play a significant role and their fruit bodies represent a remarkable phenomenon especially in the summer and autumnal aspect of plant communities. Their principal function consists in their contribution to humus formation, to the decomposition of wood – nor is it possible to overlook their role as a means of sustenance.

The shape of basidia underlies their division into two subclasses – Heterobasidiomycetidae and Holobasidiomycetidae.

The subclass **Heterobasidiomycetidae** includes Basidiomycetes with either simple or – most frequently – septate (i.e. multicellular) or more or less deeply divided basidia. It is formed by the following four orders:

Fungi of the order **Protoclavariales** have basidia consisting of a globular or cylindrical part (hypobasidia) to which inflated or elongate epibasidia are attached, bearing sterigmata with spores. The fruit bodies are often remarkably gelatinous or elastic. These small fungi usually live as saprophytes on dead wood. They are classed into two families, Tulasnellaceae and Dacrymycetaceae; a common representative of the last-mentioned family, *Calocera*, is dealt with in this book.

Fungi of the order **Auriculariales** have cylindrical or clavate basidia divided into several cells by transverse septae. A single sterigma ending in a spore develops from each of these cells. The family Auriculariaceae has been included here.

Fungi of the order **Tremellales** produce almost globular, cruciately septate basidia, divided by one or two longitudinal septae perpendicular to each other into two or four parts. The fruit bodies are mostly gelatinous and are of various shapes. This order includes predominantly wood saprophytes, of the larger ones particularly various species of the genus *Tremella* and *Pseudohydnum* belonging to the family Tremellaceae.

The order **Uredinales** (rusts) includes micromycetes parasitizing green plants in which they cause the so-called rustiness: the attacked plant is covered with minute rusty, orange, brown to black-coloured deposits in the form of tubercles or other structures. The tissue of the infested plants often withers, in other cases rusts may cause hypertrophic growth. Rusts that attack cultivated plants, especially cereals, are of considerable importance. Numerous rust species produce four types of spores: aeciospores (spring) in cupulate aecia, urediospores (summer) in uredia, teliospores (winter) in telia; teliospores germinate into the promycelium from which sporidia arise (the fourth type of spores). A characteristic of the rusts is an alternation of sexual and asexual generations; in some of them there is also an alternation of hosts on the one hand, and a narrow specialization on a certain (often a single) type of host on the other. The substantial part of species is concentrated in the genera *Puccinia* and *Uromyces*.

In the past, smuts (Ustilaginales) used to be introduced here as the following order. Today they are included in the class Endomycetes which represents the natural transition between moulds (Phycomycophytina) and primitive Ascomycetes. Other authors, however, join smuts and rusts into the independent class Teliomycetes. Smuts, like rusts, parasitize vascular plants.

The subclass **Holobasidiomycetidae** is the developmentally most advanced group of Basidiomycetes. Fungi belonging to this subclass have unicellular basidia usually bearing four sterigmate spores at their apex. The hymenium is either freely expanded or enclosed in the fruit-body tissue. The subclass is divided into six orders. The first five are the so-called Hymenomycetes in which the hymenium is freely opened before the spores have reached maturity and covers either the entire fruit-body surface or some of its parts. The spores are actively discharged from the basidia, forming the

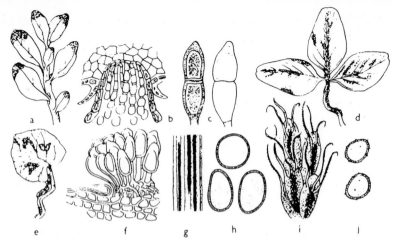

27) Examples of some parasitic rusts and smuts: **a** – *Exobasidium vaccinii* on Cowberry leaves; **b** – cross section through a rust aecium; **c** – teliospores of the rust *Puccinia*; **d** – deposits of the rust *Uromyces trifolii* on clover leaves; **e** – telia of the rust *Uromyces ficariae* on the Lesser Celandine; **f** – teliospores of *Uromyces ficariae*; **g** – deposits of the smut *Ustilago longissima* on *Glyceria* leaves; **h** – spores of the smut *Ustilago longissima*; **i** – cereal grains attacked by the smut *Ustilago segetum*; **j** – spores of *Ustilago segetum*.

deposited spore mass. The sixth order, **Gasterales**, includes fungi with closed fruit bodies within which spores are formed; these, however, are not actively discharged from the basidia and fail to form any spore deposit.

The Gasterales do not form a developmentally homogenous group – in fact it is an extremely heterogeneous grouping. Perhaps they represent the termination of several developmental lines of different origin. Different views are therefore supported in their classification, manifesting themselves in the unequal evaluation of the individual groups. Many mycologists regard the group discussed here as an order (Gasterales), others (including the author) as a higher category – a class (Gasteromycetes).

The order **Aphyllophorales** (non-gilled fungi) have either a resupinate fruit body spreading out loosely on the surface, or one of a definite shape. Resupinate species are most frequently found on the underside of uprooted tree trunks and fallen branches, on putrescent wood logs, in stump cavities, etc. So far a definitive classification of this large order has not been worked out; several families including a great number of genera are distinguished.

The following survey again presents families included in this book:

Stereaceae are lignicolous fungi having tough, resupinate to pileate fruit bodies usually surviving for several years, often densely arranged one above the other.

Thelephoraceae have brown-coloured, mostly angular, echinulate or verrucose spores. This holds for the genera *Tomentella* and *Thelephora*, as well as for the pileate fruit bodies of Hydnaceae – such as the genera *Hydnellum*, *Sarcodon* and *Phellodon*.

A characteristic of lignicolous fungi of the family Ganodermataceae are also brown-coloured spores, but these are truncate and ornamented. The fruit bodies of Ganodermataceae are tough to ligneous.

The family Coniophoraceae has relatively large, coloured, smooth spores – e.g. genera *Serpula* and *Coniophora*.

Clavariaceae and Sparassidaceae have erect, cylindrical or clavate, simple or ramose fruit bodies. The hymenium covers most of the outer surface of the fruit body. There are a large number of genera including *Clavaria*, *Ramaria* and *Sparassis*.

Hydnaceae and Auriscalpiaceae are fungi with an echinate (spiny) hymenophore – for example *Auriscalpium*, *Hericium*, *Hydnum*.

The family Poriaceae includes the greater part of polypores whose tubular hymenophore is

36

inseparable from the tough context to which it is firmly accreted. Besides many true polypores (e.g. *Albatrellus, Fomes, Laetiporus, Trametes, Piptoporus*) the genus *Fistulina* also belongs here, though it is often classed with the independent family Fistulinaceae. A part of the polypores (the genus *Polyporus*) has been transferred as the family Polyporaceae into the order Polyporales, together with several genera bearing a lamellate hymenophore but similar in anatomical structure.

Cantharellaceae and Lentinellaceae are fungi with a distinctly developed fruit body whose underside is covered by the hymenium; this surface is either smooth or augmented by blunt, shallow, often anastomosing ridges, gill-folds or gills. From the well-known genera belonging to this group, which are collected for table use, let us mention the Chanterelle (*Cantharellus*), *Craterellus* and *Gomphus*, sometimes classed into the independent family Gomphaceae.

The hymenophore in the Schizophyllaceae is formed by pseudogills splitting in two along the edge.

The order **Polyporales** includes fungi having a lamellate or porous hymenophore. The fruit bodies are mostly annual, fleshy when alive, often tough in dry weather, resilient or almost hard as wood, and with a central, eccentric or lateral stipe. The hyphae are relatively thick-walled. The spore print is white, cream-coloured or lilac (greyish violet). They are mostly lignicolous fungi. The families Polyporaceae and Pleurotaceae belong to this group.

As a general rule, fungi of the order **Boletales** have a tubular hymenophore covering the lower surface of the cap as a continuous layer, quite easily separable from the cap context. The fruit bodies are fleshy in most cases, often with a developed covering (velum), usually with a central stipe. They grow on the ground, most frequently in mycorrhizal association with woody plants. The following three families are included in this book:

In the true Boletaceae the velum is either present or absent, the cap cuticle is either viscid or dry, smooth or matted-tomentose. The pores are white, yellow, olive-hued, pink or red, sometimes staining blue, green or red when bruised. The spores are ellipsoid to elongate-fusiform, mostly smooth. They are mycorrhizal fungi. Best known are the genera *Boletus, Tylopilus, Suillus, Xerocomus* and *Krombholzia*.

Paxillaceae are closely related to the foregoing family. Their hymenophore bears gills which are sometimes anastomosed or forked, relatively narrow, decurrent, yellow, orange or brown. The cap has an involute margin. The spore sprint is whitish, cream-coloured, yellow or brown; the spores are ellipsoid, ovoid, cyanophilous, nonamyloid. The genera *Paxillus, Hygrophoropsis* and *Omphalotus* belong here.

Gomphidiaceaea have thick, decurrent, distant gills, fleshy fruit bodies with a dry to markedly glutinous cap, a black or olive-black spore print, and fusiform, smooth, cyanophilous, nonamyloid spores. Cystidia are developed. The genus *Gomphidius* is sometimes divided into two genera – *Chroogomphus* and *Leucogomphidius*.

The order **Agaricales** – gill fungi – has juicy or tough-fleshed fruit bodies, usually differentiated into a cap and a stipe, which may sometimes be reduced so that the fruit body is directly attached to the substrate. The hymenophore bears gills that are exceptionally narrow, veiny or ribbed, or the hymenophore is entirely smooth. The spore print varies in colour; the spores are colourless or coloured, sometimes dextrinoid or amyloid, smooth or ornamented. When young the fruit body is sometimes encased in a veil, leaving remnants of various kind on its surface (patches on the cap, filaments or scales on the stipe, a volva at the stipe base, etc.). The gill fungi are usually divided into ten families:

Hygrophoraceae have soft, juicy or waxy fruit bodies often covered with slime, light to variegated in colour, with or without a fugacious veil, thick and distant gills, markedly long and narrow basidia, and colourless and smooth spores.

The family Tricholomataceae is one of the largest gill-fungi families. It includes fungi of various size, with or without a velum, with a fleshy to fibrillose context, with a central or lateral stipe, and with adnate to deeply decurrent gills. The spore print is white or yellowish, exceptionally it may be pale pink or violet. The spores are often amyloid, rarely cyanophilous, and smooth or ornamented. With a view to the vast amount of genera not even their selection is introduced here, and the reader is referred to the illustrated section of this book where he will find a number of representatives of this family.

Similar to the above family in appearance are the Entolomataceae. They also include fungi of various size and colouring, with a central or lateral stipe or maybe entirely stipeless. They differ from the Tricholomataceae in having a pale to vivid pink spore print. The spores are mostly angular, elongate, nonamyloid. The basic genus is *Entoloma*. This name is nowadays used by some mycologists as the only generic designation covering all the species which, in the original conception, represented altogether five independent genera: *Entoloma, Nolanea, Leptonia, Eccilia* and *Claudopus*. On the other hand, French mycologists apply the collective designation *Rhodophyllus* to the genera referred to above.

Pluteaceae are fleshy fungi with a central stipe, with thin, broad, crowded, free to remote gills formed by an inverse trama. In some species, a volva is developed at the stipe base. The spore print is pale pink, spores are smooth, without any germ pore, nonamyloid, and cyanophilous. The Pluteaceae often grow on wood. The genera *Volvariella* and *Pluteus* are included here.

Amanitaceae are characterized by fleshy fruit bodies; the stipe can easily be removed from the context of the cap. When young the fruit bodies are enveloped in a velum, leaving warts or patches on the cap cuticle and an annulus on the stipe. A sheath (volva) is often developed at the stipe base; it assumes various forms and is sometimes reduced to mere flocci. The gills are free, broad, the gill trama is bilateral, the spore print is white, rarely tinged with green, the spores are colourless, mostly smooth, sometimes amyloid. The very plentiful genus *Amanita* is classed with this family, as well as the small genus *Limacella* formerly regarded as one of the *Lepiota* species.

Agaricaceae have fleshy fruit bodies with a central stipe which can easily be disconnected from the cap context and bears an annulus. The gills are crowded, free, broad, thin. The cap cuticle is often squamulose or floccose; the gill trama may be regular or irregular; the spore print is white, greenish, pink, reddish brown, rusty or purple-brown; the spores are smooth, rarely verrucose, often thick-walled. The fruit bodies grow on the ground, on dung and humus. Of the principal genera included, *Agaricus, Lepiota, Macrolepiota,* and *Cystoderma* should be mentioned.

The fleshy fruit bodies of the Coprinaceae have a central stipe and thin, free or adnate gills; their trama is regular. In the genus *Coprinus*, fruit bodies develop extraordinarily quickly and, as the spores ripen, at first the gills and ultimately the whole fruit body start dissolving into a pulpy mass (autolysis). This process does not take place in the genera *Panaeolus, Panaeolina,* and *Psathyrella*. The spore print

28) Examples of some Agaricales fruit-bodies: **a** – *Lactarius* sp.; **b** – *Russula* sp.; **c** – *Hygrocybe* sp.; **d** – *Armillaria mellea;* **e** – *Clitocybe* sp.; **f** – *Collybia* sp.; **g** – *Mycena* sp.; **i** – *Coprinus* sp.; **j** – *Lepiota* sp.; **k** – *Tricholoma* sp.; **l** – *Amanita* sp.; **m** – *Agaricus* sp.; **n** – *Inocybe* sp.; **o** – *Pholiota* sp.; **p** – *Psathyrella* sp.; **r** – *Cortinarius* (*Phlegmacium*); **s** – *Boletus* sp.

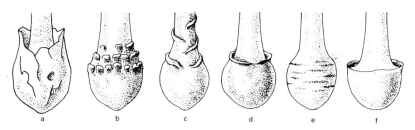

29) Examples of the basal end of the stipe in some species of *Amanita*: **a** – *Amanita phalloides*; **b** – *A. muscaria*; **c** – *A. pantherina*; **d** – *A. gemmata*; **e** – *A. rubescens*; **f** – *A. citrina*.

is dark brown, purple-brown to black, the spores are smooth or ornamented, mostly possessing a discernible germ pore. Coprinaceae grow on the ground, on dung, excrements, wood, and on the remains of herbs or grasses.

Bolbitiaceae are smaller-sized and often thinfleshed fungi with a central stipe. The gills are thin, broad, adnate, the gill trama is regular, the spore print is rusty brown, rusty ochre to umber-brown, the spores are smooth, with a a germ pore. The cap cuticle is composed of globular to pyriform cells; cheilocystidia of a characteristic shape are often developed. Bolbitiaceae grow on excrements, on the ground, on wood and other plant remains. Important genera are *Conocybe*, *Bolbitius*, and *Agrocybe*.

Variously sized fleshy fungi with a central stipe belong to the family Strophariaceae. The cap cuticle consists of long hyphae, the sometimes distinctly developed velum leaves a ring or other remnants on the stipe. The spore print is pale violet or tinged with various shades of brown. The spores are smooth, mostly furnished with a germ pore. Cheilocystidia and also pleurocystidia are developed, some genera have chrysocystidia. Strophariaceae grow on the ground, often on decaying wood or on other plant remains, sometimes also on excrements. The main genera belonging here are *Stropharia*, *Hypholoma*, *Psilocybe* and *Pholiota*.

Cortinariaceae greatly resemble Tricholomataceae and represent the second largest family of gill fungi. The characteristic feature common to all Cortinariaceae is the colour of the spore print which, as a rule, is brown or rust-coloured; it is white only exceptionally. The spores are often ornamented, verrucose, and usually lack a distinct germ pore; the cap cuticle is composed of radially arranged hyphae; the gill trama is regular. The universal veil (velum generale) is either developed or absent; the partial veil is usually present in the form of a cortina. Cystidia are often present. Cortinariaceae grow on humus, wood and moss, and many species form ectotrophic mycorrhizae. The name of the family is derived from that of the most plentiful genus of gill-bearing fungi, *Cortinarius*, comprising approximately 500 species and divided into several subgenera which some considered to be independent genera. Of the other large genera belonging to this family, let us mention *Inocybe*, *Hebeloma* and *Galerina*.

The order **Russulales**. Originally the Russelales were regarded as a family of the order Agaricales; at present, however, they are taken to be an independent order. A characteristic feature here is the structure of the fruit-body context containing – besides long, cylindrical hyphae – groups of globular cells (spherocysts) nidulariaceously arranged in its tissue. It is the spherocysts that cause the characteristic friability, that is the pomaceous brittleness of the broken context. Lactifers are also present in the context. In the *Lactarius* species they are filled with latex, i.e. a milky-white juice oozing from bruised places in fresh fruit bodies. The cap cuticle is often variegated; the spore print is white to bright yellow; spores are broad, subglobose, and broadly ovoid or ellipsoid, with a conspicuous strongly amyloid ornamentation on the surface. Cystidia are present in the hymenium. The order has a single family – the Russulaceae, including the genera *Russula* and *Lactarius* represented in the European forests by a large number of species. For the most part, they are mushrooms living in ectotrophic mycorrhiza with woody forest plants.

The class of **Gasteromycetes** (stomach fungi) includes fungi with an angiocarpous, predominantly globular fruit body which is either permanently closed or opens only in connection with the maturation of basidiospores. The fruit body consists of an external cover (peridium) and the part enclosed within (the gleba) containing the spore-bearing tissue. The gleba is often composed of cavities whose walls are partly formed by thick-walled hyphae; in the mature fruit body, these hyphae are transformed into the capillitium, while the other hyphae of the gleba disintegrate simultaneously with the basidia. The basidia are distributed throughout the fruit body either evenly or like birds' nests; sometimes they line the inner walls of the chambers or cavities in palisades. The development of the gleba is typical of individual families and genera of the Gasteromycetes. Ripe spores are not actively discharged (as for instance in the gill fungi).

Phallaceae are conspicuous and sometimes very ornamental fungi. The young fruit body is egg-shaped. The peridium is often composed of three layers, the middle layer being thick and gelatinous. At maturity it is pierced through at the apex by the receptaculum (i.e. the infertile part of the gleba). The receptaculum carries the fertile part upward, while the rest of the peridium remains at the base in the form of a cup (volva). At maturity the fertile part of the gleba covering the surface of the receptaculum decomposes into a pulpy matter emitting an unpleasant odour. This odour attracts insects and these subsequently disperse the basidiospores contained in this matter. A number of tropical genera belong here, the genera indigenous to Europe are *Phallus* and *Multinus*. The genera *Clathrus*, *Anthurus*, *Lysurus* and *Dictyophora* are sometimes classed with the independent family Clathraceae.

Hysterangiaceae have hypogeous, tuberiform or subglobular fruit bodies often overgrown with mycelial threads, and a cartilaginous or gelatinous gleba composed of a tissue radially developing from the infertile base or from a gelatinous columella. The spores are smooth, ellipsoid or cylindrical, and are almost colourless. The genus *Hysterangium* belongs to this family.

Earth stars (Geastraceae) are terrestrial, and in the tropics even lignicolous fungi. When young, the globular or pyriform fruit bodies are usually embedded in the ground. In mature fruit bodies the outer peridium bursts and lifts the fruit bodies above the ground. The outer peridium splits into rays, in the centre of which the inner peridium with a globular gleba is seated. The gleba contains the capillitium and spores. The Geastraceae often remain in their spot for a long time.

Lycoperdaceae are mostly epigeous (at least maturity). They are globular, pyriform or clavate in shape; the gleba fills the whole interior of the fruit body or passes over into a sterile tissue in its basal portion. The peridium consists of a thin and readily decomposing outer layer (exoperidium), and a usually thin, papery layer (endoperidium) opening by a small peristome or irregularly decomposing. In the members of the genus *Geastrum* it splits to form regular rays, the endoperidium is either attached to the exoperidium or is borne on a pedicel; the peristome is situated at the apex of the endoperidium. The capillitium is usually developed. Spores are globular, small, and coloured. The main genera include *Lycoperdon*, *Bovista*, *Calvatia*, *Langermannia*, and *Geastrum*. *Langermannia gigantea*, whose fruit bodies grow up to 50 cm in diameter, are among largest of fungi.

Sclerodermataceae have tuberiform, fleshy, sometimes stipitate fruit bodies developing on under the surface of the ground. The peridium either opens by an apical pore or bursts irregularly. At maturity the gleba is reduced to powder – either directly, or following an intermediate disintegration into pip-like structures. The basidia are either regularly distributed in the gleba, or form nidi, or fill in the cavities. Spores are globular, ornamented, and coloured. The best-known genera of this family are *Scleroderma* and *Pisolithus*.

Closely related to the Sclerodermataceae are Astreaceae, even though, in appearance, they markedly resemble members of the genus *Geastrum* to which they are not linked.

Nidulariaceae have globular or cup-like, sessile fruit bodies with a chambered gleba disintegrating into single peridioles. These either remain attached to the inner wall of the peridium, or are discharged. The basidia form the hymenium covering the walls of the peridioles, or assemble into nest-like structures situated within the gleba. Spores are ellipsoid, smooth, and colourless. The Nidulariaceae thrive on decaying plant remains or on old dung. On the whole, they are small fungi interesting both in appearance and in biology.

Deuteromycetes (*Fungi imperfecti*)

This vast group includes all fungi characterized by purely asexual reproduction (without any foregoing nuclear association either by decomposition of hyphae, or by the formation of special spores, known as conidia). They are known only in this form (nowadays termed anamorph), or demonstrably belong to other fungus groups – mostly to Ascomycetes – as their particular developmental stage. They mostly

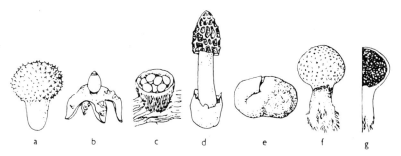

30) Examples of some Gasteromycetes fruit bodies: **a** – *Lycoperdon;* **b** – *Geastrum;* **c** – *Crucibulum laeve;* **d** – *Phallus impudicus;* **e** – *Rhizopogon;* **f, g** – *Scleroderma verrucosum.*

involve minute organisms which, for the most part, can be distinguished only under the lens, and only a first-rate microscope makes possible their identification and study. They occur practically everywhere, as saprophytes or parasites. Approximately 20,000 species have been described hitherto. They are divided into two main groups – Coelomycetes and Hyphomycetes. In the Coelomycetes, conidia are borne on conidiophores or arise directly from conidiogenous cells growing out the sterile hyphal tissue which forms closed or open fruit bodies. Several hundred genera including many thousand species belong to this group.

In the Hyphomycetes, conidia arise either directly from the mycelium or, most frequenty, they originate on conidiophores from specific, so-called conidiogenous cells. Conidiophores grow freely on the substrate as fibrillose, hirsute or matted-tomentose layers. These so-called pseudomoulds are of considerable importance in phytopathology, technical mycology, veterinary science and medicine as organisms causing various diseases in plants, animals and man. The colouring of conidiophores substantiates their division into colourless ones (Moniliales or Moniliaceae) and dark-coloured ones (Dematiales or Dematiaceae). Of the most important genera at least the following should be referred to: *Aspergillus, Penicillium, Botrytis, Monilia, Cladosporium* and *Fusarium.* Also the Hyphomycetes include a great number of genera and species.

The designation Blastomycetes covers a group of microscopic fungi which are explicitly gemmiparous. This is also why they are termed 'asporogenous (anascosporogenous) yeasts'. The genera included here are *Candida* and *Cryptococcus;* some of them cause skin and other diseases in Man.

31) Examples of some microscopic fungi of the group Deuteromycetes: **a** – pycnidia of *Phoma* sp.; **b** – section through the pycnidium of *Septoria* sp. with conidia; **c** – conidiophore of *Penicillium* sp. with conidia; **d** – conidiophore of *Aspergillus niger* with conidia; **e** – conidia of *Aspergillus* sp.; **f** – conidiophore of *Alternaria tenuis* with conidial chains.

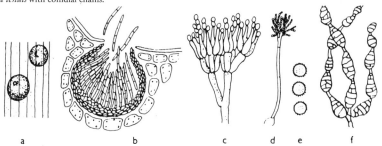

GLOSSARY OF BASIC MYCOLOGICAL TERMS

acyanophilous – not staining blue when touched with cotton blue.

aethalium – a pulvinate or semiglobular fruit body of some slime moulds arising from the association of a large number of sporangia.

allantoid spores – curved cylindrical spores, sometimes also referred to as sausage-shaped.

amyloid – spore walls or hyphae staining blue in solutions containing iodine. In mycology, Melzer's reagent is used for testing amyloidity; the colouration appears in various shades of blue (from bluish grey over deep blue or bluish green to black).

anamorph – a stage of the fungal thallus which is either sterile (e.g. sclerotium, rhizomorph), or producing asexual spores (conidia, chlamydospores). Most of the conidial stages in fungi are anamorphs.

annulus – ring; in general it is a remnant of the veil (*velum partiale*) on the fruit-body stipe, usually in the form of a membranous collar.

anthracophilous – inhabiting burned-over soil or growing directly on burned wood.

apical – at the apex.

apiculus – a minute projection at the basal end of the spore by which the spore is attached to the sterigma.

apothecium – the fruit body of the Discomycetes with an open thecium.

ascocarp – the pseudoperithecium of some Pyrenomycetes.

ascospore – a spore of the Ascomycetes borne in an ascus.

ascus – a saclike, cylindrical or claviform structure in the Ascomycetes where, after nuclear association and a subsequent reduction division, spores (ascospores) develop.

asexual reproduction – vegetative reproduction; in general, this implies reproduction through elements arisen without any foregoing fusion of the plasmatic and nuclear contents of two sexually different cells.

assimilative pigment – photosynthetic pigment (particularly chlorophyll in green plants).

autotropic nutrition – the capacity of the plants to transform absorbed inorganic substances into organic ones.

basidiole – a sterile basidium (without sterigmata) or other sterile hymenial cells resembling the basidia in both shape and size.

basidiospore – a spore of the Basidiomycetes separated from the basidium by a sterigma (pedicel).

basidium – a cell mostly clavate or cylindrical in shape, bearing pedicellate (sterigmate) spores (basidiospores) developing subsequent to nuclear association and the reduction division following thereon. It is characteristic of the Basidiomycetes.

bilateral gill trama – see trama.

binding hyphae – mostly thick-walled, richly branched fruticose hyphae with a short basic pedicel, aseptate, lacking clamp connections.

bitunicate ascus – a double-walled ascus.

capillitium – sterile fibres mixed with the spores within the fruit bodies of some Gasteromycetes or Myxomycetes.

carminophilous basidia – see siderophilous basidia.

caulocystidium – a cystidium developed on the stipe cuticle.

cheilocystidium – a cystidium occurring on the edge of a gill.

chemical reagents – are used in identifying fungi as well as in preparing microscopic mounts. The most common ones are a 3–10 per cent aquaeous solution of ammonia, a 2–5 per cent solution of potassium hydroxide (KOH), lactophenol, lactic acid, Melzer's reagent, cotton blue, acetocarmine. Colour reactions of the context in fresh fruit bodies are tested e.g. by an aquaeous green-vitriol solution, phenol, sulphovanillin, benzidine, etc.

chlamydospore – a thick-walled vegetative spore developed from a hyphal cell.

chrysocystidium – a claviform cystidium in gill-bearing fungi filled with an amorphous, often yellow-coloured matter.

clamp connection – a protuberance arching over the hyphal septum in numerous Basidiomycetes.

cleistothecium – a closed globular fruit body of the Ascomycetes opening by rupture.

collarium – a collar-like arrangement of gills about the apex of the stipe.

columella – a sterile part of the sporangium or fruit body, usually leading from the apex of the stipe or from the base into the spore-bearing part (in slime fungi, moulds and some Gasteromycetes).

conidiogenous cell – a cell bearing conidia.

conidiophore – a specialized independent hypha, either simple or branched, bearing conidiogenous cells and conidia.

conidium – an asexually (vegetatively) produced spore on a hypha or conidiophore.

coprophilous – inhabiting excrements or dung.

copulation – the fusion of two sexual cells, or of the contents of sexually different cells.

cortina (*cobweb*) – a membranous veil covering the hymenium only, eventually a part of the epicutis of the cap.

cotton blue (CB) – dissolved in lactic acid, it is used to colour hyphae, spore walls, and particularly the spore ornamentation, mostly in the Discomycetes.

cyanophilous – readily turning blue to violet in a cotton-blue solution; the opposite is acynophilous.

cystidiole – a sterile cell in the hymenium situated between the basidia, arising from the same hymenial level as the basidium but differing from it in shape.

cystidium – a sterile cell in the hymenium of the Basidiomycetes; it is larger, different in shape from the basidium, and usually more deeply embedded in the hymenium.

dendrophysis – much branched, often dendriform cell found in the hymenium or in the cap cuticle.

dermatocystidium – a cystidium growing from the cuticle of the fruit body; the pileocystidium develops on the pileus cuticle, the caulocystidium on the stipe cuticle.

detritus – a layer of decomposed remains of organic matter (mostly of plant origin) lying on the surface of the ground.

dextrinoid – staining yellowish to reddish brown or vinaceous (purplish) brown in Melzer's readent; it means the same as pseudoamyloid.

diploid – having a twofold number of nuclear chromosomes, as e.g. in the zygote.

eccentric stipe – attached to the pileus extracentrally but not laterally.

epicutis – the outermost layer of the multistratal cuticle covering the pileus of gill fungi; it differs from the other layers in structure.

epigeous – developing above the surface of the ground.

excipulum – the external tissue forming the apothecium.

fimicolous – growing on dung or excrements.

fructification – the stage or period when the fungus produced fruit bodies.

fruit body – a part of the thallus differentiated in shape, consisting of hyphae and reproductive spore-producing cells.

gametangium – an organ producing gametes, i.e. sexual-reproduction cells.

generative hyphae – basic ramified, thin-walled, septate (partitioned) hyphae with or without clamp connections, filled with plasma (see hyphal systems).

germ pore – a usually flattened spot in the thinned part of the spore wall through which the spore germinates.

gill folds – the hymenophore assumes the form of thick and narrow ribs covered with a continuous hymenial layer.

gleba – the fruit-body tissue of the Gasteromycetes producing basidia.

gloeocystidium – a thin-walled cystidium generally having a refractive or granul (often oily) content. It is elongate, claviform or cylindrical, usually deeply anchored in the hymenium, sometimes also in the trama or cap cuticle.

haploid – having half the number of chromosomes in the nuclei of germ cells (gametes).

heterotrophic organisms – having no assimilative pigments, they derive organic substances directly from the living or dead tissues of autotrophic organisms (green plants) or animals.

hilar depression – a slightly depressed spot on the ventral spore wall right above the apiculus.

host – a plant or animal with which either the entire life cycle of a parasite or saprophyte, or at least a part of it is connected.

hydnoid – having a spinulose hymenophore.

hygrophanous – the cap in gill fungi is darker-coloured when damp than after drying out. With the moisture disappearing it fades in colour and is often divided into two contrasting colour zones (the apical and the marginal), or is radially striped with darker and lighter colour shades.

hymeniderm – the structure of the hymenidermal cuticle of the cap is similar to that of the hymenium (all cells are arranged on the same level).

hymeniform – a layer of globular, pyriform, shortly cylindrical or claviform cells arranged in a palisade (e.g. the cap cuticle in some gill fungi).

hymenium – a layer of basidia arranged palisade-like.

hymenophore – part of the fruit body bearing the hymenium.

hypha – filament; the basic structural unit of the fungus body, usually divided by septae into longer and shorter cells; hyphae constitute the mycelium and the major part of the fruit body.

hyphal systems – the fruit body can be composed of one, two or three types of hyphae: the monomitic system consists exclusively of basic (generative) ramose hyphae with or without clamp connections; the dimitic system is made up of generative and skeletal, or generative and binding hyphae; the trimitic system has generative, skeletal and binding hyphae.

hypogeous – growing underground.

hypothallus – also subiculum; a mass of intertwined surface hyphae forming a felted or cobweb-like layer from which fruit bodies arise.

hypothecium – a layer of tissue immediately beneath the thecium of the Discomycetes.

hysterothecium – the usually elongate fruit body of Ascomycetes or lichens with a narrow longitudinal slit in the middle.

incrustation – the surface of hyphal walls is coated with a hard crust, granules or small crystals of frequently refractive colourless matter (incrusted hyphae).

irpicoid – the hymenophore assumes the shape of irregular, flattened (foliated) teeth or short lamellae.

irregular – see (gill) trama.

jellification – coagulation into jelly; the walls of jellified hyphae are coated with a layer of usually colourless jelly.

lactifers (*latifers*) – long, nonseptate hyphae bearing thick, granular lasma or latex (milky-coloured juice).

lamellae – gill-like structures of the hymenophore radially spreading out from the stipe to the cap margin.

lamellules – short gills beginning in the cap margin but not reaching the stipe.

lamprocystidium – a thick-walled cystidium in gill fungi.

lateral stipe – attached to one side of the cap.

lignicolous – growing on wood.

macromycetes – an auxiliary term applied to large fungi whose fruit bodies are visible with the naked eye (they usually exceed 0.5 cm in size).

margo – marginal edge of the apothecium.

meiosis – one of the two successive nuclear divisions of a diploid nucleus is reductional, the result being four daughter nuclei having a haploid (n) number of chromosomes.

Melzer's reagent – the solution of chloral hydrate in water with an admixture of potassium iodide (KI) and iodine (I) used for testing amyloidity (KI, 1.5 g; I, 0.5 g; distilled water, 20 cc; chloral hydrate, 22 g). It was discovered and used for the first time by the Czech mycologist V. Melzer and is one of the most generally applied and most important reagents in taxonomic study and in identifying fungi.

metachromatic – a layer of cells or hyphae changes colour through the application of a given colouring agent, yet the newly acquired colour differs from that originally borne by the colouring agent – e.g. cresylic blue discolours to red.

metuloid – a thick-walled cystidium with a strongly incrusted surface arising in the deep layers of the hymenophore tissue.

micromycetes – an artificial grouping of fungi of predominantly microscopic dimensions whose fruit bodies usually do not surpass the limit of discernibility with the unaided eye. This group includes all imperfect fungi, rusts, smuts, moulds, and the greater part of Ascomycetes.

micron – 1 μm = one thousandth of a millimetre. In mycology, all microelements subjected to microscopic study are indicated in microns.

monomitic – see hyphal systems.

mycelium – the vegetative of the fungal thallus obtaining nutritional substances from the substrate.

mycology – the science of fungi.

mycorrhiza – a symbiotic association of fungus hyphae with the roots of green plants.

nonamyloid – failing to turn blue in Melzer's reagent.

ocrea – partly membranous remnants of the universal veil (*velum generale*), attached to the base of the stipe like a sheath, having a distinct upper margin. They are typical of the *Cortinarius* species belonging to the subgenus *Telamonia.*

oidium – a thin-walled cell arising from the disintegration of a vegetative hypha.

oogonium – a female sexual organ.

oosphere – an egg cell.

oospore – a thick-walled spore formed as the result of fertilization of the oosphere.

ornamentation of spores – the spore-wall surface is sculptured with various excrescences (warts, spinules, ridges, reticulation).

ostiole (ostiolum) – a part of the perithecium narrowing down into a neck-shaped extension provided with a canal lined with hyphae and opening by a pore.

palisade tissue – more or less parallel claviform or cylindrical elements usually situated on the pileus surface or composing the hymenium.

paraphyses – sterile filaments filling up the space between asci (see ascus).

parasite – an organism living or growing upon other living organisms from which it derives nourishment and, in doing so, damages or destroys them.

peridium – the cover enveloping the fruit body in Gasteromycetes; outer peridium = exoperidium, inner peridium = endoperidium.

perithecium – a closed, usually more or less rounded fruit body characteric of the Pyrenomycetes, provided with a wall which, as a rule, opens at the apex by an ostiole.

phialide – a specific cell on the conidiophore, giving rise to conidia.

pileocystidia – cystidia situated on the pileus surface.

plage – suprahilar disc; a more or less circumscribed, smooth spot on the spore wall immediately above the apiculus.

plasmodiocarp – the extending, sessile and ramose fruit body of slime moulds.

plasmodium – a body of plurinucleated, naked protoplasm in Myxomycetes exhibiting slow motion and ultimately changing into fruit bodies.

pleurocystidium – a cystidium occurring on the face of gills.

pore – an opening at the apex of the ascus, or an opening in the ostiole of the perithecium.

poroid – a hymenophore consisting of tubes.

pseudoamyloid – see dextrinoid.

pseudoparaphyses – paraphysoid filaments; sterile threads in some Pyrenomycetes separating the single asci contained in the pseudothecium.

pseudoparenchyma – fungous tissue composed of globular or subglobular cells.

pseudothecium – the perithecium-like fruit body of some Pyrenomycetes; developmentally, however, it is a stroma containing bitunicate asci and pseudoparaphyses – i.e. remnants of the inner tissue.

pycnidium – a closed, mostly ball-shaped fruit body producing nothing but conidia.

radial – spreading out radially from the centre to the margin (for example, fibres on the pileus surface).

receptaculum – an alternative designation for the apothecium or for its greater part; also the bearer in Phallales.

resupinate – reclining over the surface and mostly attached to the substrate (fruit bodies of numerous Aphyllophorales).

rhizoid – a rootlike or strandlike mycelium at the base of the fruit body.

rhizomorph – mycelial strands with a thickened (sclerotized) outer layer.

ring – see annulus.

saprophyte – living on dead organisms, their remains, and on organic matter or mineral soils.

sclerotium – a tuberiform, lenticular or irregular structure composed of firmly intertwined hyphae; it is a resting stage from which, under certain conditions, fruit bodies or hyphae may develop.

sections through the gills – the tangential section is made across the gills in the marginal part of the cap;
– the longitudinal (radial) section is cut through the centre of the cap so that it mostly passes between the gills or longitudinally bisects them;

45

– the cross (transverse) section is cut horizontally to the surface of the ground (in fruit bodies growing on the ground).

septum – partition; a transverse or longitudinal wall in fungus hyphae and spores.

seta – a thick-walled, tough, usually dark-coloured cystidium tapering upward, or a structure similar to it.

sexual reproduction – fusion of the plasmatic and nuclear content of two sexually differentiated cells, and the subsequent development of spores.

spherocystidium – a globular cell in the tissue of Basidiomycetes (e.g. in the genus *Russula*).

siderophilous basidia – their plasma contains a large quantity of granules turning dark in ferric acetocarmine; the same as carminophilous basidia.

skeletal hyphae – thick-walled, unbranched, long, nonseptate hyphae; see also hyphal systems.

sporangiophore – a hyphal branch bearing the sporangium.

sporangium – an asexually produced cell bearing one or more spores (e.g. mycetozoan fruit bodies).

spore – the reproductive monocellular or multicellular body functionally corresponding to the seed in higher plants but lacking an embryo.

sterigma – the minute pedicel on the surface of the basidium upon which a spore is borne.

stroma – a rigid structure composed of hyphae wherein fruit bodies or cavities containing asci or conidiophores are embedded (mostly in Pyrenomycetes).

subhymenium – a layer of tissue under the hymenium (its structure is sometimes different from that of the trama).

subiculum – see hypothallus.

substratum – the nutritive base (e.g. earth, soil, plant remains, wood, excrements).

suprahilar disc – see plage.

terrestrial – growing on the ground.

thecium – the uppermost part of the Discomycetes fruit body with the hymenium; the latter consists of asci and paraphyses arranged in a palisade.

thallus – a simple plant- or fungus body undifferentiated in roots, stalks or leaves (gills).

trama – the tissue supporting the hymenium in Basidiomycetes; in gill fungi, the following four types of gills are distinguished: regular trama (the hyphae are parallel to each other); irregular trama (some hyphae diverning in various directions are interwoven with the parallel hyphae); bilateral trama (the hyphae are parallel only in the mediostratum of the gills, while in the margins they diverge towards the hymenium in a curve); inverse trama (similar to the bilateral trama but the hyphae are diverging backwards).

trichoderm – the cuticle consisting of densely clustered and erect hairs.

trimitic – see hyphal systems.

tubes (tubules) – vertically arranged tubular structures composing the hymenophore.

vegetative reproduction – see asexual reproduction.

velum (veil) – the cover enveloping the whole fruit body or a part of it; *velum universale (generale)*, universal veil, enfolds the entire fruit body; *velum partiale*, partial veil, connects the cap margin to the apex of the stipe, covering the hymenophore when young.

volva (cup, sheath) – a usually membranous, cup-shaped structure around the base of the stipe (a remnant of the universal veil).

zygospore – a resting spore resulting from the conjugation of the contents of two gametangia or two gametes.

zygote – a cell in which two nuclei of the opposite sex have fused together. It is diploid, having a double number of chromosomes.

KEY TO SYMBOLS USED:

 - edible

 - inedible

 - poisonous

The black squares in the text refer to the respective photographs on the opposite pages.

Slime fungi – Myxomycetes

Flowers of Tan
Fuligo septica (L.) WIGGERS   V–X   ◼️◻️◻️◻️

Fruit-body (aethalium) cushion-shaped, 2–20 cm wide, 1–3 cm tall, broadly sessile to membranous hypothallus with a fragile, crumbling crust which disintegrates into powder. Its surface is soft and slimy at first, then most frequently whitish or ochre when mature; the inside is dark purple or black-violet with a mass of spores. Spores are 6–9 μm in diameter, spherical with fine spikes, purple brown. Abundant after heavy rainfall on rotten wood or rotting leaves, but also on other substrates, for example on lower parts of live plants. Inedible.

Lycogala epidendron (L.) FR.   V–X   ◻️◼️◻️◻️

Fruit-body (aethalium) almost spherical or cushion-shaped, sessile, 3–15 mm wide, reminiscent of small Puff-balls or *Bovista* species; grows individually or in small groups, with a thin, shell-like crust, soft and pale pink when young, later pinkish-grey, yellowish-brown or reddish; bursts irregularly, with a dusty grey-pink mass of spore powder. Spores are 6–7.5 μm wide, spherical, pinkish-grey on the surface with a fine network, later pale ochre. This most common representative of Slime moulds flourishes on tree stumps and fallen tree trunks of various woodland species. Inedible.

Nectriaceae

Byssonectria luteovirens (FR.: FR.) Z. MORAVEC
Syn. *Hypomyces viridis* BERK. et BR.   VIII–IX   ◻️◻️◼️◻️

Parasitic hard fungus, forming felt-like or woolly stroma, coloured yellow-green to dark green, in which are embedded numerous densely packed, egg-shaped perithecia 0.2–0.3 mm long; pale at first, later turns brown to almost black. Cylindrical, thin-walled asci with eight spores. Ascospores 27–45 × 5–6 μm, narrow, spindle-shaped, pointed at both ends, covered with fine warts, monocellular, colourless. Stroma covers gills of live fruit-bodies of some *Russula* species and deforms them so that in places the gills are replaced by low ribs or are missing altogether. Attacked *Russula* fruit-bodies are conspicuously hard. Inedible.

Xylariaceae

Xylaria hypoxylon (L.: HOOK.) GREV.   I–XII   ◻️◻️◻️◼️

Stromatic, hard wood fungus. Stroma is erect, very tough and flexible, 3–8 cm high; either sterile, without perithecia, antler-like, flattened, tips powdered with white conidia which develop on their surface, lower part black and hirsute, or unbranched or only slightly forked, fertile with spherical perithecia on the surface. Ascospores 11–15 × 5–6 μm, bean-shaped, non-transparent black, smooth, monocellular. Grows abundantly in groups on tree stumps and fallen branches of various deciduous trees. Inedible.

Sclerotiniaceae

Sclerotinia tuberosa (HEDW.: MÉRAT) FUCKEL   IV–V

Fruit-body (apothecium) 1–3 cm in diameter, deep cup-shaped, all chestnut brown. Fruit-bodies bald with relatively thin, crooked tough stalk up to 10 cm long; grow solitary or in clusters of tough, black, tuberous sclerotia with white flesh, 1–2 cm tall. Spores 12–17 × 6–9 μm, ovoid, ellipsoid, smooth, develop in eights in long, cylindrical asci. Abundant in growths of *Anemone nemorosa*, parasitizing its rhizomes. Inedible.

Helotiaceae

Leotia lubrica (SCOP.) ex S. F. GRAY   VIII–IX

A Discomycete with erect fruit-bodies, 3–8 cm tall, made up of a stalk and a head-like broadened fertile part, 1–2 cm wide, arched, folded, edge enrolled and lobed, tough, gelatinous, coloured cloudy yellow to olive green. Stalk 3–6 mm thick, cylindrical, narrowing at base, pale yellow, slightly dotted with greenish particles. Ascospores 20–25 × 5–6 μm, cylindrical, spindle-shaped, with 5–7 transverse partitions, colourless, arranged in eights in asci. Grows on the ground in damp, mainly deciduous woods, sometimes in dense clusters. Inedible.

Geoglossaceae

Mitrula paludosa FR.   VI–VIII

Fruit-body erect, 1–4 cm tall, divided into fertile section and stipe. Fertile section is club-, pear-shaped or cylindrical, often rather irregular, folded and lobed, bright orange or yolk yellow, fragile and watery. It is sharply separated from the thin, cylindrical, white, transparent stipe, 2–5 cm long and 1–3 mm thick. Ascospores 10–15 × 2.5–3 μm, narrow, cylindrically spindle-shaped, filled with drops, monocellular, colourless, develop in eights in elongated, club-shaped asci. It usually grows in clusters on rotting grass, needles, foliage and branches submerged in clear water in woodland fens and moorland. Inedible.

Sarcoscyphaceae

Scarlet Elf Cup
Plectania coccinea (SCOP.: ST. AM.) FUCKEL   X–V

Fruit-body (apothecium) 2–7 cm wide, deeply cup-shaped, later bowl-shaped, flesh is thin but tough and leathery with a bright scarlet disc inside, whitish or reddish on the outside, softy silky. It is attached to the substrate by an extended base or a 1–2 cm long, white, felt-like stalk. Ascospores 24–32 × 12–14 μm, cylindrically ellipsoid with two drops, smooth, colourless. The asci have nonamyloid walls and carry eight spores. It grows on rotting branches and deciduous tree trunks lying on the ground, especially those of lime and maple; it is locally abundant. Young fruit-bodies become established in autumn and often ripen when the snow melts at the end of winter or in early spring. Inedible.

Humariaceae

Orange Peel Fungus
Aleuria aurantia (PERS.: HOOK) FUCKEL   IX–XI

Fruit-body (apothecium) 2–10 cm wide, at first cup-shaped, later bowl-shaped, and finally almost expanded; broadly sessile, thin and fragile flesh with bright orange disc, whitish, downy on the outside. Ascospores 17–24 × 9–11 μm, ellipsoid with two large drops; decorated on the surface with a network of square, usually regular hexagonal eyelets which can be intensively coloured by cotton blue. Asci are cylindrical, have nonamyloid walls with eight spores. Paraphysis club-shaped at top and filled with orange pigment: It grows in damp, sandy-clayey soil, especially along woodland tracks and ditches. Inedible.

Tarzetta velata (QUÉL.) SVR.   VI–IX

Fruit-body (apothecium) 10–18 mm wide, 10–15 mm tall, with a stalk; deeply cup-shaped, greyish outside, ochre yellow to pale brown, felt-like, with brown of grey-brown speckles near the edges. The greyish-ochre disc is at first covered by a whitish, cobweb-like veil, later opens out and remainder of veil is left on edges. Stalk 1–3 cm long, whitish to yellow. Asci cylindrical with nonamyloid walls and eight spores. Spores 20–25 × 12–14.5 μm, broadly ellipsoid, narrowing towards the ends, with two large drops, smooth, colourless. It grows on clay, bare soil in gardens and in woods. Inedible.

Otideaceae

Hare's Ear
Otidea onotica (PERS.) ex S. F. GRAY   IX–X

Fruit-body (apothecium) 2–8 cm tall, 1–3 cm wide, erect, in the shape of hare's ear, tapers down into a short stalk, pitcher-shaped and enrolled, on one side lobed to the base, with a rusty brown disc, ochre on the outside, bare, smooth; thin, leathery flesh. The stalk-like stipe is whitish, felt-like. Asci are cylindrical, with a nonamyloid wall, having eight spores. Paraphyses terminate in a hook. Spores 12–15 × 6–8 μm, ellipsoid with two drops, smooth, colourless. Grows among needles and moss in acid soil in coniferous woods. Inedible.

Sowerbyella radiculata (SOW.: FR.) NANNF.   VIII–XI

Fruit-body 2–5 cm wide, cup-shaped, later bowl-shaped, regularly circular, later lobed; narrows at the base into a tough, long, deeply rooted stalk which is whitish, felt-like on the outside. The disc is pale yellow or yolk yellow, smooth. The outer surface is white, finely felted, later becoming bare and yellow. Asci are cylindrical with eight spores, and with a nonamyloid wall. Paraphysis has a pronounced curve at top. Ascospores 12–14 × 7–7.5 μm, uniseriate, ellipsoid, with two large drops, warty, colourless. Grows mostly under coniferous trees, often in circles. Inedible.

Pezizaceae

Peziza badia PERS.: MÉRAT   VI–IX

Fruit-body (apothecium) 2–8 cm wide, sessile, at first globular and enclosed, later deep cup- to bowl-shaped, finally almost flat. Disc is dark brown with an olive-green tinge, outer surface is pale red-brown with small rusty brown flakes. Flesh is thin, fragile and juicy; when cut, it produces colourless liquid. Ascospores 17–20 × 9–12 μm, longitudinally ellipsoid, with two drops, on the surface decorated with thin, irregular, branched and joined ribs, which in places form incomplete network. Ascus wall is strongly amyloid at top. Grows on bare ground, especially in sand or clay, by woodland paths and in ditches. Inedible.

Peziza micropus PERS.   V–X

Fruit-body 2–10 cm wide, at first cup-shaped, narrowing at base, sessile, but soon widely bowl-shaped, and finally flattened or concave with involuted margin. Flesh is fragile and watery, disc in various shades of ochre yellow to ochre brown; outer surface is white felted and floury, margins densely cracked or covered with small warts, edge serrated or broken. Flesh 2–4 mm thick, whitish with central filamentous layer. Asci are cylindrical with eight spores and wall strongly amyloid at top. Ascospores 14–18 × 8–10 μm, ellipsoid, smooth, colourless. It grows on rotting wood of deciduous trees, especially on beech in mountain forests. Rare or absent in Great Britain. Inedible.

Rhizinaceae

Rhizina undulata FR.: PERS.
Syn. *Rhizina inflata* (SCHAEFF.) ex KARST.   VIII–X

Fruit-body 2–10 cm wide, arched, with lobed margin, up to 5 mm thick, relatively tough, whitish on the underside, attached to the substrate by numerous root-like, yellowish filaments; disc is chestnut brown to black-brown, with a wide and thick white edging. Asci cylindrical, with eight spores located in one row, and with non-amyloid wall. Paraphysis colourless, club-shaped at the top and covered with a brown spore mass. Ascospores 22–40 × 8–11 μm, spindle-shaped, pointed at both ends, with several large drops, slightly rough on surface, colourless. It grows on burnt ground on roots of coniferous trees. It is considered a pest for seedling pines. Inedible.

Helvellaceae

Neogyromitra gigas (KROMBH.) IMAI
Syn. *Gyromitra gigas* (KROMBH.) COOKE   IV–VI
Syn. *Discina gigas* (KROMBH.) SVR. et J. MOR.

Fruit-body 8–25 cm tall and wide, hollow. Cap is sub-globose, lobed and convolute, 6–15 cm wide, with margins almost attached to the stipe, ochre yellow to pale brown. Stipe is short, up to 5 cm wide, grooved with depressions, white, greyish when old, granulated. The white flesh has a pleasant smell. Spore powder is white, spores 28–40 × 12–14 μm, spindle-shaped, with cap at apex and with ornamental network. It grows on old tree stumps and their roots. Edible.

Helvellaceae

 Discina fastigiata (KROMBH.) SVR. et J. MOR.
Syn. *Gyromitra fastigiata* (KROMB.) REHM   IV–V

Cap 3–12 cm wide, 2–8 cm tall, saddle-shaped with two to three (occasionally four) free, pointed lobes, disc convoluted, veiny, pink to reddish-brown, or pinkish-chocolate brown, creamy outside. Stipe, up to 6 cm thick, often broadens at base; it is white pruinose, slightly wrinkled. Asci cylindrical, with nonamyloid walls, eight spores. Paraphysis at the top slightly broadened and filled with brown pigment. Spores 24.5–32.5 × 11–15 μm, ellipsoid, with large drop in the centre and two smaller at both apexes, covered with fine warts and low network; several unevenly long warts at either end. It grows on the ground in warm, deciduous woods. Rare or absent in Great Britain. Edible.

 Gyromitra esculenta (PERS.) FR.   III–IV

Fruit-body is 3–15 cm tall and wide, hollow. Cap is irregularly globular, with brain-like convolutions, rounded lobes. Chestnut or reddish-brown, but also white or blackish-brown. Stipe up to 3 cm tall and 4 cm wide, finely pitted, white to whitish. Flesh is white and has a pleasant mushroom smell. Spore powder is white, spores 18–22 × 9–12 μm, smooth, with 2 drops of oil, transparent. It grows on bare ground in sandy pine woods and also under deciduous trees, especially in Scotland. Poisonous.

Morchellaceae

The Common Morel
Morchella esculenta PERS.: ST.-AMANS   IV–V

Erect fruit-body, hollow inside. Cap 3–10 cm high, 3–7 cm wide, globular, obtusely ovoid with deep pits surrounded by irregularly shaped sinuous ridges, attached to stipe below, brownish, ochre, greyish, or with an olive green tint. Stipe 3–7 cm high, widened towards the base, whitish or slightly ochre, partly pitted. Flesh fragile. Ascospores 18–23 × 11–15 μm, ellipsoid, faintly grained at both ends, smooth, yellowish. Spore powder light ochre. It grows on grassland, in gardens, parks and light woodlands. Edible, very tasty.

Morchellaceae

Morchella conica PERS.   IV–V

Erect fruit-body, hollow inside. Cap 2–6 cm wide, 2–7 cm high, pointed ovoid to cylindrical, brown to blackish brown, hispid, with deep, elongated, square pits, edged by main, horizontal ridges from the apex of the cap to its lower edge and by vertical thin lines. Stipe is narrower than the cap, usually broadens towards the base, whitish ochre, slightly wrinkled. Spore powder is ochre. Spores 18–21 × 12–12 μm, ellipsoid, with several grains at either end, yellowish, smooth. It grows on grassland, waste ground in towns, in gardens and woods. Edible, tasty.

Morchella pragensis SMOTL. ex VESELSKÝ   V–VI

Fruit-body 6–28 cm high, 4–8 cm wide, long and conical, tapering towards the top or flattened like a ping-pong bat, lower edge 2–4 cm overlapping the stipe, yellowish to olive brown, with horizontal and vertical ridges, pits elongated to circular. Stipe 4–9 cm long, 2–4 cm wide, cylindrical, often pitted or grooved, white to ochre yellow. Spore powder is light ochre. Spores 19.5–25.5 × 12–13.5 μm, longish ellipsoid, with grains at apex, smooth pale ochre. It grows on waste ground and in various places of human activity (e.g. yards, warehouses, ditches, between cobbles), especially in eastern Europe. Edible.

Verpa bohemica KROMBH.   III–V

Cap 2–6 cm wide, 3–8 cm high, campanulate, attached to the top of the hollow stipe, with transversely lobed ridges, pale ochre, yellow-brown to brown. Stipe 7–14 cm long, 1–2.5 cm thick, cylindrical, white or whitish, faintly granular, fragile. Spore powder ochre yellow. Spores 55–80 × 15–22 μm, unusually large, longish ellipsoid, smooth, developing in cylindrical asci, usually in twos. The ascus wall is non-amyloid. It grows in warm areas in deciduous woods, on fallen leaves, especially under aspen, sometimes in clusters. A similar species, *V. conica*, is found in Great Britain. Edible, tasty.

Terfeziaceae

Choiromyces venosus (FR.) TH. FR.
Syn. *Choiromyces meandriformis* VITT.   VII–IX

Subterranean fruit-body of irregular tuber-like shape, 5–15 cm wide, surface whitish, greyish-white, yellowish to light brown; very tough to hard consistency, heavy (reaches up to 500 gms in weight); flesh is meaty, whitish at first, later greyish, with a network of sinuous, faintly yellow or yellow-brown veins. When mature it emits a strong, unpleasant, spicy smell. Asci broadly club-shaped, with two, four or eight spores. Spores 16–22 μm wide (including thorns), globular with short and blunt thorns, colourless, later yellowish. It grows in all types of forest, close to the surface of the ground and partly penetrating above. Edible as spice.

Tremellaceae

Yellow Brain Fungus or
Witches' Butter   IX–IV ■□/□□

Tremella mesenterica RETZ. ex HOOK.

Fruit-body 2–4 cm wide, sessile, roundish, divided into numerous brain-like folds, golden-yellow, elastic gelatinous in damp conditions, hard and shrivelled in drought; emits pleasant aroma. Hymenium covers the whole surface of the fruit-body. Spore powder is white. Spores 10–12 μm wide, globular, smooth, colourless. Basidia are divided by two planes at right angles to one another into four sections. It grows on fallen branches of deciduous trees, especially on oak and hornbeam. Inedible. Related *Tremella foliacea* is bigger, up to 15 cm wide, brown-yellow, sometimes with purple tinge.

Hirneola auricula-judae (BULL.: ST.-AM.) BERK.   IV–XII □■/□□

Fruit-body 3–12 cm wide, cup-shaped at first, later bowl-shaped, attached to the substrate by its narrow base, later concave with ear-shaped folds, scaly; the living fruit-body is soft and elastic, gelatinous, horny hard and almost black in drought, but becomes pliable again when moistened. The surface is velvet hirsute, grey-brown, hymenium veiny wrinkled, light to date-brown, covered with white spore powder. Spores 13–20 × 4–6 μm, narrow, ellipsoid, colourless. It grows on dead tree trunks and branches, mostly on common elder and false acacia, less often on other deciduous trees and shrubs. Edible.

Exidia plana (WIGG.: SCHLEICH.) DONK
Syn. *Exidia glandulosa* FR. sensu NEUHOFF   IX–IV □□/■□

Fruit-body 3–10 cm wide, 0.5–1 cm high, attached to the substrate by its broad base; coloured olive black to black, with brain-like lobes, sparsely covered with club-shaped, blunt, black warts. In damp weather it becomes softly elastic and gelatinous; in drought it shrivels into a thin, black, glassy or gumma coating which breaks easily. Hymenium covers only the upper surface of the fruit-body. It has no specific smell. Spore powder is white. Basidia are longitudinally divided into four bottle-shaped sections. Spores 10–16 × 4–5 μm, cylindrical, curved and colourless. It grows in abundance on dead branches and stumps of deciduous trees, most frequently on beech and oak. Inedible.

Pseudohydnum gelatinosum (SCOP.: FR.) KARST.   VII–X □□/□■

Fruit-body 1–8 cm wide, 1–2 cm thick, ligulate, attached to the substrate by a short, eccentric stalk, tough gelatinous and elastic, coloured milky white, bluish, greyish, also dark brown, with felted surface. The lower surface is covered with dense spikes up to 1 cm long, bearing the hymenium. Basidia are divided by two division at right angles into four sections with neck-like protrusions which terminate in a single spore. Spore powder is white. Spores 5–8 × 4.5–6.5 μm, almost globular, smooth and colourless. It grows on stumps and fallen trunks of coniferous trees, particularly of spruce and pine in subalpine forests. Edible.

Dacrymycetaceae

Yellow Antler Fungus
Calocera viscosa (PERS.: FR.) FR.   VI–X

Fruit-body 3–10 cm high, erect, branched like a stag's horn into cylindrical, forked protrusions; slimy, elastic and tough, deeply rooting in the substrate, golden-yellow or orange. Hymenium covers the surface of branches. Basidia forked into two branches, which terminate in spores. Spore powder is white. Spores 8–12 × 3.5–4.5 μm, cylindrical, curved, colourless. It grows abundantly on old coniferous tree stumps, particularly on spruce. Inedible. Unbranched species *C. cornea* is only 1–1.5 cm high and grows on deciduous trees.

Corticiceae

Hyphoderma radula (FR.) DONK
Syn. *Radulum orbiculare* (FR.) FR.   I–XII

Flat (resupinate) fruit-body in the form of white, later yellowish coating which is firmly attached to the substrate; white, filamentous edging at the perimeter; circular or irregularly shaped, 2–8 cm wide; thin, wax-like flesh when growing. Surface covered with individual or clustering spikes which are cylindrical, often flattened and terminate in pointed or forked protrusions up to 5 mm long. Spore powder is white. Spores 8–13 × 3–3.5 μm, cylindrical, slightly curved, smooth and colourless. It grows on dead branches of deciduous trees, namely on cherry, birch and aspen. Inedible. There are a number of similar species difficult to identify on macroscopic characters.

Amylostereum areolatum (FR.) BOIDIN   I–XII

Fruit-body semi-resupinate, protruding in short (0.5–2 cm wide), thick, little caps with blunt ends, tough, up to 10 cm in diameter, 1–1.5 mm thick, with brown felt-like surface, hymenium smooth, ochre-brown to grey-brown, often with violet tinge. Spores 5–8 × 2.5–4 μm, ellipsoid, smooth, colourless, amyloid. It is abundant on spruce stumps. Similar species is *A. chailletii* (PERS.) BOIDIN which grows mainly on firs and differs in thin, almost bald fruit-bodies (only 0.5–0.7 mm thick), protruding in very short caps (max. 1 cm wide). Inedible.

Stereum hirsutum (WILLD.: FR.) S. F. GRAY   I–XII

Fruit-body usually less than 6 cm wide, adpressed to the substrate or with upper part forming thin brackets with hairy upper surface. It is tough, leathery, hirsute on the surface, yellowish, greyish or brownish. Sometimes also forms saucer-shaped fruit-bodies like *Trametes versicolor*, but is always distinguished by the yellow margin. Hymenium is smooth and bare, yolk yellow or orange-yellow, becoming pale with age, yellow colouring of margins remains. It does not change colour when bruised. Spore powder is white. Spores 5–8 × 2.5–3.5 μm, cylindrical, smooth, colourless and amyloid. It grows in profusion on live and dead wood of decisuous trees. Inedible.
Note: In the picture you can see very young fruit-bodies.

Corticiaceae

Merulius tremellosus FR.   IV–XII   ■□ □□

Fruit-body resupinate or semi-resupinate, protruding in filaments, lobed, gelatinously soft, leathery, up to 10 cm wide, 3–4 mm thick, white or greyish felt-like to hirsute on the surface. Hymenium brownish, wrinkled, with combs, with a dense network of veins, sometimes up to orange or reddish yellow. Spores 3.5–5 × 1–1.5 μm, thin, cylindrical, arched, colourless. It growns on stumps, rotting trunks and branches of deciduous trees, rarely of conifers, in damp places. Inedible.

Gomphaceae

Ramaria botrytis (PERS.: FR.) RICKEN   VIII–IX   □■ □□

Fruit-body 5–12 cm wide, 5–20 cm high, sub-globose, with numerous branchlets growing out of a short, thick, fleshy, white stipe. Branchlets are smooth or longitudinally grooved, pale to light ochre, at tips flesh or vine red, later brownish; tips are blunt. Flesh is white and fragile, almost colourless; the taste is at first mild, later becoming slightly bitter to sour. Spore powder is pale yellow. Spores 11–18 × 4–6 μm, cylindrical, wedge-like, points, pale ochre, striate. It grows on the ground in deciduous or coniferous forests. Edible. Care must be taken not to confuse it with the related species *R. formosa* which has buff to rose branches and buffer flesh, bruising blackish.

Ramaria flava (SCHAEFF.: FR.) QUÉL.   VI–IX   □□ ■□

Fruit-body 10–20 cm high, 6–15 cm wide, densely branched. Stipe is fleshy, whitish, turning brownish-red when bruised. Branchlets continue to fork upwards and terminate in blunt tips. They are sulphur or lemon yellow when young, ochre when mature. Flesh is fragile, white, aroma and taste pleasant. Spore powder is pale creamy, spores 11–18 × 4–6.5 μm, cylindrical, yellowish and tuberculate. It grows mainly in deciduous forests, especially beechwoods. Edible.

Ramaria eumorpha (KARST.) CORNER
Syn. *Ramaria invalii* (COTT.: WAKEF.) DONK   VI–X   □□ □■

Fruit-body 4–8 cm high, grows individually or in clusters, with a short stem enveloped at the base with white mycelium, which changes into numerous thin white rhizomorphes; the stem is divided into numerous erect thin branches coloured ochre, later yellowish-cinnamon to ochre brown. Flesh is white and firm, without a distinctive smell. Spore powder is ochre yellow. Spores 6–10.5 × 3.5–6 μm, cylindrical ellipsoid, densely covered with spikes, ochre yellow. It grows in needles and foliage of spruce and pine forests, but also under larch and in mixed woods. Inedible. Similar species is *R. ochraceo-virens*, which turns green when bruised.

Clavariaceae – Club Fungi

Clavariadelphus ligula (SCHAEFF.: FR.) DONK   VIII–X

Fruit-body 3–8 cm high, 5–12 mm wide, erect, unbranched, clavate or cylindrical, tapering towards the base; lower surface is usually encrusted by coniferous needles and is matted together by white mycelium. It is coloured pale ochre, rarely pinkish-yellow, its surface is wrinkled, its texture soft and elastic. Flesh is white and has no odour. Hymenium covers whole surface of the broadened section of the fruit body. Spore powder is white. Spores 10–15 × 5–6 μm, cylindrical, bare and colourless. It grows abundantly in spruce woods where it often forms dense patches and stripes on the rotting coniferous needles. Inedible.

Clavulina rugosa (BULL.: FR.) SCHROET.   VII–X

Fruit-body 4–10 cm high, clavate, usually longitudinally flattened, deeply wrinkled or verrucose on the surface, as if deformed. Unbranched or irregularly divided into several short, erect branches with blunt tips. It is coloured whitish, light grey to purple-greyish. Flesh is brittle, whitish. Spore powder is white. Spores 9–14 × 8–12 μm, globular ovoid, smooth and colourless. It grows on bare ground in coniferous forests, particularly plentiful in damp and shaded places alongside forest tracts and ditches. Edible.

Clavulina cristata (HOLMSKJ.: FR.) SCHROET   VII–X

Fruit-body 3–10 cm high, stipe branching into numerous protrusions with irregular, comb-like, pointed and laterally flattened tips. Its colour varies from pure white to dirty yellow and light grey; the grey form is sometimes called *C. cinerea*. Fruit-body is brittle and breaks easily. Spore powder is white. Spores 7–11 × 6.5–10 μm, almost globular, smooth, with a large drop inside, colourless. It can be distinguished from similar species by the pointed tips of comb-shaped ends of its branches. It grows profusely on damp bare ground alongside woodland tracks, in ditches and also in woods, often in large masses. Edible.

Clavaria purpurea FR.   VIII–IX

Fruit-body 3–12 cm high, unbranched, cylindrical or belt-shaped, often flattened or longitudinally grooved, usually pointed at tip; it is coloured pale amethyst purple or lilac purple, later grey or brown purple. Lower surface is covered with white down, rest of body is bare and smooth; it is hollow and breaks easily. Hymenium covers the whole surface of the fruit-body; long, thin-walled cystidia protrude among basidia. Spore powder is white. Spores 5.5–9 × 3–5 μm, elongated, smooth and colourless, filled with drops. It grows in damp places in spruce forests in sub-alpine regions. Rare or absent in Great Britain. Edible.

Sparassidaceae

Cauliflower Fungus
Sparassis crispa (WULF.) ex FR.   VII–IX

Fruit-body 10–35 cm in diameter, almost globular, whitish or light cream, later brownish. Firm, deeply rooted stipe profusely branches out above the ground, the ends of flat, gill-like branches are curled. Flesh is white and brittle and has a pleasant spicy aroma. Hymenium covers the surface of branches on both sides. Spore powder in white. Spores 6–7.5 × 4–5 μm, ellipsoid, smooth and colourless. It grows at the foot of pines or on their roots. At first sight it resembles a sponge. It can be kept in a bowl of water and slices can be cut off as required. Edible, very tasty.

Thelephoraceae

Thelephora palmata (SCOP.) ex FR.   VII–IX

Fruit-body up to 10 cm high, densely branched from the base. The erect branches are flattened and closely crowded, with lobed, irregularly toothed tips, which are often longitudinally grooved, dark brown with whitish tips. Hymenium covers the whole surface of the branches. The mushroom is elastic, tough and leathery. It has a repulsive smell similar to old rotting cabbage. Spore powder is brown. Spores 8–12 × 7–9 μm, irregularly angular, spiky and brown. It grows on the ground and in moss in coniferous woods, often alongside grassy woodland tracks and at the edges of woods. Inedible.

Thelephora terrestris EHRH.: FR.   VIII–X

Fruit-body is entirely or semi-resupinate, circular, fimbriate or funnel-shaped, attached to the substrate by a concentric, tapering base; sometimes all shapes can be found growing together. The most frequent are circular fruit-bodies 3–10 cm wide, leathery, dark brown with paler fringed margin; upper surface is fibrillose. Hymenium is on the lower surface of the caps, it is slightly tuberculate or wrinkled, grey-brown. Spore powder is brown. Spores 7–12 × 5–9 μm, irregularly angular, with fine spikes, yellow-brown. It is abundant on bare sandy ground in coniferous forests and on heaths. Inedible.

Hydnellum caeruleum (HORNEM.: PERS.) KARST.   VII–X

Fruit-bodies single or clustered. Cap up to 11 cm in diameter, convex, soon flat, later depressed, smooth at first, velvet, later undulated with shallow depressions, felt-like, blue, soon turning pale and whitish. Flesh is grey-blue, later whitish to light orange brownish, bluish striate when cut. Stipe is 1.5–6 cm long, 1–2.5 cm thick, felt-like, yellow-orange to orange-brown. Spikes up to 5 mm long, attached to the stipe, bluish, later white, brownish, purple brown. Spores 5–6 × 3.5–4.5 μm, brownish, coarsely warty. It grows on the ground in coniferous woods, less common in deciduous woods, mainly under beech. Inedible.

Thelephoraceae

Hydnellum ferrugineum (FR.) KARST.   VIII–X

Fruit-bodies single or clustered. Cap up to 10 cm in diameter, shallowly convex to slightly depressed, undulated or grooved, velvet-like to hirsute felt-like on the surface, at first white, then whitish pink, later yellow-brown to red-brown, turning dark brown. It releases drops of red liquid when fresh. Stipe 0.5–6 cm long, 0.7–3 cm thick, cylindrical or spindle-like, velvet and of similar colours as the cap. Spikes up to 6 mm long, converging towards the stipe, whitish, later purple brown. Flesh smells of flour when cut. Spores 5.5–6 × 3.5–4.5 μm, brownish, bluntly undulate. It grows in the ground in coniferous woods. Inedible.

Hydnaceae – Tooth Fungi

Hydnum scabrosum (FR.) KARST.   VIII–X

Cap 4–10 cm wide, irregularly rounded, slightly curved, later flat, with a shallow and wide depression in the middle; chestnut brown, smooth, later cracking into a large number of small scales. Its flesh is firm. Spikes are long and closely packed, converging towards the stipe, brown-grey, whitish at tips. Stipe is short and stout, tapering towards base, white-grey or brownish, blackish or black-green at the base. Spore powder is brown. Spores 5–6 μm wide, brownish, with fine spikes. A rare species that grows in pine woods. Inedible.

Hydnum imbricatum L.: FR.   VIII–X

Cap 6–20 cm wide, irregularly roundish, slightly curved, later flat, deeply depressed in the middle; it is coloured dark brown, covered with large, loose, rough, thick, black-brown scales which are concentrically arranged; its flesh is tough and thick. Stipe is short, stout and tough, coloured grey-brown. Spikes are long and crowded, converging towards the stipe, at first ashy, later pale grey-brown. Flesh is white-grey and has a bitter taste. Spore powder is brown. Spores 5–7 μm wide, brownish, covered with fine spikes. It grows in large numbers on the ground in pine and spruce forests in acid soil.

Dentinaceae

Dentinum repandum (L.: FR.) S. F. GRAY   VIII–X

Cap 6–10 cm wide, flat, irregularly lobed. Although it resembles the Chanterelle (*Cantharellus cibarius*) in general form and colour, and often grows with it, it is at once distinguished by the spore-bearing surface being carried on needle-like spines. stipe is short, 1–3 cm thick, often eccentric. Flesh is white and brittle, has no smell but is mild in taste. Spore powder is white. Spores 6–9 μm in diameter, almost globular, smooth and colourless. It grows on the ground in coniferous and deciduous woods usually in large numbers.

Auriscalpiaceae

Auriscalpium vulgare S. F. GRAY   III–XI

Cap 1–2 cm wide, semi-circular or reniform, entirely brown or black, hispid, tough and elastic; hymenophore in the shape of grey-brown, long, dense and tough spikes is on the lower surface of the cap. Stipe is 5–8 cm long and slender, eccentric or almost concentric, black-brown and also covered with coarse hair. Spore powder is white. Spores 4–5 × 3.5–4 μm in diameter, slightly globular, tuberculate, colourless and amyloid. It grows abundantly on fallen pine cones which are buried in humus. Inedible.

Fistulinaceae

The Beef Steak Fungus
Fistulina hepatica (SCHAEFF.) ex FR.   VII–IX

Cap 5–20 cm wide, usually attached laterally, ligulate or semi-circular, with thick and juicy flesh; red to brown-red, shortly hispid, later glabrous. Whitish or yellowish tubes turn brown-red in old specimens or when bruised. They are free and individually separable and form a continuous layer. Flesh is dark red marbled with paler lines; it is juicy and release red liquid. Its colour and taste is acid. Spores 4–5.5 × 3–4 μm, subglobular to ovoid, smooth, colourless and dextrinoid. It grows at the foot of living oak trunks or on their stumps. Edible.

Cantharellaceae

Horn of Plenty
Craterellus cornucopioides (L.: FR.) PERS.   VIII–X

Fruit-body 4–10 cm high, trumpet-shaped, entirely hollow, in the centre deeply funnel-shaped, wavy at the edges; its colour is brown-black or dark grey, surface is scaly. Hymenophore on the outer surface of the fruit-body is smooth or wrinkled, grey-brown with blue bloom. Spore powder is white. The thin, tough and membranous flesh is grey-brown and has a mild taste. Spores 12–16 × 7–10 μm, ovoid ellipsoid, smooth and colourless. It grows in large groups and clusters on the ground in fallen leaves in deciduous woods, especially under beech. Edible. Fruit-bodies last for a long time.

Chanterelle
Cantharellus cibarius FR.   VI–IX

Cap 3–9 cm wide, convex, later concave, funnel-shaped, with lobed and wavy margin. The lower surface displays low, transversely interconnected blunt ledges, which are forked and concentric to the stipe. Stipe is often short and tapers downwards. The whole fruit-body is yolk yellow, less frequently whitish. Flesh is yellowish, has a pleasant smell but its flavour can be slightly bitter. Spore powder is white. Spores 7–10.5 × 4–6.5 μm, ellipsoid, smooth and colourless. It grows in clusters in all types of forest but is most prolific in damp spruce and pine woods, especially on moss. In Great Britain it tends to be found under frondose trees. Edible.

Cantharellaceae

Cantharellus tubaeformis FR.
Syn. *C. infundibuliformis* (SCOP.) ex FR.   VIII–X

Fruit-body 2–6 cm wide, up to 10 cm high, cap deeply depressed to funnel-shaped towards centre, thin with lobed and wavy margin; surface is filamentous or scaly, dark yellow-brown in damp conditions, dirty ochre in drought. Hymenium covers low gill-like folds on the lower surface of the cap, which are grey-yellowish with grey bloom convergent towards the stipe, branches transversely interconnected. Stipe tapers towards the base, is yellowish and hollow. Spore powder is white. Spores 8–9.5 × 7–8 μm, sub-globular and smooth. Flesh has no specific smell and is mild in taste. It grows gregariously on the ground and in moss in damp places often in coniferous woods. Similar species is *Cantharellus lutescens*, which differs in vivid reddish-orange hymenium, which is almost smooth or its gill-like folds are only slightly developed. It grows abundantly in clusters in damp, subalpine forests. Some mycologists also distinguish *C. tubaeformis* FR. (with yellow to pale orange gill-like folds which later become grey-brown, and an orange stipe) from *C. infundibuliformis* (with pale yellow gill-like folds which later have grey bloom, and a pale yellow stipe).

Schizophyllaceae

Schizophyllum commune FR.: FR.   I–XII

Cap 1–3 cm wide, fan-shaped or shell-like, laterally attached, soft but leathery, elastic in damp weather, on the surface white or grey tomentose, thin. Hymenophore consists of irregular pale violet-grey or flesh-grey pseudo-gills, split at the edges in two convoluted halves. Spore powder is white. Spores 3–4 × 1–1.5 μm, narrowly cylindrical, smooth and colourless. It grows usually on dead deciduous branches and trunks which lie on the ground, rarely on conifers and sometimes also on living trees, often in clusters. It decomposes the sap of trees into a felt-like substance. Inedible. In Britain rare outside southeast England.

Polyporaceae

Phellinus robustus (KARST.) BOURD. et GALZ.   I–XII

Cap 5–30 cm wide, laterally attached, at first irregularly bracket-shaped, later irregularly semi-circular, very thick. Its edges are rounded, grey-brown and velvety, later bare; rest of cap is blackish with cracked surface. Tubes 3–5 cm long, arranged in layers, yellow-brown, with very small rounded pores. Flesh is as hard as wood, saffron yellow-brown, silky filamentous. Spore powder is white. Spores 6–8 × 5.5–7 µm, sub-globose, smooth, colourless and dextrinoid. Fruit-bodies are perennial. It grows on living trunks of deciduous trees, especially on old oaks. Inedible.

Hapalopilus nidulans (FR.) KARST.
Syn. *Phaeolus rutilans* (PERS.: FR.) PAT.   VII–X

Cap 2–10 cm wide, semi-circular or kidney-shaped, laterally attached to the substrate, thick; the flesh is soft in fresh state, brittle in drought. It is pale cocoa brown or cork-coloured, velvety, later bare. Tubes are the same colour as cap, openings are rounded square and vary in size. Flesh turns red-brown when bruised. Ammoniac vapours or any alkaline solution (KOH, NaOH) colours it immediately vivid purple. Spores 3–5.5 × 2–3.5 µm, ellipsoid, smooth and yellowish. It grows on branches of deciduous trees, including oak, mountain ash, lime and birch; rare on conifers. Inedible. A related species, *H. schweinitzii*, occurs on coniferous wood.

Hymenochaetaceae

Coltricia perennis (L.: FR.) MURR.   V–XII

Cap 3–10 cm wide, tunnel-shaped, thin and leathery, cinnamon in colour, concentrically zoned; at first finely silky hairy, later bare. Tubes are low and rusty, openings small, circular. Stipe is central or eccentris, slightly cylindrical, 2–6 cm long, the same colour as cap, velvety. The leathery flesh is brown-coloured. Spores 6–9 × 3.5–5 µm, ellipsoid, thick-walled, yellowish and dextrinoid. Annual mushroom, growing abundantly in places on forest soil, especially along sandy tracks and in heather in coniferous. Inedible. Formerly assigned to *Polporus*.

Ganodermataceae

Common Ganoderma
Ganoderma applanatum (PERS.) PAT.   I–XII

Cap 5–50 cm wide, semi-circular, laterally attached, thin and flat; upper surface with semi-circular ridges and humps, grey-brown, often sprinkled with cocoa-brown spore powder. Tubes are white and turn brown when bruised. Flesh is firm, deep brown. Spores 7–9 × 5.5–6.5 µm, ovoid globular, consists of two membranes: outer membrane is smooth and colourless, sharply terminated at the tip of the spore; inner membrane has an ornamental pattern, is tuberculate, brown. Apart from the spores 8 µm conidia are formed. They are ovoid ellipsoid and brown. It grows profusely on living and dead beech, birch, hornbeam and other deciduous trees, rarely on coniferous species. Inedible.

Polyporaceae

Tyromyces caesius (SCHRAD.: FR.) MURR.
Syn. *Leptoporus caesius* (SCHRAD.: FR.) QUÉL.   VII–X

Cap 1–6 cm wide, laterally attached, velvety, white at first, turns blue with age or when bruised; long, whitish tubes also bruise. Caps usually grow in several layers one above the other. Flesh is white or greyish, soft but hard when dry. Spore powder is bluish. Spores 3.5–5.5 × 1–1.5 μm, narrow and cylindrical, slightly curved, smooth and colourless. It grows on stumps and fallen trunks of conifers, especially on spruce; rare on deciduous trees, but sometimes grows on fallen beech branches. Inedible.

Oligoporus ptychogaster (LUDWIG) R. et O. FALCK   VIII–IX

It usually has only the chlamydosporic stage (*Ptychogaster albus*) during which it produces 4–10 cm wide, semi-globular to cushion-shaped formations. There are hispid and white, later light brown. Cross-section displays concentric zones of hyphal filaments, which radiate from one place and enclose radially arranged cavities filled with a powdery matter. The material consists of chlamydospores, which are 3.5–6 × 3.5–4.5 μm, ovoid ellipsoid, smooth, thick-walled and golden yellow. Spores 4–5.5 × 2.5–3.5 μm, ellipsoid, smooth and colourless. A rare species which grows on stumps and roots of spruce and pine. Inedible.

Bjerkandera adusta (WILLD.: FR.) KARST.   I–XII

Cap 1–5 cm wide, laterally attached, thin and semi-circular, ash or grey in colour, filamentous, with white, later blackish, margin. Caps usually grow in large numbers in a rootlike formation or produce individual effusoreflexive or resupinate fruit-bodies. Tubes are short, grey or red coloured, separated from the cap by concolorous line visible in cross-section; they turn black when bruised. Spore powder is white. Spores 4–6 × 2–3 μm, cylindrical and colourless. It grows abundantly on trunks and stumps of deciduous trees such as hornbeam, beech and maple. Inedible.

Trichaptum fusco-violaceum (EHRENB.: FR.) RYV.
Syn. *Hirschioporus fusco-violaceus* (EHRENB.: FR.) DONK   I–XII

Fruit-body 2–20 cm wide, resupinate or effusoreflexive with upturned margins, resembling greyish caps 1–3 cm wide, thin, often arranged in rows, one above the other. Hymenophore has a shape of serrate, irregularly cracked ridges, which are at first bright purple, later brownish. Flesh in damp conditions is soft and gelatinous, in drought it becomes parchment-like and leathery, thin and greyish. Hymenium covers the entire surface of ridges. Spore powder is white. Spores 6–8 × 3–4 μm, cylindrical, smooth and colourless. Cystidia are thick-walled and encrusted. It grows abundantly on branches, trunks and stumps of conifers, especially on pine. Inedible.

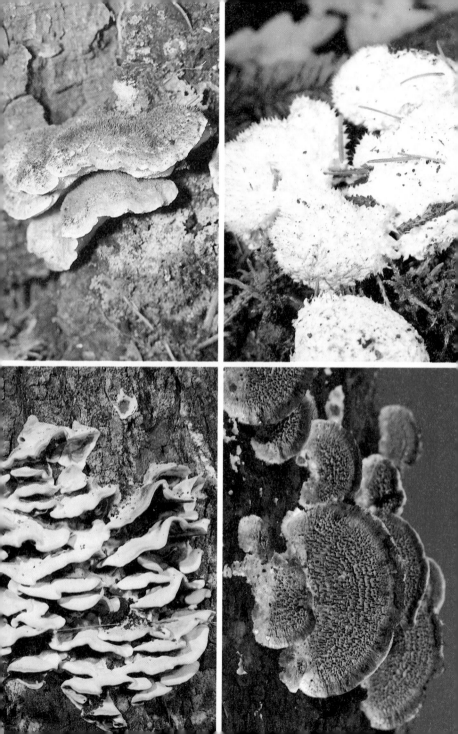

Polyporaceae

Laetiporus sulphureus (BULL.: FR.) MURR.   V–VIII

Cap 5–30 cm wide, laterally attached to the base; young fruit-bodies are juicy and fleshy, thick, whitish yellow, sulphur to orange, old specimens brittle and pale. Tubes are vivid sulphur yellow, later pale ochre. Yellowish flesh is soft and juicy when growing, in dry weather fragile and crumbling; smell is slightly acid. Spore powder is white. Spores 5–7 × 3.5–4.5 μm, ellipsoid, smooth and colourless. This annual polypore grows abundantly in large numbers on living and dead trunks of deciduous trees, particularly on oak, willow and poplar. It causes red-brown rot in wood.

Pycnoporus cinnabarinus (JACQ.: FR.) KARST.   VII–X

Cap 2–10 cm wide, semi-circular, laterally attached, surface is uneven, narrowing towards the margin. Young specimens are bright vermilion red, later becoming dark and bare. Tubes are 2–6 mm long, vermilion red, their openings are small and rounded or square. Flesh is vermilion red, has cork-like consistency and no smell. Spore powder is white. Spores 4.5–6.5 × 2–3 μm, ellipsoid, smooth and colourless, It grows on dead trunks and branches of deciduous trees, especially beech, mountain ash, birch and cherry. A distinctive, but rather uncommon species, which can sometimes be found referred to the genus *Trametes*. Inedible.

Piptoporus betulinus (BULL.: FR.) KARST.   VI–IX

Cap 5–20 cm wide, semi-circular, attached by its tapering side, thick, hoof-shaped, with a broad sterile ridge at the margin; the surface is covered with a smooth, pale ochre or grey-brown, later whitish, papery but firm skin which cracks with age. Tubes, 2–8 mm long, are whitish, detached from cap's flesh in old specimens; openings are minute, rounded, whitish or greyish, later ochre. Flesh is soft at first, later dry and firm, white; acid in smell. Spore powder is white. Spores 5–6.5 × 1.5–2 μm, cylindrical, smooth and colourless. This annual polypore grows exclusively on birch trunks, damaging them completely. Inedible.

Polyporaceae

Trametes versicolor (L.: FR.) LLOYD — I–XII ■□ / □□

Cap 2–8 cm wide, semi-circular, laterally attached, in cross-section uniformly narrow, edge are sharp; it has leathery consistency and bears conspicuous grey, brown, bluish and yellowish concentric stripes; young fruit-bodies have white or yellow margins. Caps are usually arranged in dense groups one above the other. Tubes are white, later yellowish. Flesh is tough, filamentous, white, and has mushroom scent. Spore powder is white. Spores 6–7 × 1.5–2.5 μm, narrow and cylindrical, colourless. It grows abundantly on stumps and dead trunks of various, mostly deciduous trees. Inedible.

Antrodia serialis (FR.) DONK
Syn. *Trametes serialis* FR. — I–XII □■ / □□

Fruit-body partly resupinate, partly composed of vertically projecting, 2–3 cm wide caps laterally attached to the substrate and arranged in rows one above the other, often merging together. Its colour is white, later pale cream to pale yellowish, amber brown; surface of caps is finely felt-like with humps and narrow stripes; edge is blunt and pale. Tube pores are small and rounded, blunt and white. Flesh is elastic, leathery, white, invariable, without specific smell. Spores 7–10 × 3–4 μm elongated and colourless. It grows on coniferous stumps. Completely resupinate fruit-bodies have been classified as *Poria callosa* FR. Inedible.

Trametes hirsuta (WULF.: FR.) LLOYD — I–XII □□ / ■□

Cap 3–12 cm wide, laterally attached, semi-circular, thickish, cross-section displays uniform thickness; surface is hispid with semi-circular ridges, coloured pale yellow or light grey, rounded at the edges. Tubes are white or whitish, later yellowish or light grey, openings are minute and rounded. Flesh is white, tough and filamentous, leathery. Spore powder is white. Spores 5–8 × 1.5–2.5 μm, cylindrical, colourless and smooth. It grows in abundance on dead trunks and branches of various deciduous trees, such as beech, birch, sallow and aspen. Inedible.

Daedaleopsis confragosa (BOLT.: FR.) SCHROET.
Syn. *Daedalea confragosa* (BOLT.: FR.) FR. — I–XII □□ / □■

Cap 3–15 cm wide, laterally attached, semi-circular, sharp at the edge; the light brown surface bears variously shaped protuberances, semi-circular stripes and radiating grooves. Hymenophore has variable shape; it is either formed by tubes with elongated openings, or by gill-like ridges forming a maze-like pattern, which turn pink when bruised and later become brown. In old fruit-bodies they are woody brown. Flesh is brownish, corky and elastic. Spore powder is white. Spores 7–10 × 2–2.5 μm, cylindrical, smooth and colourless. It grows in damp places on dead and living trunks and branches of deciduous trees, especially on sallow and birch. Inedible.

Polyporaceae

Daedalea quercina (L.) ex FR.   I–XII

Cap 5–20 cm wide, 2–5 cm thick, semi-circular or hoof-shaped, attached to the substrate with its broad side. One or several in a roof-like formation, one above the other, narrowing towards the edge, smooth or with protuberances, coloured ochre or grey, black-brown in old age. Tubes have elongated and irregular maze-like openings, wide and wavy, rarely square or rounded, with thick walls of pale woody colour. Flesh elastic like cork, dirty yellow to pale ochre. Spore powder is colourless. Spores 5–7.5 × 2.5–3.5 μm, ellipsoid cylindrical, smooth and colourless. It grows only on oak trees, especially on their stumps. Fruit-bodies last several years. Inedible.

Osmoporus odoratus (WULF.: FR.) SING.   I–XII
Syn. *Gloeophyllum odoratum* (WULF.: FR.) IMAZ.

Perennial fruit-body has a cap, it is laterally attached or semi-resupinate, 3–12 cm wide, yellowish-brown to rusty-brown, later almost black, velvety or felt-like, with protuberances. Tubes are quite long, brownish-ochre, with large openings, rounded or elongated. Flesh of fresh fruit-bodies is juicy, soft and corky, later tough and woody, rusty brown. Fruit-bodies smell of aniseed and fennel. Spore powder is white. Spores 6–7.5 × 3–4 μm, longitudinally ellipsoid, smooth and colourless or lightly yellowish. Very abundant on stumps of spruce, rare on other coniferous trees. Inedible.

Gloeophyllum sepiarium (WULF.: FR.) KARST.   I–XII

Cap 2–10 cm wide, laterally attached, semi-circular or disc-shaped, rusty brown with yellow edge when young, completely covered with protrusions, tomentose to hispid, tough. Hymenophore consists of thick, leathery, radially arranged lamellae which are yellow at first, later rusty. Flesh is rusty brown, leathery and tough. Spore powder is white. Spores 7–12 × 3–4.5 μm, cylindrical and colourless. It grows in large numbers on trunks and stumps of conifers in dry places, very frequently on timber of fences, beams and wooden bridges. Inedible.

Heterobasidion pannosus (FR.) BREF.   I–XII

Fruit-body 5–20 cm wide, 1–3 cm thick, resupinate, semi-resupinate or even laterally attached, irregular, woody, surface covered with bubbly humps and resinous crust; chestnut brown to black-brown. Tubes arranged in several layers, white or pale ochre, with small openings. Flesh is tough and woody, whitish or woody yellowish. Spore powder is white. Spores 4–6 × 3.5–4.5 μm, wide ellipsoid, rough and colourless. It grows most frequently in cavities of stumps, on coniferous roots and rarely on deciduous trees. It is a dangerous pest, particularly in spruce monocultures. Inedible.

Polyporaceae

Fomitopsis pinicola (Sw.: Fr.) Karst.
Syn. *Polyporus marginatus* (Pers.) ex Fr.   I–XII

Cap 5–30 cm wide, 2–8 cm thick, semi-circular, laterally attached, with semi-circular ridge; surface is grey-black, covered with hard, resinous crust. It is brown-red and glossy towards the edges; edge is rounded, coloured white or yellowish. Tubes are tall, layered, yellowish, their openings are minute, rounded with drops of water. Flesh is corky, yellowish and has an acid smell when fresh. Spore powder is white. Spores 6–8 × 3–4.5 μm, ellipsoid, smooth and colourless. Fruit-bodies last for several years and grow on living and dead trunks and stumps of deciduous and coniferous trees. It is most commonly found on spruce and birch. Its mycelium causes dangerous decomposition of wood, which is revealed by the characteristic red colouring. *E. pinicola* also attacks many fruit trees; in some areas it can cause a mass destruction of improperly tended trees, especially of cherry and apple. Inedible.

Fomes fomentarius (L.: Fr.) Kickx   I–XII

Fruit-body 5–50 cm wide, at first hoof-shaped, later broadly resupinate; surface is grey or grey-brown, covered with smooth crust and glossy when cut. Tubes are layered, brownish, pores are small and rounded. Flesh is ochre-rusty, firmly woolly, dry. Spore powder is white. Spores 14–20 × 5–8 μm, cylindrical, smooth and colourless. Grows abundantly on living and dead trunks of deciduous trees, especially on beech in mountains forests, where it is the most common parasite of these wood species and causes intensive rotting. Inedible. Rare in Great Britain.

Polyporus umbellatus (Pers.) ex Fr.
Syn. *Grifola umbellata* (Pers. ex Fr.) Pil.   VII–IX

Fruit-bodies grow in clusters, 10–40 cm wide, with numerous, richly branched stipes which fuse into a tuberous trunk. Caps at the ends of stipes are 1–4 cm wide, rounded, with thin flesh, scaly, flat and slightly curved, depressed at the centre; pale brownish or yellowish. White tubes are very short with small pores and radiate towards the stipe. Stipes are concentric, white. Flesh is white, juicy, and has a pleasant smell of fennel. Spore powder is white. Spores 7–10 × 2.5–4 μm, almost cylindrical, smooth and colourless. It forms large clusters up to 50 cm in diameter and 4 kg in weight at the foot of old deciduous trees, especially oak. Edible.

Polyporaceae

Polyporus badius (PERS.: S. F. GRAY) SCHW.   ■□
Syn. *Polyporus picipes* FR.   V–VII   □□
Cap 2–15 cm wide, funnel- to mussel-shaped, fleshy and leathery, thin at the edges, fragile in drought; lobed and wavy, pale yellowish-brown to red-brown, greasily glossy, bare when old. Tubes converge towards the stipe; they are short, white or yellowish, with small and rounded openings. Stipe is concentric or eccentric, very short, black-brown to black, velvety, paler at the top. Flesh is white or yellowish, tough. Spore powder is white. Spores 6–8 × 3.5–4 μm, ellipsoid, smooth and colourless. It grows on trunks of deciduous trees, especially old willows and poplars in light woods. Inedible.

Polyporus ciliatus FR.: FR.   III–XII   □■
                                                   □□
Cap 2–10 cm wide, flat, slightly depressed in centre, tough leathery, roundish; ochre yellow, yellow-brown or grey-brown, covered by filamentous scales, with felt-like to tomentose edge, bare when old. Tubes converge towards the stipe, are narrow, whitish, later yellowish; openings 0.5 mm in diameter at the most, rounded. Stipe is central, 3–6 cm long, narrowly cylindrical, entirely grey, covered with fine brown scales. Spore powder is white. Spores 5–7.5 × 2–2.5 μm, cylindrical, smooth and colourless. It grows profusely on fallen branches and stumps of deciduous trees, especially on birch and beech. There are several closely related species.

Polyporus squamosus (HUDS.) ex FR.   V–VIII   □□
                                                   ■■
Cap 10–60 cm wide, semi-circular or fan-like, thinning towards the margin, tough and fleshy; it is coloured ochre yellow, covered with large brown, adpressed scales. Tubes are narrow and yellowish, their openings large and elongated, striate to scaly, finely serrate. Stipe is usually lateral or eccentric, short and stout, yellowish, brown-black below. Flesh is white, of cucumber-like taste and smell. Spore powder is white. Spores 9–14 × 4–5.5 μm, cylindrical, smooth and colourless. It grows in large clusters on dead or living trunks of deciduous trees, sometimes on their stumps, particularly on willow and walnut. Edible when young.

Polyporaceae

Albatrellus ovinus (SCHAEFF.: FR.) QUÉL.　　　　　　　VIII–X

Cap 3–10 cm wide, shallowly convex, irregularly shaped, whitish or yellowish, often cracked. Tubes are very short (1–2 mm) and decurrent, white, turning lemon yellow when bruised, pores are very small. Stipe is central, eccentric or lateral, short 1–3 cm thick, irregular with uneven surface, firm, tapering and curving at the base. Flesh is white, later lemon yellow, with firm and tough flesh; it has a pleasant almond flavour and scent. Spore powder is white. Spores 3.5–4.5 × 3–4 µm, subglobose, smooth, nonamyloid and colourless. It grows individually or in clusters on the ground in spruce forests, especially in subalpine regions. Rare or absent in Great Britain. Edible.

Albatrellus confluens (ALB. et SCHW.: FR.) KOTL. et POUZ.　　　VIII–IX

Fruit-body often forms lobed clusters, sometimes up to 50 cm in diameter, these are composed of small caps 3–8 cm wide, ochre yellow, pale yellow to reddish; lower surface is covered with shallow, white and very dense tubes which converge to the short, white stipe. Flesh is white, juicy and brittle, solution of green vitriol colours it brisk red. Spore powder is white. Spores 4.5–5 × 3–3.5 µm, broadly ellipsoid, smooth, colourless and amyloid. It grows on the ground in coniferous forests with acid soil. Edible.

Lentinellaceae

Lentinellus cochleatus (PERS.: FR.) KARST.　　　　　　VII–IX

Cap 3–8 cm wide, irregular, deeply funnel-shaped, split on one side; smooth, ochre to red-brown. Gills decurrent, shallow and whitish with serrated blades. The red-brown, grooved stipe is eccentric or lateral, fuses at base with other stipes. Flesh is brownish, tough, has a strong aniseed smell and a sweet taste. Spore powder is white, spores sub-globose, 4–5 µm, tuberculate, colourless and amyloid. It grows in dense clusters on stumps and roots of various deciduous species. Edible.

Pleurotaceae

Panus tigrinus (BULL.: FR.) SING.　　　　　　　　　VI–X

Cap 2–10 cm wide, convex, with deeply funnel-like depression in the middle, with thin leathery flesh, white, creamy pale ochre, covered with blackish hairy scales. Gills dense, white, then pale ochre, with finely serrated edges. Stipe 3–5 cm long, 3–6 mm thick, elastic, almost eccentric, white, whitish yellow, with blackish filaments and scales. Flesh is white and has no smell. Spores 6–8 × 2.5–3 µm, ellipsoid, colourless. It grows on trunks, branches and stumps of deciduous trees, especially willows, mainly in swampy woods. Inedible.

Pleurotaceae

Oyster Fungus
Pleurotus ostreatus (JACQ.: FR.) KUMM.   I–XII

Fruit-bodies usually grow in clusters in a roof-like formation, rarely individually. Cap 5–15, sometimes up to 30 cm wide, circular, ligulate to shovel-like, convex, later flat, margins involuted in young fruit-bodies; colour varies from dark grey to olive black, sometimes pale to whitish, young specimens are usually darker than mature fruit-bodies. Its surface is smooth and bare, white-felted near the stipe. Gills are decurrent, dense, white to greyish, often purplish on old fruit-bodies. Stipe is usually eccentric or lateral, short, sometimes strongly reduced, 1–4 cm long, 0.5–2 cm wide, white or greyish, strigose at base. Flesh is white, rather tough but juicy and has a sweetish taste but no specific smell. Spore powder is white to purplish. Spores 8–11 × 3–4 μm, ellipsoid, cylindrical and colourless. It grows on trunks of deciduous trees, rarely on conifers. Edible, tasty. Now usually divided into several forms, or rather independent species: *P. ostreatus* (p. 93, above right), *P. pulmonarius* (p. 93, above left), *P. salignus* (p. 93, below left and right), *P. columbinus* and *P. cornucopiae*.

Hygrophoraceae

⚔ *Hygrophorus leucophaeus* (SCOP.: FR.) FR.   IX–X   ■■□□

Cap 4–7 cm wide, convex, later flat with a hump in the centre, thin fleshed, margin white silky, yellowish to orange-brownish towards the centre, slimy. Gills are long and decurrent, sparse, yellowish to creamy with pink tinge. Stipe is 5–8 cm long, 2–4 mm wide, narrowly cylindrical, pale yellow or orange-brownish, with longitudinal fine filaments, dry, not slimy. Flesh is whitish, without a specific smell or taste. Spore powder is white. Spores 6–8 × 3.5–4 μm, ellipsoid, smooth and colourless. It grows among fallen leaves in beech and hornbeam forests, especially on limestone substrate. There are several similar white *Hygrophorus* species. Edible.

⚔ *Hygrophorus nemoreus* (PERS.: FR.) FR.   IX–X   □■□□

Cap 4–8 cm wide, convex, later flat with a rounded hump in the centre, then slightly depressed, firm flesh; coloured pale orange to brick red or brownish-orange, with ingrown darker striae, dry and sometimes pruinose. Gills are thick and sparse, broadly attached and shortly decurrent, pale cream with orange tinge. Stipe is 4–8 cm long, 1–1.5 cm wide, whitish to ochre, tapering at base; its surface is covered with longitudinal lines and fine scales. Flesh is pale orange, colourless, of mild taste. Spore powder is white. Spores 6–7 × 3–5 μm, cylindrical ellipsoid and colourless. It grows in small numbers in deciduous forests. A rather similar species *H. pratensis* is often encountered in grass in Britain and North America. Edible.

⚔ **Pinewood Wax Cap**
Hygrophorus hypothejus (FR.) FR.   X–XI   □□■□

Cap 3–5 cm wide, convex, later flat, depressed in the centre, margin involuted, its flesh is thin, skin very slimy and easily detachable, coloured coffee brown with cloudy olive shade. Gills are sparse, elastic, deeply decurrent yolk yellow. Stipe is 5–10 cm long, 3–7 mm wide, narrowly cylindrical, often crooked, yellow, covered with a layer of colourless slime, remnants of slimy veil in upper part under the gills. Flesh has no specific smell or taste. Spore powder is white. Spores 7–9 × 4–5 μm, ellipsoid and colourless. It grows gregariously in pine woods after first autumn frosts. Edible.

⚔ *Hygrophorus erubescens* (FR.) FR.   VII–X   □□□■

Cap 4–8 cm wide, convex, with deeply involuted margin, later shallowly rounded, fleshy; coloured whitish with red and lemon yellow patches, later completely covered with purple or red scales; slimy. Gills are sparse and decurrent, considerably thick, white with reddish edge, sometimes entirely covered with red spots. Stipe is long and cylindrical with firm flesh; white, scaly, covered with red drops under the gills. Flesh is white, later turning red and yellow. Spore powder is white. Spores 8–10 × 4–5 μm, ellipsoid and colourless. Grows particularly in coniferous woods. Inedible.

Hygrophoraceae

Hygrophorus olivaceo-albus (FR.) FR. IX–X

Cap 2–7 cm wide, arched, with a hump in the centre, later flat or with a shallow depression, dark brown with an olive tinge, covered with a thick layer of slime. Gills are decurrent, sparse, pure white. Stipe is 8– 12 cm long, 8–12 mm wide, narrowly cylindrical, tapering downwards, whitish surface is covered with olive brown slimy velum which forms a disappearing ring; the surface is cracked so that the stipe has dark stripes. Flesh is white, without a specific smell or taste. Spore powder is white. Spores 10–15 × 6–8 μm, ellipsoid and colourless. It grows in coniferous forests, especially in mountainous regions. Edible.

Hygrophorus pustulatus (PERS.: FR.) FR. IX–X

Cap 3–6 cm wide, shallowly convex, with a hump in the centre, grey to grey-brown, darker in the centre, with small seed-like warts, slimy when damp, thin flesh. Gills are sparse, decurrent and white. Stipe 4–8 cm long, 5–10 mm wide, cylindrical, white, dry, entirely or partly dotted in grey or black-grey. Flesh is white, invariable, without smell or taste. Spore powder is white. Spores 7–10 × 4.5–6 μm, ellipsoid and colourless. Occasional, particularly in coniferous forests. Edible.

Hygrophorus marzuolus (FR.) BRES. II–V (VI)

Cap 4–12 cm wide, firm and thick flesh, convex, later flat, often irregular and wavy, dry; coloured at first white, later pearl grey or with grey-black patches, then entirely grey-black, mat or finely pruinose. Gills are sparse, thick and shortly decurrent; whitish or white, later bluish-grey to grey. Stipe 3–6 cm long, 1.5–4 cm thick, short, tapering downwards, white, later greyish, fibrous and dry. Flesh is firm, white, smells of honey, has a pleasant taste. Spore powder is white. Spores 6–8 × 4–5.5 μm, ovoid ellipsoid, colourless. Its habitat is mainly limited to pine forests, usually at high altitude. Rare in mixed and deciduous woods. Fruit-bodies are deeply rooted and therefore are covered with soil for a long time. Rare or absent in Great Britain. Edible.

Hygrophorus virgineus (WULF.: FR.) KUMM. VIII–X

Cap 2–6 cm wide, shallow and convex, later flat with a hump in the centre, fleshy, pure white, dry, smooth, later cracked, sometimes flecked in red when old. Gills are dense, deeply decurrent, white. Stipe 3–7 cm long, thick and cylindrical, tapereing downwards, white, dry and bare. Flesh is white, without a smell or taste. Spore powder is white. Spores 7.5–10 × 5–6 μm, cylindrical ellipsoid and colourless. It grows in grass in forest meadows, on slopes and moors. A smaller grassland species is *H. niveus*. Edible.

Hygrophoraceae

¶¶ Sweet-scented Wax Cap
Hygrophorus agathosmus (Fr.: Secr.) Fr.   VIII–X   ■□
                                                                        □□
Syn. *Limacium agathosmum* (Fr.: Secr.) Wünsche

Cap 4–7 cm wide, at first slightly convex, soon flat with slightly involuted margin, slimy when young, greyish to grey-brown. Gills are arched, shortly decurrent, white to pale greyish. Stipe is cylindrical, white, with white, greyish or golden-yellow granules or scales at the top. Flesh is white with a strong almond smell and a sweet taste. Spore powder is white, spores 7–10 × 5–6 μm, ellipsoid, colourless, smooth and nonamyloid. It grows in small groups in mossy spruce forests. Edible.

¶¶ Goat Moth Wax Cap
Hygrophorus cossus (Sow.: Fr.) Fr.   VIII–X   □■
                                                                        □□
Syn. *Limacium cossus* (Sow.: Fr.) Wünsche

Syn. *Hygrophorus eburneus* var. *cossus* (Sow.: Fr.) Quél.

Cap 3–6 cm wide, convex when young, soon flat with involuted margin; slimy, later dry, bare, glossy and white. Gills are arched, shortly decurrent, white when fresh, ochre when dried. Stipe is cylindrical, pointed at the base, white, slimy for a long time with white flakes at the top. Flesh is white, smells of the Goat Moth caterpillar. Spore powder is white, spores 8–9 × 5–6 μm, ellipsoid, smooth, colourless and nonamyloid. It grows in small groups on the ground in deciduous forests. Edible.

¶¶ Ivory Wax Cap
Hygrophorus eburneus (Bull.: Fr.) Fr.   VIII–X   □□
                                                                        ■□
Syn. *Limacium aburneum* (Bull.: Fr.) Fr.

Cap 3–6 cm wide, at first convex, later flat with rounded margin; young skin is slimy, later dry, smooth, bare and pure white. Gills are arched, lightly decurrent, pure white even after drying. Stipe is cylindrical; slightly tapering at the base, white with white granules at the top. Flesh is white, smells unpleasantly of the Goat Moth caterpillar. Spore powder is white, spores 8–9 × 5–6 μm, ellipsoid, smooth, colourless and nonamyloid. It grows in small groups on the ground in oak and beech woods. It resembles *H. cossus* for which it is often mistaken. Edible.

¶¶
Hygrophorus russula (Schaeff.: Fr.) Quél.   □□
Syn. *Limacium russula* (Schaeff: Fr.) Ricken   IX–X   □■

Cap 5–15 cm wide, convex when young, later flat with deeply involuted margin, slightly depressed in the centre, fleshy. Slimy when young, soon dries up; it is smooth with small scales in the top. Coloured white at first, later has pink to red patches. Stipe is cylindricval, white with red patches. Flesh is white, turns pink when cut; skin is often bitter in taste. Spore powder is white, spores 6–7 × 4–6 μm, widely ellipsoid, colourless and nonamyloid. It grows in small groups in warm oak and beech woods. Rare in Great Britain. Edible.

Hygrophoraceae

¶ *Hygrophorus lucorum* KALCHBR.   X–XI ⬛⬛⬜⬜

Cap 2–6 cm wide, bell-shaped, later flat with a hump, finally depressed in the centre; thin flesh, entirely lemon yellow, slimy. Gills are decurrent, sparse, thick whitish, later yellowish to lemon yellow. Stipe narrowly cylindrical, long, pale yellow, whitish at the top and often with slimy granules. Flesh is white, without smell or taste. Spore powder is whitish. Spores 7–10 × 4–6 μm, ellipsoid, smooth and colourless. It grows under larch, late in the autumn, usually after the first frost; often in groups. Edible.

¶ *Hygrocybe conica* (SCOP.: FR.) KUMM.   VI–X ⬜⬛⬜⬜

Cap 2–6 cm wide, club-shaped and bell-shaped, later flat, pointed in the centre, slightly fleshy and brittle, coloured orange to red, slimy in damp conditions, silky glossy, cracking in radiating lines in drought. Gills are sparse, deep and curved, pale yellow. Stipe is cylindrical and long, pale yellow, turning black from the base, filamentous, dry, hollow. Flesh is yellow and odourless. Fruit-body turns black when bruised or getting old, so that old or dry fruit-bodies are charcoal black. Spore powder is white. Spores 7–10 × 4–6 μm, ellipsoid and colourless. Inedible.

¶ *Hygrocybe psittacine* (SCHAEFF.: FR.) WÜNSCHE   VII–IX ⬜⬜⬛⬜

Cap 1–3 cm wide, convex, later flat with a hump in the centre, brittle with thin flesh, gills are transparent at the edge. It is usually green with yellow to orange patches, sometimes almost entirely yellow-red with a few greenish spots. Gills are sparse, thick, curved, coloured greenish or yellow to orange. Stipe is narrowly cylindrical, often crooked and slimy, greenish or beige; at the base yellow or orange. Flesh has no smell. Spore powder is white. Spores 8–10 × 4–5.5 μm, ellipsoid and colourless. It grows in grass and moss at the edge of woods, on lawns, pastureland and woodland meadows. Inedible.

Tricholomataceae

¶ *Hohenbuehelia petaloides* (BULL.: FR.) SCHULZER   ⬜⬜
Syn. *Pleurotus petaloides* (BULL.: FR.) QUÉL.   VI–IX ⬜⬛

Cap 3–12 cm high and 2–6 cm wide, fan-like or shovel-like, constricted where attached to the stipe, ochre to brown, smooth skin, bare and gelatinous. Gills are considerably decurrent, shallow, whitish or brownish. Stipe is short and lateral, with fine granules, moulting. Flesh is thin, yellowish and sweet in taste. Spore powder is white, spores 5–6.5 × 3.5–4.5 μm, shortly ovoid, colourless, smooth and non-amyloid; hymenium contains pronounced spindle-shaped cystidia. It grows in small numbers on rotting wood of deciduous trees. This species may also be found referred to as the genus *Geopetalum* or *Acanthocystis*. Edible.

Tricholomataceae

Lyophyllum fumosum (PERS.: FR.) KÜHN et ROMAGN.   IX–X

It forms large clusters with fused bases. Cap 4–10 cm wide, fleshy, shallowly convex, light or dark brown or grey-brown, smooth, bald. Gills are sparse, attached or shortly decurrent, whitish. Stipe 5–8 cm long, 1–1.5 cm thick, fleshy, white, finely filamentous. Flesh is white and smells of flour. Spores 5–6 µm, almost globular, smooth, colourless. It grows in woods, often in groups arranged in circles. Inedible.

Lyophyllum connatum (SCHUM.: FR.) SING.
Syn. *Tricholoma connatum* (SCHUM.: FR.) RICKEN   VIII–X

Cap 3–15 cm wide, convex, involuted margin, cuticle is smooth and bare, white or whitish. Gills are arched, slightly decurrent, white, turning brown with age. Stipe is white, cylindrical, fusing with others at the base into a tuber-like formation. Flesh is white, tastes and smells of cucumber; solution of $FeSO_4$ colours it violet, later pink. Spore powder is white, spores 6–8 × 3.5–4.5 µm, cylindrical, smooth, non-amyloid and colourless; basidia contain basidiophile grains. It grows in very dense clusters, mostly in frondose woods, but is not common in Britain. Edible, not first-rate.

Lyophyllum loricatum (FR.) KÜHNER   VIII–IX

Cap 5–10 cm wide, shallowly convex, later flat, coloured a chestnut to sooty brown with a thick, bare, gristly cuticle; flesh is thick and tough. Gills are cirved, attached by a tooth to the stipe, sparse, elastic, whitish and later dirty yellow. Stipe is 5–10 cm long, 10–15 mm wide, filamentous, pale brownish, with small scales at top. The bitter-tasting flesh is white, slightly cartilaginous and colourless. Spore powder is white. Spores 6–8 µm, wide, globular, smooth and colourless. It grows individually or in clusters on the ground in forests of all types especially in beech woods. It is considered sometimes a variety of *Lyophyllum decastes,* or *L. aggregatum.* Edible.

Tephrocybe anthracophila (LASCH) P. D. ORTON
Syn.: *Tephrocybe carbonaria* (VELEN.) DONK   VI–X

Cap 1–3 cm wide, shallowly convex, slightly depressed at the centre, black-brown when damp, with transparent gills, grey-brown in drought, smooth, bald. Gills are sparse, adnate to shortly decurrent, whitish to light grey. Stipe 1–5 cm long, 1–2 mm thick, dark grey, blackish towards the base, paler and powdered at the top. Flesh has a strong smell of flour. Basidia with carminophile grains. Spores 4.5–5.5 µm, globular, smooth, colourless. It grows on old burnt ground. Inedible.

Tricholomataceae

Tephrocybe palustris (PECK) DONK   VI–VII

Cap 2–2.5 cm wide, at first semi-circular, later convex, sometimes with a hump in the centre, then depressed; very fragile, pale sooty when young, finely pruinose towards the edges, later moulting, strongly hygrophanous; gills are transparent to the centre. It is coloured brown or brown-yellow, dry and paler, sometimes almost whitish. Gills are curved, shortly attached, high, sparse, whitish, later pale brown-yellow. Stipe is very fragile, slender and thin, up to 11 cm long, 1.5–2 mm wide, brownish to sooty, finely filamentous, attached to the peat bog moss by web-like hyphae on the lower surface. Flesh is almost colourless; smells of fresh meal. Spore powder is white. Spores 6–9 × 4–5 μm, ellipsoid, smooth, colourless. It usually grows in communities on living *Sphagnum*. Inedible.

Calocybe gambosa (FR.) DONK   IV–V

Cap 3–10 cm wide, shallowly convex, rounded, later flat, margin deeply involuted, usually white with creamy tinge, rarely pale lemon yellow (see the illustration); smooth, bare, thick flesh. Gills are very dense, sinuated towards the stipe, with a shortly decurrent tooth; shallow and white. Stipe is short and cylindrical, thick, tough and white. Flesh is white, smells and tastes of new meal. Spore powder is white. Spore 4–7 × 2–4 μm, ellipsoid, smooth and colourless. Basidia carminophile. It grows in groups in grass at the sunny edges of forests and under bushes. Often confused with *Inocybe patouillardii*. Edible, tasty.

Laccaria amethystea (BULL.: MÉRAT) MURR.
Syn. **Laccaria amethystina** (HUDS.: HOOK.) COOKE   VII–X

Cap 2–6 cm wide, convex, later flat, depressed in the centre, strongly hygrophanous; thin flesh is dark purple, lilac or purple-grey to whitish in damp conditions, pale in drought. Gills are sparse, deep and shortly decurrent, rather thick, pale purple dusted with white spore powder. Stipe is slender and cylindrical, long, longitudinally filamentous, purple. Flesh is purple, without a specific smell or taste. Spore powder is white. Spores 8–10 μm wide, globular, spiky and colourless. It grows abundantly in all forests, predominantly in damp places and on rotten wood. Edible.

Laccaria laccata (SCOP.: FR.) COOKE   VI–X

Cap 2–6 cm wide, convex, later flat, depressed in the centre; thin flesh. In damp weather coloured flesh, red-brown or pink, transparent and grooved at the margin; in drought pallid, beige. Gills are sparse, shortly decurrent, deep and thick, pale flesh red or pink, pruinose with white spore powder. Stipe is narrowly cylindrical and filamentous, concolorous with cap. Flesh is pinkish, without a specific smell or taste. Spore powder is white. Spore 7–10 μm wide, globular, with short spikes, colourless. Abundant in all types of forests, especially in damp places. Edible.

Tricholomataceae

Laccaria bicolar (R. MAIRE) P. D. ORTON   VII–X

Cap 1–4 cm wide, broadly convex and rounded, thin and smooth, later finely scaly at the top, coloured flesh red to red-brown. Gills remotely attached and slightly decurrent, rather tough, sparse. Stipe is cylindrical, tough, filamentous, red-brown, base is enveloped in lilac felt. Flesh is brownish. Spore powder is pale lilac, spores 7–9 × 6.5–8 μm, wide and ellipsoid, spiky, colourless and nonamyloid. A rare mushroom which grows in small groups in pine and oak wood. Edible.

Tricholomopsis rutilans (SCHAEFF.: FR.) SING.   VI–X

Cap 5–15 cm wide, shallow and convex, usually umbonate in the centre, later flat, fleshy, yellow, at first entirely covered with red scales; these are later arranged in narrow lines. Gills are sinuate, attached to stipe with a tooth, deep, dense, golden yellow or light yellow. Stipe is cylindrical, 6–10 cm long, 10–15 mm thick, golden yellow, with red velvety patches. Flesh is pale yellow with a faint resinous scent. Spore powder is white. Spores 6–8 × 4.5–5.5 μm, ovoid ellipsoid, smooth and colourless. Cheilocystidia are large. It grows abundantly on stumps and dead roots of coniferous trees, especially on pine and spruce. Edible.

Tricholomopsis decora (FR.) SING.   VII–X

Cap 3–8 cm wide, broadly, convex, regular but also eccentric. Cuticle is golden yellow and felt-like, with dark olive to brown-black scales. Gills are slightly arched, sulphur yellow, edge is pruinose. Stipe is erect or ascending, fibrous to finely scaly, golden yellow. Flesh is yellow and slightly bitter. Spore powder is white, spores 6–7 × 4–5 μm, ovoid, colourless, smooth and nonamyloid. It grows on stumps and fallen branches of spruce, pine and fir. Inedible.

Tawny Funnel Cap
Lepista inversa (SCOP.: FR.) PAT.   VIII–X
Syn. *Clitocybe inversa* (SCOP.: FR.) QUÉL.

Cap 4–8 cm wide, funnel-shaped, with thin, often lobed margin, thin and elastic flesh; coloured red-yellow, orange-yellow, ochre orange-yellow, bare. Gills deeply decurrent, considerably dense and shallow, paler than the cap. Stipe is short and cylindrical, 3–5 cm long, 4–6 mm thick, lighter than the cap, bare, base enveloped in felt-like mycelium. Flesh is pale ochre. Spore powder is white. Spores 3–5 μm wide, globular, tuberculate. It grows in clusters in humus of spruce forests. Edible.

Tricholomataceae

Wood Blewits
Lepista nuda (BULL.: FR.) W. G. SMITH   IX–XII

Cap 5–14 cm wide, shallow and convex, slihtly umbonate, deeply involuted margin, fleshy, smooth and bare; deep purple or brownish purple in damp conditions, turning pale to beige-brown during drought and when mature. Gills are attached to the stipe with a tooth, dense, easily detached from cap's flesh, purple, later brown-purple. Stipe is relatively short, cylindrical, broadened at the base, purple with finely fibrillose tough flesh. Flesh is light purple, later greyish to whitish, with pleasant scent. Spore powder is dirty pink. Spores 6–8 × 4–5 μm, ellipsoid, tuberculate, pale pink. It grows abundantly in humus on forest floors, especially spruce growths, often forming clusters or large rings. Edible.

Blewits
Lepista personata (FR.) COOKE
Syn. *Lepista saeva* (FR.) P. D. ORTON   IX–XII

Cap 6–15 cm wide, shallowly convex, without an umbo; involuted margin, smooth and bare, fleshy, dirty yellow or greyish ochre, without the purple tinge. Gills are attached to the stipe with a tooth, dense, yellowish-grey. Stipe is short and cylindrical, usually enlarged at the base, light purple and roughly striated in bluish purple; tough flesh. Its stipe differentiates it from the Wood Blewits. Flesh is whitish and has a pleasant scent. Spore powder is dirty pink. Spores 6–8 × 4–5 μm, ellipsoid, tuberculate, pale pink. It grows in grass in meadows and pastureland along edges of woods, specially in warm areas. Edible.

Lepista sordida (FR.) SING.   VII–IX

Cap 3–7 cm wide, broadly bell-shaped, soon flat, later concave with a low umbo in the centre, narrow at the edge with thin flesh, hygrophanous; light purple in damp conditions, grey-purple or lilac brown to brownish, pallid in drought with a prevailing brownish tinge, smooth and bare. Gills are curved, attached to stipe by a tooth, dense, purple, pale lilac to fleshy, later grey easily detached from the cap's flesh. Stipe 3–7 cm long, 5–10 mm thick, short and cylindrical, often curved at the base, longitudinally fibrillose. Flesh grey-purple, pleasant scent, mild taste. Spores 6–8 × 3–4.5 μm, ellipsoid, tuberculate, pale pinkish. It resembles Wood Blewits (*Lepista nuda*), whose young fruit-bodies are vivid purple and which always grows in forests. The similar *Lepista sordida* grows on old, overgrown compost heaps and in grass on damp manured soil along roadsides and in the fields. It is usually clustered. The bottom left illustration shows older soaked specimens, the bottom right illustration shows young and dry specimens.

Lepista nebularis (FR.) HARMAJA
Syn. *Clitocybe nebularis* (BATSCH: FR.) KUMM.   IX–XI

Stout and fleshy fungus. Cap 7–15 cm wide, arched with a low hump in the centre, later flat with involuted margin; thick fleshy, coloured ash grey to grey-brown, white pruinose when young. Gills are dense, shortly decurrent, white, later yellowish. Stipe 5–15 cm long, 2–4 mm thick, cylindrical, clavate at the base, white to greyish. Flesh is white, with a strong, slightly unpleasant aroma and no specific taste. Spore powder is pale creamy yellow. Spores 6–8 × 3–4 μm, ellipsoid and smooth. Grows in all types of forests, usually in large numbers.

Tricholomataceae

Common Funnel Cap
Clitocybe infundibuliformis (SCHAEFF.: WEINM.) QUÉL.   VI–IX
Syn. *Clitocybe gibba* (PERS.: FR.) KUMM.

Cap 3–8 cm wide, funnel-shaped, with a small umbo in the centre, thin flesh, margin serrated and grooved, entirely pale ochre yellow, pale beige to whitish, filamentous and felt-like. Gills are deeply decurrent, dense, white. Stipe is slender and cylindrical, whitish, base is enveloped into white, felt-like mycelium. Flesh is whitish, with a pleasant bitter-almond scent. Spore powder is white. Spores 5–7 × 3–4 μm, almost globular, smooth and colourless. It grows abundantly in coniferous woods in moss and grass. It is very similar to *Clitocybe incilis*, with which it is often classed as one species. Both are edible.

Clitocybe cerussata (FR.) KUMM.   VIII–X

Cap 5–10 cm wide, flat but slightly convex with an umbo, later flat to depressed, shiny as if lacquered, with concentric circles when mature. Coloured white, slightly grey when mature. Gills are dense, slightly decurrent, white, greyish. Stipe is cylindrical, whitish to brownish, broadening at the base which is covered with white felt. Flesh is greyish; smells of green cabbage. Spore powder is whitish, spores 4–5 × 3–4 μm, broadly ellipsoid, smooth and colourless. It grows in rings or groups in foliage, rarely in coniferous needles. Poisonous.

Clitocybe geotropa (BULL.: FR.) QUÉL.   X–XI

Cap 8–15 (20) cm wide, convex, with inrolled margin, flat, broadly funnel-shaped, with a blunt umbo in the centre, whitish yellow, buff to light brown, finely silky filamentous and also with minute scales. Gills are dense, decurrent, whitish, bay to brownish. Stipe 8–15 cm long, 2–4 cm thick, longer than the cap diameter when young, filamentous, covered with white felt at the base, of the same colour as the cap. Flesh is pale, without specific smell and taste. Spores 6–7 × 5–6 μm, almost globular, smooth, colourless. It grows in grass on forest meadows, rarely in light woods, sometimes is arranged in circles. Edible.

Clitocybe pithyophila (SECR.) GILL.
Syn: *Clitocybe nivea* VELEN.   VIII–X

Cap 3–10 cm wide, soon flat, later with a shallow depression in the centre, wavy margin; coloured entirely pure white, cuticle at the edges is woolly and felt-like with concentric cracks when old; thin, soft flesh. Gills are short and decurrent sparse, deep, white with a butter yellow tinge. Stipe 5–8 cm long, 8–10 cm thick, white, smooth and bare, felt-like at the base. Flesh is white and colourless. Spore powder is white. Spores 6–9 × 4–5.5 μm, ellipsoid, smooth and colourless. It grows in groups or in clusters in spruce forests on rotting needles. Inedible. Rare or absent in Great Britain.

Tricholomataceae

Clitocybe tornata (FR.) QUÉL. VIII–IX

Cap 3–6 cm wide; perimeter is regularly rounded, shallowly convex, with a low umbo in the white to leathery brown centre. Pruinose, dry, cracked when old, with involuted margin. Gills are shortly decurrent, very dense, whitish with a grey-brown tinge. Stipe 2–4 cm long, 4–8 mm thick, white. Flesh is white with a specific smell. Spore powder is white. Spores 4–6 × 2.5–4 μm, ellipsoid, smooth and colourless. It grows in coniferous and deciduous forests. Rare. Inedible.

Clitocybe ditopa (FR.: FR.) GILL. IX–X

Cap 2–5 cm wide, shallow and convex, soon flat, depressed to funnel-shaped in the centre, thin flesh, hygrophanous; in damp conditions dark brown-grey, in drought pale grey, smooth. Margin white pruinose when young. Gills decurrent, slightly dense, light brown-grey. Stipe is slender and cylindrical, hollow, longitudinally fibrillose, light grey or brown-grey, pruinose under the gills. Flesh is grey and smells strongly of new meal. Spore powder is white. Spores 3–3.5 × 2.5–3 μm, minute, sub-globose, smooth and colourless. It grows in needles in pine and spruce woods, sometimes in communities. Inedible.

Clitocybe phyllophila (FR.) KUMM. VIII–X

Cap 4–8 cm, convex, later flat, only slightly depressed, smooth and silky, glossy, white; yellowish in the centre. Gills are relatively dense, adnexed and shortly decurrent, shallow, creamy white to yellowish. Stipe is cylindrical or slightly compressed, pointed at the base, elastic, soon hollow, white. Flesh is white with a slightly aniseed scent. Spore powder is creamy, spores 4–5 × 3–4 μm, soon globular, colourless and nonamyloid. It grows in foliage and needles in groups, stripes or rings. Poisonous.

Clitocybe rivulosa (PERS.: FR.) KUMM. VIII–X

Cap 2–6 cm wide, at first broadly convex, soon slightly depressed. Involuted margin, later rather wavy. Cuticle is hygrophanous, reddish when damp, white pruinose in drought, margin almost white. Gills adnexed, crowded and whitish. Stipe is cylindrical, elastic, whitish at the top, fleshy in the centre, brownish with mycelial filaments at the base. Flesh is whitish, smell is slightly earthy. Spore powder is white, spores 4–5 × 2–3 μm, ellipsoid, colourless and nonamyloid. Commonest is short grass, often in lawns. Sometimes considered as a variety of *C. dealbata*. Poisonous.

Tricholomataceae

Clitocybe odora (BULL.: FR.) KUMM.   VIII–X

Cap 3–7 cm wide, convex with umbo in the centre, soon flat, broadly funnel-shaped in the centre, thin flesh, in damp conditions coloured cooper green or blue-green, in drought pallid to whitish, pale grey-greenish, smooth and silky. Gills are shortly decurrent, dense, grey-greenish, later pallid. Stipe is greenish, short and cylindrical, tapering and felted downwards. Flesh is pale, smells pleasantly of aniseed. Spore powder is white. Spores 6–7 × 3–4 μm, ellipsoid and colourless. It grows profusely in coniferous, particularly spruce, forests where it can be easily found by its scent. This usually disappears after drying. Edible.

Honey Fungus
Armillariella mellea (VAHL: FR.) KARST.   IX–XI
Syn. *Armillaria mellea* (VAHL.: FR.) KUMM.

Cap 3–15 cm wide, shallowly convex, of various brown or yellowish colours, covered with flaky brown to black-brown scales, later bald; margin attached to the stipe by a white or yellowish velum. Gills are slightly decurrent, sparse, white or yellowish, later fleshy red. Stipe is 5–20 cm long, 1–3.5 cm thick, cylindrical, with a yellowish or brownish tinge, getting dark towards the base, fibrillose to scaly, with a membranous ring. Flesh is white or yellowish, and has an unpleasant bitterish taste and sometimes also unpleasant smell. Spore powder is white or cream. Spores 7–9 × 5–6 μm, ellipsoid, colourless, smooth, nonamyloid. It grows usually in rich clusters on stumps, roots and live trunks of coniferous and deciduous trees. It belongs among most abundant wood mushrooms, its mycelium attacks live shrubs and trees. There is a complex of the so called lesser species, differing mainly in cap and velum colouring. The typical variety with an olive-blackish, later olive-brown to honey-yellow cap and a thick ring, has white or yellowish with yellow scales and white, later rusty-brown gills. More abundant is *Armillaria polymyces* (PERS.: S. F. GRAY) SING. et CLEM. with a whitish ring, honey-brown to red-brown, dark brown to blackish filamentous cap and white or cream gills, turning red to violet-brown with age. *A. ostoyae* ROMAGN. and *A. bulbosa* (BARLA) ROMAGN. have underdeveloped velum and a white and yellow ring, respectively. Both of them grow on wood of deciduous trees, exceptionally also on pines. All raw honey fungi are poisonous. Even a tiny piece of flesh causes stomach problems. Edible only when cooked properly.

Tricholomataceae

¶ *Tricholoma focale* (Fr.) Ricken   IX–XI ⬛⬜ / ⬜⬜

Cap 5–12 cm wide, broadly convex with involuted margin which carries remnants of volva; sticky when young, orange to red-brown, radially striate, later cracked. Gills attached to the stipe, cream-coloured when old with red patches. Stipe is stout, white above the fleshy ring, reddish underneath. Flesh is tough, white, turning slightly reddish, smell and taste resembles cucumber. Spore powder is white, spores 4–5 × 3–3.5 μm, ovoid, colourless. It grows rarely in sandy coniferous woods, particularly in pine. Rare. Sometimes regarded as a variety of *T. robustum*. Edible.

☠ *Tricholoma pessundatum* (Fr.) Quél.   VIII–IX ⬜⬛ / ⬜⬜

Cap 6–12 cm wide, tough fleshy, semi-globular, later shallowly convex to flat, with inrolled margin, red-brown, lighter towards the margin, with red-brown patches between the margin and the centre of the cap, slimy or sticky when damp. Gills sinuate, dense, whitish or light cream, later with red-rusty patches. Stipe 4–7 cm long, 2–3.5 cm thick, cylindrical, firm, full, pale, whitish cream, turning brown at the base. Flesh hard, whitish, of strong cucumber-flour taste and smell. Spores 4–6 × 2.5–3 μm, ellipsoid, smooth, colourless. It grows in coniferous woods, particularly in spruce. It is not recommended to collect. A milder poisoning can be caused.

☠ *Tricholoma fulvum* (Bull.: Fr.) Sacc.
Syn. *T. flavobrunneum* (L.: Pers.) Kumm.   VIII–X ⬜⬜ / ⬛⬜

Cap 3–10 cm wide, broadly convex with rounded top, red-brown, sticky when damp, glossy in drought. Gills are dense, sinuate with a decurrent tooth; pale yellow with rusty patches when old. Stipe is cylindrical, relatively slender and long, hollow when mature, yellowish with brown filaments. Flesh on the cap is white, on the stipe yellow; it smells of new meal. Spore powder is white, spores 5–7 × 3–4.5 μm, ellipsoid, colourless and smooth. It grows under birch in woods or outside woods in small groups. Poisonous.

¶ *Tricholama populinum* Lange   VIII–X ⬜⬜ / ⬜⬛

Cap 5–18 cm wide, permanently broadly convex, fleshy, coloured brown, smooth and bare, sticky when young. Gills are dense, sinuate, attached to stips with a small decurrent tooth; whitish, turning rusty. Stipe is cylindrical, often swollen at the base, 2.5 cm wide with minute pale rusty scales. Flesh is white, fleshy and compact, smell and taste is of new meal; slightly bitter. Spore powder is white, spores 5.5–6 × 3.5 μm, ellipsoid, smooth and colourless. It grows exclusively under poplar in clusters or large groups. Can be mistaken for poisonous brown *Tricholoma* species. It is not recommended to collect.

Tricholomataceae

☠ *Tricholoma albobrunneum* (PERS.: FR.) KUMM.   VIII–X   ⬛⬛⬜⬜

Cap 4–8 cm wide, broadly flat, later slightly convex, sticky when damp, glossy when dry, chestnut brown with small scales. Gills are sinuate, white, turning brown. Stipe is cylindrical, 5–10 cm long, 1–2 cm thick, white and slimy at the top, brown and scaly at the base. Flesh is firm, white, turning slightly pink, smells of new meal. Spore powder is white, spores 4–5 × 3–4 μm, broadly ellipsoid, hyaline and smooth. It grows in coniferous woods and also under oak and birch. Inedible, rather poisonous.

🍴 *Tricholoma vaccinum* (PERS.: FR.) KUMM.   IX–XI   ⬛⬜⬜⬜

Cap 3–8 cm wide, convex with rounded umbo and involuted, rusty tomentose margin; scaly, red-brown. Gills are attached, whitish, soon with flesh-coloured patches, then entirely reddish. Stipe is cylindrical, 5–8 cm long, 1–1.5 cm thick, hollow, white, granulate under the cap; the base is often swollen, red-brown and striate. Flesh is white, turning red; smell is earthy. Spore powder is white, spores 3–5.5 × 4–4.5 μm, almost globular, smooth and colourless; it grows abundantly in coniferous woods, particularly in limy soil. Inedible.

🍴 *Tricholoma imbricatum* (FR.) KUMM.   IX–XI   ⬜⬜⬛⬜

Cap 5–10 cm wide, broadly bell-shaped, later flat, margin involuted, finely felt-like, coloured red-brown; cuticle is dry, soon scaly except for the top of the cap. Gills are white, turning brown when bruised, patchy. Stipe is cylindrical, 5–10 cm long, 1–2 cm thick, white under the cap, red-brown at the base. Flesh is white, rusty in the stipe, insipid in smell. Spore powder is white, spores 5–5.5 × 3.5–4 μm, broadly ovoid to globular, smooth and colourless. It grows in warm areas in sandy soil under pine. Inedible.

🍴 *Tricholoma portentosum* (FR.) QUÉL.   VIII–X   ⬜⬜⬜⬛

Cap 3–10 cm wide, flat and umbonate, often irregular, old specimens have radiating cracks; sticky, fibrous, grey with purple or olive tinge. Gills are sinuate with a small decurrent tooth, not very dense, white with lemon tinge. Stipe is cylindrical, 4–8 cm long, 1–2 cm thick, full, striate and tough when old; white to yellow. Flesh is white or yellowish, tastes of hazel nuts, smells of flour. Spore powder is white, spores 5–6 × 3.5–5 μm, ellipsoid, smooth and colourless. It grows in coniferous forests, particularly in sandy pine woods. Can be confused with other greyish but inedible *Tricholoma* species.

Tricholomataceae

Tricholoma flavovirens (PERS.: FR.) LUND.   IX–XI   ■□ □□

Cap 4–10 cm wide, fleshy, at first bell-shaped, later flat with a low umbo in the centre, margin involuted, often wavy, coloured entirely greenish brown, brownish yellow to green-yellow, with dark, ingrown radial lines; slimy when damp. Gills are
deep, not very dense, deeply sinuate by the stipe, equipped with a decurrent tooth,
vivid sulphur yellow. Stipe is short, cylindrical, with tough flesh, green-yellow, sometimes with a brown tinge, longitudinally filamentous. Flesh is white, lemon yellow
in the cap under the detachable cuticle, pleasant mealy smell, does not change colour
when bruised. Spore powder is white. Spores 6–8 × 3.5–5 μm, ovoid ellipsoid,
smooth and colourless. It grows, often gregariously, in pine woods late in the autumn until the first frosts, especially in sandy soil. Related species *T. portentosum*
can be found in similar locations. It differs by the reddish-grey cap and white gills,
which have a lemon yellow tinge.

Tricholoma orirubens QUÉL.   VIII–IX   □■ □□

Cap 5–8 cm wide, shallowly convex, light to dark grey, dry, with dense blackish filaments and scales, fleshy. Gills are white or have a grey tinge at first, later light pink,
with patches, dense, sinuate. Stipe 5–12 cm long, 10–15 mm thick, white, with reddish patches with age, finely filamentous, sometimes with blue patches at the base.
Flesh is white, tasteless. Spores 5–7 × 5–6 μm, broadly ellipsoid, smooth, colourless. It grows in deciduous woods, especially in limestone substrate. Inedible.

Sulphurous Tricholoma
Tricholoma sulphureum (BULL.: FR.) KUMM.   VII–X   □□ ■□

Cap 2–6 cm wide, broadly bell-shaped when young, later broadly convex with a low
umbo; smooth, with ingrown fibres, sulphur yellow, brownish at the centre. Gills
are attached with a tooth; sparse, thick, fragile, coloured sulphur yellow. Stipe is cylindrical, sulphur yellow with brown filaments. Flesh is sulphur yellow; unlike *T.
flavovirens* it smells unpleasantly of gas. Spore powder is white, spores 9–11 × 5–6
μm, ellipsoid and colourless. It grows scattered under deciduous and coniferous
trees. Inedible.

Soap-scented Tricholoma
Tricholoma saponaceum (FR.) KUMM.   VIII–XI   □□ □■

Cap 4–12 cm wide, roundish-convex, soon irregularly expanded, viscid, in drought
bare, with laciniate cracks; greyish olive green with white, brown and reddish tones.
Gills are thick, attached to stipe with a small tooth; white, later with greyish to reddish patches. Stipe is cylindrical, 5–10 cm long, 1–3 cm thick, tough, whitish, often with grey scales. Flesh is white, turning red, smells of soap. Spore powder is
white, spores 5–6 × 3–4 μm, ellipsoid and colourless. It grows in small groups under
coniferous and less frequently under deciduous trees. Inedible.

Tricholomataceae

Tricholoma scalpturatum (FR.) QUÉL.   IX–XI

Cap 3–8 cm wide, broadly convex with rounded umbo, dry, slightly scaly, fibrillose, pale grey. Gills are sinuate, white to greyish, turning lemon yellow when bruised or old. Stipe is cylindrical, pruinose at the top, filamentous at the base, white to greyish; turns yellow with age when bruised. Flesh is greyish, brittle, mealy and cucumber-like in smell and taste. Spore powder is white, spores 7–9 × 4–5 μm, smooth and colourless. It grows in communities at the edges of spruce forests in grass and needles. There are several similar species. Edible.

Tricholoma terreum (SCHAEFF.: FR.) KUMM.   IX–X

Cap 3–8 cm wide, broadly expanded with a low umbo, black-grey, light grey during drought, felt-like, scattered with scales. Gills are sinuate, edges are serrated, whitish and turning grey; brittle. Stipe is cylindrical, white and granular at the top, fibrillose and greyish at the base. Flesh is thin and fragile, grey in the cap, white in the stipe; it smells of raw potatoes and has an insipid taste. Spore powder is white, spores 5–7 × 4–5 μm, smooth and colourless. It grows in communities in all woods, especially on limestone. It resembles *T. portentosum*, but it has neither yellow-tinged stipe, nor floury taste and smell. Edible.

Tricholoma album (SCHAEFF.: FR.) KUMM.   VII–X

Cap 5–12 cm wide, broadly convex, later with a rounded umbo, involuted margin; dry, glossy and silky, white, later yellowish. The top is brownish. The top is brownish. Gills are sinuate with a decurrent tooth, white, later creamy. Stipe is cylindrical, curved at the base, white, slightly ochre. Flesh is tough, white, at first with a mealy smell, later unpleasant, taste bitter and astringent at the same time. Spore powder is white, spores 4.5–6 × 3–4.5 μm, ellipsoid, smooth and colourless. It grows particularly under birch at the edge of woods, in avenues of trees. Inedible.

Tricholomataceae

 Tricholoma virgatum (FR..) KUMM.   VIII–X

Cap 3–7 cm wide, pointed, later expanded with a pointed tip, smooth and glossy, grey; radially striate with clusters of grey-brown or purple fibres. Gills are white, attached by a tooth, turning grey with age. Stipe is cylindrical, slightly broadened at the base, white to greyish. Flesh is whitish. Spore powder is white, spores 6–8 × 5–6 µm, broadly ellipsoid, smooth, colourless and nonamyloid. It grows in small groups under coniferous trees. Inedible. It may be confused with *T. portentosum*. Inedible, rather poisonous.

 Omphalina ericetorum (PERS.: FR.) M. LANGE
Syn. *Omphalina umbellifera* (L. HOOK.) KUMM.   VII–X
Syn. *Omphalina umbellifera* (L. HOOK.) QUÉL.

Cap 1–2 cm wide, shallowly but broadly concave, grooved close to the margin, margin serrated; skin white, brownish to greenish at the centre. Gills are deeply decurrent, sparse and considerably thick, whitish. Stipe is 1–2 cm long, thin (1–2 mm) and hollow, cartilaginous, whitish to yellowish. Flesh is thin, whitish, without specific smell. Spore powder is white, spores 7–8 × 6–7 µm, broadly ellipsoid, smooth, colourless and nonamyloid. It grows in woods on stumps and timber of coniferous trees, but particularly in peat. Inedible.

Rickenella fibula (BULL.: FR.) RAITH.
Syn. *Gerronema fibula* (BULL.: FR.) SING.   V–XI

Cap 5–15 cm wide, convex, deeply depressed in the centre, vivid orange-yellow, later turning pale, thinly membranous grooved, bare. Gills are deeply decurrent, not too dense, white, later pale orange. Stipe 2–6 cm long, 1–1.5 mm thick, thin, orange, bare and smooth. Flesh has no smell. Spore powder is white. Spores 4–5 × 2–2.5 µm, ellipsoid, colourless and smooth. The skin of the cap and the gills carries thin, club-shaped cystidia. It grows abundantly, individually or in small groups, in moss and grass along woodland tracks, clearings and edges of woods. Inedible.

Tricholomataceae

Wood Woolly-foot
Collybia peronata (Bolt.: Fr.) Kumm.   VI–X
Syn. *Marasmius urens* Fr.

Cap 2–5 cm wide, smooth, shallowly convex, later flat; margin is faintly grooved, flesh is thin and elastic, colour pale flesh brownish, pale beige when dry. Gills are sinuate and broadly attached, sparse, pale yellow to yellow-brown, later brown. Stipe is slender and cylindrical, 3–5 mm thick, broadened at the base, hispid and felt-like, yellowish to reddish brown, elastic. Flesh is pale yellow, with slightly acid smell. Spore powder is white. Spores 6–7 × 3–4 μm, ellipsoid, smooth, colourless. It grows individually or in clusters in rotting leaves or needles. Inedible.

Collybia confluens (Pers.: Fr.) Kumm.   VI–X

Cap 2–4 cm wide, shallowly bell-shaped, later flat and sometimes umbonate, pale leathery to brownish, sometimes whitish; flesh thin and elastic, skin bare. Gills are very dense and shallow, sinuate and attached by a tooth; whitish, later brownish, edges finely hairy. Stipe is slender and cylindrical, sometimes compressed, tough and elastic, light brown, densely covered by white granules, hollow. Spore powder is white. Spores 7–10 × 2–3 μm, spindle-shaped, smooth and colourless. It grows often in large clusters on rotting leaves and needles, which become firmly attached to the base of the stipe. Inedible.

Russet Shank
Collybia dryophila (Bull.: Fr.) Kumm.   V–X

Cap 2–6 cm wide, convex, soon flat, most frequently pale ochre, yellow-brown or even chestnut brown; flesh is thin and elastic. Gills are sinuate, narrow, very dense, white, whitish to pale yellow. Stipe 4–8 cm long, 2–5 mm thick, tube-like, ochre yellow, bare, smooth, elastic, white-felted at the base. Flesh is whitish or yellowish pleasantly smelling of *Boletus*, mild in taste. Spore powder is white. Spores 4–6 × 2–3 μm, ellipsoid, smooth, colourless. It grows abundantly in all types of forest, most frequently in oak woods.
Lower left: *Collybia dryophila* subsp. *exsculpta* (Fr.?, Bres.), yellowish to olive-coloured.

Tricholomataceae

Collybia asema (Fr.) Kumm.   VII–X

Cap 3–5 cm wide, bell-shaped, later flat with a central umbo, strongly hygrophanous, coloured ash grey, greenish-grey with a dark brown centre; thin flesh. Gills are sinuate and narrowly attached, dense, whitish. Stipe 4–9 cm long, 5–20 mm thick, light grey to brown-grey, soft; base is broadened and has white mycelium. Flesh is white, without specific smell and taste. Spore powder is white. Spores 6–8 × 3–3.5 μm, ellipsoid, smooth and colourless. It grows abundantly in all woods, particularly coniferous and mixed. Some authorities regard this as the same species as *C. butyracea*. Edible.

Greasy Tough Shank
Collybia butyracea (Bull.: Fr.) Kumm.   VII–X

Cap 4–8 cm wide, bell-shaped and convex, later flat with a low umbo in the centre, deep red-brown or chestnut brown, cocoa cap brown during the drought, hygrophanous, gills are sinuate and narrowly attached, dense, whitish. Stipe 4–8 cm long, 5–20 mm thick, cylindrical, swollen at the base, longitudinally coarsely fibrillose to ribbed; red-brown, lighter at the top. Flesh is white without specific smell or taste. Spore powder is white. Spores 6–8 × 3–3.5 μm, ellipsoid, smooth and colourless. It grows in moss and needles in damp coniferous woods. This and the preceding species are very similar in appearance, differing only in colour. Edible.

Spotted Tough Shank
Collybia maculata (Alb. et Schw.: Fr.) Kumm.   VII–X

Cap 5–12 cm wide, firm flesh, semi-globular, later flat; pure white, later with red-brown to rusty brown patches. Gills are sinuate and attached by a tooth, very dense, white, edges finely serrated. Stipe is often twisted, tapering or pointed at the base, finely longitudinally striate, white with reddish patches, tough. Flesh is white and tough. Whole fruit-body gradually turns red-brown with age or when bruised. Spore powder is yellowish pink. Spores 5–6 × 4–5 μm, sub-globose, smooth. It grows on rotting wood concealed in the ground or on the stumps in coniferous woods, especially in pine woods. Inedible.

Collybia marasmioides (Britz.) Brsky. et Stangl
Syn. *Collybia acervata* (Fr.) Kumm. ss. Konrad et Maubl.   VI–X

Cap 1.5–4 cm wide, at first semi-globular or bell-shaped, later flat with a central umbo; margin is often wavy; cuticle is smooth and bare, deep red in damp conditions, paler during drought. Flesh is thin and elastic. Gills are sinuate and attached by a tooth, very dense and shallow, tapering towards the edges, whitish, later reddish. Stipe is 5–12 cm long, 2–5 mm thick, slender and cylindrical, red or red-brown, base is red-brown felted. Spore powder is white. Spores 6–8 × 2.5–3 μm, ellipsoid, smooth and colourless. It grows in clusters on stumps and remnants of timber, sometimes even at the base of live trunks. Edible.

Tricholomataceae

Collybia platyphylla (PERS.: FR.) KOTL. et POUZ.   VII–IX

Cap 5–15 cm wide, shallowly convex, slightly fleshy, dark grey or grey-brown, sharply radially fibrillose, later cracked. Gills adnate to the stipe, conspicuously deep (2–3 cm), sparse, white; edges irregularly serrated, sometimes brown tomentose. Stipe is cylindrical, tough, hollow, whitish or greyish, longitudinally grooved, base has numerous, tough, black or white mycelial cords which penetrate humus. Flesh is white, without specific smell or taste. Spore powder is white. Spores 7–8 × 6–7 μm, sub-globose, smooth. It grows on rotting wood in the ground or on disintegrated stumps. Sometimes referred to the genus *Tricholomopsis*. Edible.

Baeospora myosura (FR.) QUÉL.   VII–X

Cap 1–2 cm wide, shallowly convex, sometimes with a wart in the centre, thinly elastic and membranous, coloured pale beige to leathery brown, with delicate white flakes or filaments, dry and smooth. Gills are very dense, shallow and narrow, white or whitish, rounded at the stipe. Stipe 2–5 cm long, 1–2 mm thick, slender, tough, light brownish, white pruinose; base often extended by roots and white tomentose. Spore powder is white. Spores 3–4 × 1.7–2 μm, small, ellipsoid, smooth and amyloid. Cheilocystidia are blunt spindle-shaped. It grows on fallen spruce, rarely pine, cones. Inedible.

Panellus stipticus (BULL.: FR.) KARST.   I–XII

Cap 1–3 cm wide, reniform or roundish with a very short, lateral stipe; shallowly convex, rounded at margin and strongly involuted; in damp conditions coloured ochre yellow, in drought pale clay yellow. Gills are sinuate, shallow, rusty yellow, sharply detached from the stipe. Stipe is eccentric, short and cone-shaped, tapering downwards, flattened, ochre yellow, downy at the base. Flesh is ochre. Spore powder is white. Spores 2–3 × 1–1.5 μm, spindle-shaped, amyloid. It grows in large numbers on oak stumps. Inedible.

Strobilurus conigenus (PERS.: FR.) GULDEN   III–VI
Syn. *Strobilurus stephanocystis* (KÜHN. et ROMAGN. IN HORA) SING.

Cap 1–2 cm wide, shallowly convex, later flat and expanded, flesh is thin; skin light ochre or ochre brown, smooth and bare. Gills are sinuate, dense, whitish or yellowish. Stipe is slender, 3–6 cm long, ochre yellow, smooth and bare; subterranean section is elongated and white tomentose. Flesh is whitish, with a light mushroom smell and mild taste. Spore powder is white. Spores 5–7 × 3–4 μm, ellipsoid. Cystidia are cylindrical or club-shaped, rounded tips, often covered with small crystals. It grows profusely on fallen pine cones embedded in the ground. Very similar species are found in North America. Edible.

Tricholomataceae

Stronilurus esculentus (WULF.: FR.) SING. III–V ■□□□

Cap 1–2 cm wide, shallowly convex, soon flat and expanded, with thin flesh, coloured greyish ochre, ochre to dark brown, but also whitish; smooth and bare. Gills are sinuate, dense, whitish or greyish. Stipe is slender, 3–6 cm long, ochre yellow, smooth and bare, the underground elongated tomentose section grows out of a cone. The length of the stipe is dependent on the depth in which the cone is buried. Flesh is whitish with a faint mushroom smell. Spore powder is white. Spores 4–6 × 2.5–4 μm, ellipsoid. It grows abundantly on fallen spruce cones, usually several fruit-bodies on one cone. Some authors refer this species to the genus *Pseudo-hictula*. Edible.

Slimy Beech Tuft
Oudemansiella mucida (SCHRAD.: FR.) HÖHN. VII–X □■□□

Adult fruit-body is white and looks as if made of porcelain. Cap 3–10 cm wide, broadly bell-shaped, with thin, translucent flesh, covered with a thick layer of slime. Gills are shortly decurrent, slightly sinuate, sparse. Stipe is slender and cylindrical, tough with a spreading, membranous and slimy ring. Spore powder is white. Spores 15–18 × 12–16 μm, almost spherical, smooth and colourless. It grows in clusters, rarely individually on old beech trunks, particularly in mountainous regions. Mycelium produces an antibiotic, called mucidin, which is used in treatment of some skin disease.

Rooting Shank
Oudemansiella radicata (RELHAN: FR.) SING. VII–IX □□■□
Syn. *Collybia macroura* (SCOP.) FR.

Cap 3–15 cm wide, bell-shaped, later flat with an umbo in the centre, ochre or yellow-brown with thin flesh, very slimy in damp conditions, often with pronounced, radiating wrinkles. Gills are deeply sinuate to adnexed, deep and sparse, white. Stipe up to 20 cm long, 5–7 mm thick, spindle-shaped at the base with an elongated root section up to several decimeters long and deeply sunk in the ground; white, grading to brown, bare and tough, crackling when it breaks. Spore powder is white. Spores 12–16 × 9–11 μm, broadly ellipsoid, smooth. It grows in deciduous woods on stumps and rotting wood in the ground. Edible.

Xerula longipes (BULL.: ST.-AM.) R. MAIRE VI–IX □□□■

Cap 3–6 cm wide, at first umbonate, later flat, yellow-brown, grey-brown or ochre, dry, velvety, thin-fleshed. Gills sinuate, deep and thick, joined together, sparse; yellowish white. Stipe similarly coloured as cap, velvety tomentose, tough, broadened at the base and suddenly tapering into a very long, deeply rooted outgrowth. Flesh is white, slightly bitter. Spore powder is white. Spores 8–10 × 6–7 μm, broadly ellipsoid, smooth and colourless. It grows rarely in deciduous woods, especially in beech woods. Edible.

Tricholomataceae

Velvet Shank or **Winter Fungus**
Flammulina velutipes (CURT.: FR.) SING.   X–IV   ■□
□□

Cap 1.5–8 cm wide, shallowly convex with thin flesh, ochre yellow or yellow-brown, with a chestnut brown centre; sticky when damp. Gills are sinuate, dense, white or yellowish. Stipe is cylindrical, tapering towards the base and sometimes rooting, chestnut brown; base is almost black-brown, yellowish at the top, felt-like and velvety. It can be found also in its pure white form (*F. lactea*), which is rare. Flesh is faintly scented. Spore powder is white. Spores 7–9 × 4.5–6 μm, ellipsoid. It grows in clusters on stumps and at the base of trees, especially deciduous species. Sometimes it appears even in summer during a cold spell. An important edible winter mushroom.

Myxomphalia maura (FR.) HORA   □■
Syn. *Fayodia maura* (FR.) SING.   VIII–X   □□

Cap 1–4 cm wide, expanded, with a shallow or deep depression in the centre, hygrophanous; in damp weather dark black-brown to blackish, during the drought grey and silvery glossy. Flesh is thin and elastic, with a rubbery, gelatinous, detachable cuticle. Gills are decurrent, rather dense, shallow and pure white. Stipe 3–5 cm long, 2–4 mm thick, cylindrical and black-brown, whitish pruinose, hollow. Spore powder is white. Spores 5–6 × 3.5–4.5 μm, ellipsoid, smooth, colourless and amyloid. It grows on old burnt ground in coniferous woods. Inedible.

Little Wheel Toadstool
Marasmius rotula (SCOP.: FR.) FR.   VI–X   □□
■□

Cap 5–15 mm wide, semi-globular or thimble-shaped, strongly marked with grooves, depressed in the centre, sometimes with an umbo, thinly membranous, white or whitish, bare. Gills are deep, sparse and whitish, joined near the stipe into a characteristic collar. Stipe is very slender, glossy; top is brownish, base black-brown to blackish. Spore powder is white. Spores 5–7 × 2–3 μm, ellipsoid, pointed at the base. It grows on small rotting sticks, often in large numbers. Inedible.

Marasmiellus ramealis (BULL.: FR.) SING.   VI–X   □□
□■

Cap 3–10 mm wide, thinly leathery, convex, later flat, wrinkled in dry weather, pale, whitish with a brown centre. Gills are sparse, attached, white. Stipe 3–10 mm long, 5–1 mm thick, tough, pale, brown towards the base, in lower part scaly with granules. Spores 8–10.5 × 2.5–4 μm, lanceolate-ellipsoid, colourless. It grows on dead twigs of deciduous trees, often on shoots of *Rubus* spp., under shrubs and in damp places, in groups. Inedible.

Tricholomataceae

Marasmius scorodonius (FR.) FR.   VI–X

Cap 1–3 cm wide, convex, later flat; fleshy brown or pinkish beige to whitish, smooth or wrinkled, bare. Flesh is thin and elastic. Gills are adnate, dense, white. Stipe is slender, 3–6 cm long, 1–2 mm thick, red-brown, bare, glossy, lighter under the gills. When rubbed, flesh has a strong garlic smell. Spore powder is white. Spores 8–9 × 4–5 μm, ovoid, smooth and colourless. It grows very abundantly in coniferous woods; on needles, fallen branches, stumps and roots of trees, usually individually. There are several similar species. Edible.

Fairy Ring Champignon
Marasmius oreades (BOLT.: FR.) FR.   V–IX

Cap 2–5 cm wide, bell-shaped, later expanded with a central boss, margin often lightly grooved; pale fleshy ochre or buff, bare, with thin and elastic flesh. Gills are sinuate and attached by a small tooth, sparse, deep, whitish. Stipe 4–7 cm long, 2–4 mm thick, full, elastic, whitish, with pruinose flakes. Flesh is white, with a faint bitter-almond scent. Spore powder is white. Spores 7–9 × 4–5 μm, elipsoid, smooth and colourless. It grows abundantly outside woods, on lawns, in pastures, meadows, along field tracks and sometimes in light coniferous woods, especially along their edges. Edible, tasty. Similar to the poisonous, white *Clitocybe* species.

Marasmius wynnei BERK. et BR.   VI–X

Cap 2–5 cm wide, bell-shaped and convex, later flat and expanded, grooved and serrated at the margin, with thin and elastic flesh; pure white, later turning grey, sometimes lilac or purple-grey, bare. Gills are sinuate, deep and scarce, whitish to light grey. Stipe 4–10 cm long, 2–5 mm thick, slender and cylindrical, tapering downwards; white at the top, dark brown to blackish at the base, felt-like. Flesh has a bitter almond scent. Spore powder is white. Spores 6–7 × 3–3.5 μm, ellipsoid, smooth and colourless. It grows in grass outside woods and also on fallen foliage and needles in woods. Edible.

Yellow-stemmed Mycena
Mycena epipterygia (SCOP.: FR.) S. F. GRAY   VII–XI

Cap 1–2 cm wide, bell-shaped, broadly expanded, with an elastic, slimy and crisp pellicle; yellow, pallid, but may be greyish. Turns rusty when bruised. Gills are sinuate, white turning rusty; edges have detachable membrane. Stipe is thread-like, white, yellow or greyish, sticky. Flesh is very thin and floury, turns rusty with age and has a pungent taste. Spore powder is white, spores 8–12 × 4–6 μm, cylindrical and colourless. It grows in large groups on needles and foliage in deep woods. Inedible. Similar to *Mycena viscosa* (SECR.) R. MAIRE with red-brown spots on cap and stipe.

Tricholomataceae

Milk Drop Mycena
Mycena galopus (PERS.: FR.) KUMM.   VI–XI

Cap 1–2 cm wide, bell-shaped, membranous, smooth or faintly grooved; young skin is pruinose, smooth, whitish, light to dark grey, sometimes brownish. Gills are adnexed, sparse, white or greyish. Stipe is slender, long and fragile, bare 1–2 mm thick; white, greyish or brownish. Fresh specimens produce white insipid milky fluid when broken. Flesh is very thin, whitish, inconspicuously scented; tastes slightly of radish. Spore powder is white, spores 10–14 × 5–7 μm, smooth and colourless. It grows gregariously in deciduous and coniferous woods. Inedible.

Lilac Mycena
Mycena pura (PERS.: FR.) KUMM.   V–X

Cap 2–4 cm, convex, soon broadly expanded, thin flesh, brittle, hygrophanous, in damp conditions has translucent edges; purple, but also white, yellowish. Gills are sinuate and shortly attached, deep swollen, edges are serrated, coloured white, later light purple, edges are whitish but turn light purple when dry. Stiple is 3–5 mm thick, gradually broadens towards the base, hollow and breakable, usually light purple. Flesh is brittle, light purple; it has a strong smell of radish. Spore powder is white, spores 5–8 × 2.5–3.5 μm, ellipsoid, smooth and colourless. It grows individually or in small groups in all types of woodland. Inedible.

Mycena rosea GRAMBERG   V–X

Cap 3–6 cm wide, soon expanded to convex with an umbo; cuticle is hygrophanous, pale pink. Gills are sinuate, swollen and joined together, with serrated edges, white or pale pink. Stipe is cylindrical, filamentous, curved in the substrate, broadens up to 2 cm towards base; hollow, white, pale pink with yellow base. Flesh is white to pale pink, with yellow base; smells of radish. Spore powder is white, spores 6–9 × 4–5 μm, cylindrical and hyaline. It grows in small groups under deciduous trees. Poisonous. There are several other smaller pink Mycenas.

Mycena inclinata (FR.) QUÉL.   VIII–XI

Cap 2–4 cm wide, partly translucent, margin deeply serrated, skin smooth, at first white, soon yellow to dark brown. Gills are sinuate, attached by a small tooth, white, turning grey or pink. Stipe has a root and fuses together into a cluster with others; erect, white, soon golden yellow. Cap and gills turn rusty with age. Flesh is white with a musty floury smell. Spore powder is white, spores 8–12 × 5–6 μm, cylindrical, smooth and amyloid. It grows in dense clusters on oak stumps. Inedible.

Tricholomataceae

Bonnet Mycena
Mycena galericulata (SCOP.: FR.) S. F. GRAY   V–XII

Cap 2–5 cm wide, semi-globular, soon umbonate, later expanded, sometimes radially ridged, membranous, tough and leathery. Cuticle is smooth and wrinkled, whitish, grey, brownish and crisp. Gills are sparse, joined together by veins, elastic, swollen with serrated edges, sinuate with a small decurrent tooth; white, greyish, sometimes turning pink when old. Stipe is rooting, long and slender, tough and bare, slippery, white, yellowish to light grey. Flesh of the cap is thin, tough, white to greyish; in the stipe it is tough and fibrillose. It has a mealy smell. Spore powder is white, spores 8–12 × 6–8 μm, ellipsoid, smooth and colourless. It grows profusely on stumps and timber of deciduous trees, usually in small clusters of fruitbodies. Edible (only cap).

Mycena polygramma (BULL.: FR.) S. F. GRAY   V–X

Cap 2–4 cm wide, bell-shaped, tough and furrowed, pruinose when young, whitish, grey-brown, turns rusty when bruised. Gills sinuate with a small tooth, white, grey, sometimes turning pink, finally rusty. Stipe is šrooting, rounded, tough and smooth, pruinose only when young, soon silvery or bluish shiny, with deep longitudinal grooves. Flesh is white, turning rusty. Spore powder is white, spores 8–12 × 6–8 μm, broadly, ellipsoid, smooth and colourless. It grows in small clusters on stumps of oak and other deciduous trees. Inedible.

Mycena cinerella KARST.   VIII–X

Cap 0.8–1.5 cm wide, semi-globular with a small depression at the top, sometimes also with a papilla; cuticle is hygrophanous, grey-brown when damp, greyish in drought, margin is grooved. Gills are decurrent, grey-brown, edges are lighter. Stipe is slender and erect, hollow, brittle and smooth, white, grey to dark grey. Flesh is thin, white and is intensively mealy. Spore powder is white, spores 6–10 × 4–5.5 μm, ellipsoid, smooth and colourless. It grows gregariously in spruce needles and can be smelt from a distance. Inedible.

Tricholomataceae

⚫⬜
⬜⬜

Mycena metata (FR.) KUMM.
Syn. *Mycena phyllogena* PERS. ss. SINGER   VIII–X

Cap 1–1.5 cm wide, club-shaped, striate at the margin, matt; pink, brown or grey fleshy. Gills are adnexed, not too dense, supple, pink brown or greyish. Stipe is very slender, long and erect and crackles when it breaks; hollow, glossy, smooth, whitish at the top, pale grey-brownish at the base. Flesh is thin, grey-brown, smells of iodoform when drying. Spore powder is white. Spores 9–11 × 4–5 μm, ellipsoid, smooth and colourless. It grows gregariously on fallen foliage and needles, less frequently on timber and stumps. Inedible.

⬜⚫
⬜⬜

Mycena abramsii MURRILL
Syn. *Mycena praecox* VELEN.   IV–VI

Cap 1–3.5 cm wide, semi-globular with shallow grooves, pruinose when young, later glossy, hygrophanous, smooth; white, grey and brownish. Margin of the cap rolls under when the mushroom dries out. Gills are rounded, sparse, white and greyish. Stipe, 3–7 cm long and 1–2 mm thick, is erect and hollow, cracking, smooth, white at the top, grey at the base, turns dark when old. Flesh is thin, whitish, with slightly alkaline scent. Spore powder is white, spores 7–13 × 4–6 μm, ellipsoid, smooth and colourless. It grows on branches, trunks and stumps of deciduous trees. It appears in spring, unlike most *Mycena* species. Inedible.

⬜⬜
⚫⬜

Xeromphalina campanella (BATSCH: FR.) KÜHL. et R. MAIRE   III–IX

Cap 1–2 cm wide, broadly bell-shaped, centrally depressed, thin, rather elastic membrane, grooved margin; colour vivid brown-orange or orange-yellow. Gills are deeply decurrent, sparse, joined transversely by numerous veins; pale yellow. Stipe 1–2 cm long, 1–2 mm thick, slender, usually curved, yellow-brown to rusty brown; base is tomentose. Flesh has no specific smell. Spore powder is white. Spores 5–6 × 2–3 μm, ellipsoid, smooth, amyloid and colourless. It grows in dense clusters of several hundred specimens on rotting and mossy stumps or on fallen trunks of coniferous trees, especially spruce. Inedible.

⬜⬜
⬜⚫

Giant Clitocybe
Leucopaxillus giganteus (SIBTH.: FR.) SING.   VIII–X

Cap 10–35 cm wide, soon funnel-shaped with involuted margin, smooth and silky; white, leathery yellowish. Gills are deeply decurrent, dense, white, soon leathery yellowish. Stipe 6–8 cm long and 2–5 cm wide, tough, full, whitish. Flesh is white, watery in old age; smell is strongly spermatic, taste inconspicuous. Spore powder is white. Spores 6–7 × 4–5 μm, ovoid, perfectly smooth (even under a microscope), colourless and amyloid. It grows in groups in pastures, along the edges of woods and in gardens. In some texts this may be found in the genus *Clitocybe*.

Tricholomataceae

Leucopaxillus gentianeus (QUÉL.) KOTL.   IX–XI

Syn. *Leucopaxillus amarus* (ALB. et SCHW.: FR.) KÜHN. ss. KÜHN.

Cap 5–15 cm wide, soon irregularly expanded to depressed with involuted margin, white-felted, comb-shaped, dry, matt. Gills are decurrent and dense, white to creamy, rusty. Stipe is cylindrical and short, swollen at the base, pruinose under the cap, white. Flesh is white, with mealy smell. Spore powder is white. Spores 4–6 × 3.5 – 5 μm, almost globular, finely spiked, colourless. It grows in rings in coniferous woods, less frequently in deciduous woods. Inedible.

Melanoleuca melaleuca (PERS.: FR.) R. MAIRE   VII–IX

Cap 3–8 cm wide, shallowly arched to umbonate, with relatively thin flesh, grey-brown or amber to blackish-brown, beige pallid when dry; faintly pruinose, with involuted margin. Gills are sinuate, dense, whitish, invariable, narrow. Stipe is slender and cylindrical, 4–10 mm thick, smooth, bare; lighter in colour than the cap. Flesh is white, slightly scented of bitter almond. Spore powder is white. Spores 7–8 × 4.5–5 μm, ellipsoid, finely tuberculate, colourless and amyloid. Cheilocystidia are thin with a crystal cap at the tip. It grows on grassy paths in woods. Edible.

Amanitaceae

Amanita vaginata (BULL.: FR.) VITT.   VII–IX

Cap 3–12 cm wide, bell-shaped, later flat and expanded, with a low umbo in the centre; its flesh is thin and brittle. Cuticle is usually bare, rarely with individual remnants of the white velum; coloured in various shades of grey, rarely white. Gills are free, quite dense, pure white, deep. Stipe is slender and cylindrical, white and has no ring; lower surface is covered with a high membranous white sheath with irregularly cracked edges. Flesh is white, brittle and watery. Spore powder is white. Spores 9–12 μm wide, globular, smooth, nonamyloid and colourless. It grows abundantly in all types of forest, often under birch in grassy and mossy patches. Sometimes confused with *Amanita phalloides*.

Amanaita fulva (SCHAEFF.) ex PERS.   VI–X

Cap 4–12 cm wide, bell-shaped, soon expanded, red-brown, translucent. Gills are swollen, free and white. Stipe, 15 cm lond and 1–1.5 cm thick, has no ring, is erect, hollow, gradually broadening towards the base; coloured white or brownish, with a white, later orange-brown granular vulva at the base. Flesh is brittle, very delicate, whitish and sweet. Spore powder is white. Spores 9–12 μm, globular, smooth, colourless and nonamyloid. It grows particularly in spruce woods, but also under deciduous trees. Edible (except fresh, when poisonous).

Amanitaceae

Amanita umbrinolutea SECR.   VII–IX

Cap 6–12 cm wide, at first club- to bell-shaped, later expanded with a central umbo; rather fleshy with grooves reaching half-way down the cap. Cuticle is yellow-brown, olive brown or grey-brown; rusty brown in the centre. Margin is lighter to whitish. Gills are free, dense and white. Stipe 10–20 cm long, 10–15 mm thick, tapering at the top; pale, striated brown-grey or yellow-brown, with a high pointed volva at the base. Flesh is white, watery and brittle. Spore powder is white. Spores 11–16 × 9.5–13 μm, broadly ellipsoid, smooth, colourless and nonamyloid. It is sometimes considered to be one of the colour varieties which belong to the collective species *Amanita vaginata*; this species is divided into at least eight independent microspecies. It grows in subalpine coniferous woods, particularly in spruce monocultures.

Amanita crocea (QUÉL.) SING.   VII–IX

Fruit-body resembles *Amanita vaginata* (BULL.: FR.) Quél. by its size and shape, it differs in orange or orange-brown cap (6–12 cm in diameter). Stipe is smooth at first, later striated, white, 10–15 cm long, 1–2 cm thick, with a volva at the base. Spores 8–12 (14) μm, globular, smooth, colourless. It grows in coniferous and deciduous woods. Edible.

Fly Agaric
Amanita muscaria (L.: FR.) HOOK.   VII–XI

Cap 5–15 cm wide, globular, soon broadly convex, vivid orange to scarlet red with numerous loose whitish warts. Gills are free, deep and white. Stipe is white, 2–3 cm thick, cylindrical, with a ring and a volva; ring is smooth and white, volva reduced to concentric warts. Flesh is white, yellow close to the skin of the cap and has no smell. Spore powder is white; spores 10–12 × 7–10 μm, ellipsoid, smooth, colourless and nonamyloid. It grows abundantly in all types of forest, particularly under conifers. Poisonous.

Amanita regalis (FR.) MICHAEL   VIII–X

Cap 10–25 cm wide, globular when young, soon broadly expanded and convex; margin is grooved, liver brown with ochre patches. Gills are free, yellowish. Stipe is erect, tall, 2–3 cm thick, cylindrical and yellowish with a yellowish ring at the top and a tuber encircled by rows of small warts at the base. Flesh is white, yellow to greenish under the cap's skin. Spore powder is white. Spores of 9–12 × 7–8 μm, colourless and nonamyloid. It grows abundantly in submountainous spruce forests. The illustration shows a pale specimen. Poisonous.

Amanitaceae

 Panter Cap
Amanita pantherina (DC.: FR.) KROMBH.   VII–XI

Cap 4–12 cm wide, ovoid, soon broadly convex with a grooved margin. The surface displays white, loose remnants of the veil; skin is grey or yellow-brown. Gills are free and white. Stipe is up to 15 cm long, 1–2 cm thick, cylindrical, hollow, white, with a white and smooth ring at the top and a globular bulb with a shallow edge at the base; one to two shallow loops which are usually slanting, are located above. Flesh is white and odourless. Spore powder is white. Spores 10–12 × 7–8 μm, ellipsoid, colourless and nonamyloid. It grows in all types of woodland, often even outside it; it prefers warm areas. Very poisonous.

 Amanita gemmata (FR.) GILL.
Syn. *Amanita junquillea* QUÉL.   V–X

Cap 3–10 cm wide, globular, soon expanded and convex, thin; margin is grooved. White, loose remnants of veil cover the surface. Cuticle is straw or ochre yellow, pallid. Gills are free and white. Stipe is 3–10 cm long, 1–1.5 cm thick, erect, slightly broadened at the base, brittle and white at the top with a faint white ring. Flesh is white. Spore powder is white, spores 10–12 × 7–8 μm, ellipsoid, colourless and nonamyloid. It grows individually in warm forests, particularly in sandy pine woods and sometimes also under deciduous trees. Rare in Great Britain. Slightly poisonous.

 The Death Cap
Amanita phalloides (FR.) LINK   VIII–X

Young fruit-body looks like a white egg. As it grows the veil bursts and the stipe pushes the cap above the ground. Cap 5–15 cm wide, expanded and convex, bare or with remnants of the veil; margin is without grooves. Cuticle is sticky in damp weather, shiny and smooth when dry; yellow, olive to brownish-green, often blackish in the centre, later turning pale almost to white. Surface covered with ingrown fibres. Gills are free, always white. Stipe is 5–12 cm long, 1–2 cm thick, cylindrical, erect, hollow when mature, with a white, membranous, usually smooth ring and greenish scales underneath; it grows out of a tall, whitish bulb which is greenish inside. Flesh is white and smells of raw potatoes. Spore powder is white. Spores 8–10 × 7–9 μm, shortly ovoid, colourless, amyloid. It grows predominantly in deciduous woods and under oak outside woods and can occasionally be found in pine woods. It is more common in warm regions. Deadly poisonous.

Amanitaceae

Destroying Angel
Amanita virosa (FR.) BERTILLON

VIII–IX

Young fruit-body resembles a white egg. Cap 3–10 cm wide, at first slightly clavate or globularly convex, expanded when mature; its margin is smooth. Cuticle is sticky when damp and glossy when dry. It has no traces of veil and is coloured pure white; when old, it turns brown from the top. Gills are free and white. Stipe is erect, hollow and slender (up to 1.5 cm); it is white with a faint ring with white scales underneath and a weak white bulb. Flesh is white and it smells and tastes of raw potatoes. Spore powder is pure white. Spores are globular, 7–10 μm in diameter, smooth, colourless and amyloid. It grows in subalpine coniferous woods in acid soil, individually or in small groups. It is rare in Great Britain. Deadly poisonous.

Amanita verna (BULL.: FR.) PERS. ex VITT.

V–IX

Very similar to the Destroing Angel. Cap is covered with traces of veil; spores are ellipsoid, 9–10 × 7.5–9.5 μm in diameter. Grows in deciduous woods in warmer areas (rather in southern Europe). Both species are deadly poisonous.

False Death Cap
Amanita citrina (SCHAEFF.) ex ROQUES

VII–XII

Cap 4–10 cm wide, semi-globular when young, soon expanded and convex to flat, with smooth margin. Cuticle is lemon yellow, often with whitish or brownish remnants of the veil. Gills are free and white. Stipe is erect, 7–10 cm long, 1–1.5 cm thick, hollow when mature, yellowish, with a faint yellowish ring; globular bulb at the base has a shallow, truncated volva. It is white and tastes and smells of potatoes. Spore powder is white. Spores are globular, 7–10 μm in diameter, smooth, colourless and amyloid. It grows abundantly in all forests. Poisonous. Some specimens can easily be mistaken for the Death Cap (*A. phalloides*).

Amanita porphyria (ALB. et SCHW.: FR.) SCHUMMEL

VII–X

Cap 4–10 cm wide, soon broadly expanded and convex, bare, often with grey-purple remnants of the veil, porphyric brown or grey-purple. Gills are swollen, free and white. Stipe is erect, with a globular, truncated bulb at the base, sometimes with remnants of volva; grey-purple, finely scaly under the limp ring. Flesh is white, sweet in taste and smells rather unpleasant. Spore powder is white. Spores 8–10 μm, globular, smooth, hyaline and amyloid. It grows usually individually in deciduous and coniferous woods. Poisonous.

Amanitaceae

Y *Amanita spissa* (FR.) OPIZ   VI–IX   ■□
                                                                    □□

Cap 5–20 cm wide, at first semi-globular, later shallowly convex. Young fruit-bodies are covered with a white or greyish velum which breaks into irregular remnants
usually arranged in concentric circles; these drop off in mature specimens. Cuticle
is grey or ash grey; pallid during drought. Gills are free, dense, deep and white. Stipe
6–20 cm long, 2–4 cm thick, white or grey above the ring which slants away from
the stipe; it is membranous and its upper part (similar to the section of the stipe
above it) is densely longitudinally grooved. The base of stipe is swollen into a clavate and often crooked bulb with one to two poorly defined rings of warts. Flesh is
white and smells of raw potatoes. Spore powder is white. Spores 9–10 × 7–8 μm,
ovoid ellipsoid, smooth, colourless and amyloid. It grows very abundantly in all
types of forest, especially under conifers. May be confused with the poisonous *Amanita pantherina*.

Y **The Blusher**   □■
Amanita rubescens (PERS.: FR.) S. F. GRAY   VI–X   ■□

Cap 5–15 cm wide, at first semi-globular, later convex to flat and expanded; fleshy,
usually whitish or slightly reddish when young, later light reddish to brown, often
with patches and small remnants of the veil. Gills are free, dense, deep and white,
later slightly reddish or with red-brown patches. Stipe 6–16 cm long, 1.5–3.5 cm
thick; white, wine reddish at the base, broadened into a club-shaped bulb with several rows of warts. The top section has a ring which is broad, membranous and
densely grooved on the upper surface. Flesh is white, soon becoming red under the
cap's skin. Turns red when exposed to the air and this is particularly apparent on the
bulb which is often riddled by insect larvae. The smell is inconspicuous and the taste
slightly astringent. Spore powder is white. Spores 8–9 × 5.5–7 μm, ellipsoid,
colourless and amyloid. It grows abundantly in all woods. May be confused with
Amanita pantherina.

Amanitaceae

Amanita strobiliformis (PAUL.: VITT.) BERTILLON   VII–IX

Cap 8–20 cm wide, fleshy, globular, soon convex; white or whitish on the surface with thick whitish to grey remnants of veil; the margin bears white fimbriate granules. Gills are free, swollen, white, with downy edges. Stipe is erect, white, strong and rooting, slightly broadened at the base, without a volva but with warty rings; the ring is thick, fringed, smooth and white. Flesh is white; it has a sweet taste and smells of radish and honey when it is drying. Spore powder is white. Spores 9–14 × 7–10 μm, colourless and amyloid. It grows in deciduous forests in warm areas, but also in parks. Also known as *Amanita solitaria* BULL. ex FR. Unknown in many areas, including Great Britain, or very rare.

Limacella illinita (FR.) MURR.   VIII–IX

Cap 2,5 cm wide, shallowly convex, pure white, but also yellow or greyish, covered with colourless slime. Gills are free, dense, pure white. Stipe 4–10 cm long, 2–7 mm thick, slimy, ringless. Flesh without specific taste and smell. Spore powder is white. Spores 4–6 × 4–4.5 μm, broadly ellipsoid, smooth, colourless. It grows on the ground in coniferous woods. Inedible.

Pluteaceae

Pluteus tricuspidatus VELEN.
Syn. *Pluteus atromarginatus* (KONRAD) KÜHNER   VII–IX

Cap 4–12 cm wide, shallowly convex, later flat and expanded, sometimes slightly umbonate in the centre; dark amber brown to black-brown, finely felted and fibrillose to scaly. Gills are remote, dense and whitish, later pale pink; their edges show narrow black-brown lines. Stipe 5–12 cm long, 5–15 mm thick, fragile, sparsely longitudinally striped in dark brown to reddish on white background. Flesh is whitish, watery, with faint radish smell. Spore powder is pink. Spores 6–8 × 4.5–5.5 μm, slightly angular, pale pink. The edges and surface carry bottle-shaped cystidia with three pointed hooks at the apex. It grows on stumps of coniferous trees, mainly pine and spruce.

Agaricaceae

Parasol Mushroom
Macrolepiota procera (SCOP.: FR.) SING.   VII–X
Syn. *Lepiota procera* (SCOP.: FR.) KUMMER

Cap 10–25 cm wide, at first club-shaped, later almost expanded with an umbo in the centre; cuticle is cracked to form brown, overlapping, partly loose scales; the centre of the cap remains smooth and brown. Gills are free from the stem, deep, brittle, white. Stipe 20–40 cm long, enlarged at the base into a bulb covered with felt-like, white mycelium. Entirely brown when young, gradually cracking into scales and rings which form transverse stripes on the white background; it is firm, easily detached from the cap, with a broad, brown-edged and movable ring in the upper third of the stipe. Flesh is white, invariably woolly in the cap and rather dry; in the stipe filamentous and woody. It has a strong smell and pleasant taste. Spore powder is white. Spores 15–20 × 10–13 μm, ellipsoid, smooth and colourless. It grows in grass in sunny places in woods and along their edges. Edible, tasty.

Shaggy Parasol
Macrolepiota rhacodes (VITT.) SING.   VII–IX
Syn. *Lepiota rhacodes* (VITT.) QUÉL.

Cap 10–15 cm wide, at first cylindrical, then bell-shaped, later expanded with a shallow boss in the centre; cuticle is brown or grey-brown which, except for the centre, cracks into numerous scales. Gills are free, dense, narrow, deep and whitish, covered with a veil when young. Stipe 10–20 cm long, 1–2 cm thick, bulbous at the base, whitish, bare, finely fibrillose, with a free, membranous ring at the top. The surface and flesh of fresh fruit-bodies turns orange, later red and brown when bruised. Flesh is whitish with a slight aroma. Spore powder is white. Spores 9–12 × 6–7 μm, ellipsoid and smooth. It grows in forests and on compost heaps. Edible, tasty.

Agaricaceae

Lepita aspera (PERS.: FR.) QUÉL.   VII–IX

Cap 8–14 cm wide, later broadly bell-shaped to expanded with thin flesh, white surface covered with numerous dark brown to black-brown, erect and pointed bristles. Gills are dense, free and white. Stipe is cylindrical, usually corm-like at the base, whitish, sparsely scattered with red-brown scales; it has a membranous ring at the top. Flesh is invariably white, with a strong, unpleasant smell, reminiscent of *Scleroderma*, mild in taste. Spore powder is white. Spores 7–8 × 2.5–3 μm, narrowly ellipsoid, smooth and colourless. It grows in coniferous and deciduous woods and sometimes also in gardens and parks. Inedible.

Lepiota perplexa KNUDSEN   VII–VIII

Species related and similar to *Lepiota aspera* (PERS.) QUÉL., from which it differs in smaller cap (only 2–7 cm wide), smaller spores (4–6 × 2.5 um) and narrower cystides. It grows in deciduous and coniferous woods. Inedible.

Lepiota clypeolaria (BULL.: FR.) KUMM.   VIII–IX

Cap 3–8 cm wide, bell-shaped, slightly umbonate in the centre, with thin and dry flesh; white surface is covered with yellow-brown to brown, soft, felt-like, adpressed scales; margin with numerous remnants of the veil in the form of white strips. Gills are free, dense and white. Stipe is slender and cylindrical, with fine, brown scales and with a web-like ring at the top. Flesh is white. Spore powder is white. Spores 12–16 × 5–5.5 μm,, long and narrow, ellipsoid, smooth and colourless. It grows in humus in nociferous and deciduous woods. Edible.

Agaricaceae

Lepiota cristata (ALB. et SCHW.: FR.) KUMM. VIII–X

Cap 2–4 cm wide, bell-shaped, later flat and convex, white with rusty brown centre, which cracks at the sides into fine scales decreasing in numbers towards the margin. Gills are free, dense and white. Stipe is slender, erect or slightly curved, reddish and white at the base with a loose ring. Flesh is thin and white and smells like the genus *Scleroderma*. Spore powder is white, spores 6–7 × 3–3.5 μm, wedge-shaped, colourless and nonamyloid. It grows in groups in grass, in woods and parks. Poisonous.

Lepiota fuscovinacea J. LGE. et MOELL. VIII–X

Cap 3–5 cm wide, at first semi-globular, then expanded and convex, finally flat with an umbo, felt-like to squamose; the top is prickly, purple brown or grey. Gills are free, dense and white. Stipe is erect, 2–8 long, 3–5 mm thick, white at the top, densely felt-like with coarse granules under the felt-like ring; grey- or brown-purple, grey at the base. Flesh is white without scent. Spore powder is white. Spores 6–7 × 3–3.5 μm, ovoid, smooth and colourless. It grows mainly in limy soil under spruce and pine. Poisonous, though slightly.

Red-staining Mushroom
Agaricus sylvaticus SCHAEFF. ex KROMBH. VII–IX

Cap 3–10 cm wide, convex, later broadly bell-shaped to expanded with rather thin and fragile, flesh; whitish surface densely covered with small, adpressed brown scales. Gills are free, dense, at first grey-reddish, later dark brown with whitish edges. Stipe is cylindrical, often broadened and curved towards the base; white, fibrillose, with a free membranous ring at the top. Flesh is white, turns vivid red when bruised and has a pleasant spicy scent. Spore powder is chocolate brown. Spores 5–6 × 3–3.5 μm, ellipsoid, brown. It grows profusely in coniferous, particularly spruce, woods. There are a number of similar red-staining mushrooms. Edible, tasty.

Common Field Mushroom
Agarius campestris L.: FR. VII–IX

Cap 4–10 cm wide, convex, later broadly bell-shaped to expanded, rather fleshy, entirely white, silky filamentous, sometimes cracking into scales. Gills are free, dense, at first deep pink, later grey-reddish, chocolate brown to deep black. Stipe is short and cylindrical, tapering at the base with a broad, thinly membranous, loose ring located at the top or half-way down the stipe; it is white, turning rusty brown from the base. Flesh is white and has a pleasant mushroom scent. Spore powder is chocolate brown. Spores 7–9 × 5–6 μm, broadly ellipsoid, brown. It grows very abundantly in meadows, fields, gardens, and along field tracks. Edible, very tasty.

Agaricaceae

Horse Mushroom
Agaricus arvensis SCHAEFF.: FR. VI–IX

Cap 5–20 cm wide, cone-shaped to convex, later broadly bell-shaped to expanded; white with a lemon yellow tinge, finely silky, later almost bare. Gills are free, dense, at first pale, later greyish-fleshy, finally chocolate brown to deep black, but never pink. Stipe is often enlarged at the base, as if base were cut off; tough, breakable, with a membranous, broad ring at the top. Whole fruit-body turns yellow when bruised. Flesh is white and has a pleasant aniseed scent. Spore powder is chocolate brown. Spores 6.5–8 × 4–5 μm, ellipsoid, brown. It grows profusely in humus in spruce forests, in warm places. Edible, very tasty. Can be confused with *Amanita phalloides* and *Agaricus xanthodermus*!

Yellow Stainer
Agaricus xanthodermus GENÉV. VII–IX

Cap 5–15 cm wide, globular, soon convex, smooth, white, turns yellow immediately when bruised, but yellow colouring soon disappears and changes into grey-brown colour. Gills are free, whitish, later pink, chocolate or black. Stipe is cylindrical, white with a membranous ring and with a globular or flatly depressed bulb; turns yellow when scratched. Flesh is white; the base of the stipe is chrome yellow when cut. It smells of carbolic acid. Spore powder is purple-brown; spores 5–7 × 3–4 μm, ovoid, brown-purple. It grows in coniferous and deciduous woods, also in parks and meadows. Poisonous.

Agaricus abruptibulbus PECK VII–IX

Cap 8–12 cm wide, arched, later expanded, pure white, gradually turns light yellow when bruised; flesh in thin, skin smooth and silky. Gills are free and dense, at first flesh grey, later chocolate brown, finally black. Stipe is cylindrical, broadened at the base into a large, loose bulb, white and finely striate, with a thin, membranous ring. The presence of a bulb distinguishes it from the Horse Mushroom (*A. arvensis*). Flesh is white, turns yellow when bruised and has a faint aniseed scent and mild flavour. Spore powder is chocolate brown. Spores 6–8 × 4–5 μm, ellipsoid, smooth, without a germining pore, brown. It grows in spruce woods. Edible. Sometimes, considered a variety of *A. arvensis*.

Agaricus augustus FR. VII–IX

Cap 10–25 cm wide, at first almost globular, later convex to expanded; pale yellow surface is covered with date brown to golden rusty; fibrillose, appressed scales arranged in concentric circles. Centre is brown, scaleless. Gills are free, shallow and dense, at first whitish, later greyish, chocolate to black. Stipe is broadened at the base, stout, yellowish, tough, scaly to smooth under the membranous ring; becomes rust-yellow when old. Flesh is white, with an aniseed scent and mild taste. Spore powder is brown. Spores 7.5–9 × 5.5–6 μm, ovoid ellipsoid, smooth, purple brown. It grows in warm areas in spruce woods, especially along their sunny edges. Edible, tasty.

Agaricaceae

⅋ *Agaricus semotus* FR.   VII–IX ■□□□

Cap 1.5–5 cm wide, at first semi-globular, later broadly bell-shaped to expanded, with thin, brittle flesh; at first whitish, later purple in the centre, finally purple-brown, pallid to white towards the margin with filamentous, purple scales and remnants of veil along the edge. Gills are free, dense, grey-pink, later grey-black. Stipe 2.5–6 cm long, only 3–6 mm thick, thinly cylindrical, whitish or yellowish, with a thin, membranous ring. Flesh is white to purple, with a faint aniseed smell and mild taste. Spore powder is purple-brown. Spores 5–6 × 3.5–4 μm, ellipsoid, smooth and brown. It grows in spruce or mixed woods. Edible.

⅋ **Wood Mushroom**
Agaricus silvicolus (VITT.) SACC.   VII–IX □■□□

Cap 5–10 cm wide, expanded and convex, thin, smooth and silky, white, turning yellow to orange when bruised or old. Gills are free, pale when young, later grey-purple to chocolate. Stipe is erect, 8–12 cm long, 1–2 cm thick, with a flatly depressed base, hollow, white, turning yellow, with a simple, smooth and white ring. Flesh is white, turning yellow under the skin, brown to black at the base of the stipe; it smells of aniseed and has a sweet taste. Spore powder is almost black; spores 5–6 × 3–4 μm, ovoid ellipsoid and chocolate brown. It grows usually in groups in coniferous and dediuous woods. It is sometimes included within the broader concept of *A. arvensis*. Edible.

⅋ *Cystoderma amianthinum* (SCOP.: FR.) MAUBL.   VIII–X □□■□

Cap 2–4 cm wide, broadly bell-shaped, often with a shallow umbo or a small central wart, later flat and expanded, ochre yellow, sometimes pale ochre, densely granulated and, particularly round the centre, radially wrinkled. Gills are adnate, crowded, white, later yellowish. Stipe is slender and cylindrical, ochre yellow and scaly with a limp ring in the top section. Spore powder is white. Spores 5–6 × 3–4 μm, ellipsoid, smooth and colourless. It grows abundantly in moss, grass and heather in coniferous forests. Inedible.

⅋ *Cystoderma carcharias* (PERS.: SECR.) MAUBL.   VIII–X □□□■

Cap 2–5 cm wide, broadly bell-shaped with a shallow umbo in the centre, later expanded, thinly fleshy, whitish, beige to pale buff, densely granular. Gills are crowded and white, attached to the stipe. Stipe is slender, cylindrical, whitish and densely granular at the top with an erect, membranous ring, which is a part of the detachable veil covering a large section of the stipe. Flesh is white, invariable, with a distinctive musty smell. Spore powder is white. Spores 4–4.5 × 3–4 μm, ovoid ellipsoid, smooth and colourless. It grows in damp grassy places in coniferous woods. Inedible.

Agaricaceae

Cystoderma cinnabarinum (ALB. et SCHW.: FR.) MAUBL.   VIII–IX   ◼◻ / ◻◻

Cap 2–6 cm wide, broadly bell-shaped, later flat and expanded, rounded in the centre; thin flesh, vermilion red, later pallid to yellow, entirely densely granulated. Gills are adnate, dense, pure white. Stipe is cylindrical, often broadened and curved at the base, vermilion scaly from base to the ring, bare and white above. Flesh is white, without a specific smell or taste, invariable. Spore powder is white. Spores 4–5 × 2.5–3 μm, shortly ellipsoid, smooth and colourless. It grows in grass along forest edges or directly in coniferous and mixed woods. Rare; edible.

Coprinaceae

Shaggy Caps, Lawyer's Wig
Coprinus comatus (MÜLL.: FR.) S. F. GRAY   VI–IX   ◻◼ / ◻◻

Young cap is calindrical, 5–10 cm tall, 3–6 cm wide, later bell-shaped, finally expanded; white, pinkish to pale ochre with silky cuticle torn into large, free scales. Gills are free, dense, at first white, later pink, then black and turning into a dark pupl when ripe. Stipe is bulbous, 1–2 cm thick, white, filamentous to scaly, with a narrow and loose ring. Flesh is white. Spore powder is black. Spores 10–15 × 7–8 μm, ellipsoid, opaque black, smooth, with a germinating pore. It grows usually in clusters on compost heaps, well manured ground outside forests. Fruit-bodies develop quickly and soon dissolve into pulp. Inedible.

Common Ink Cap
Coprinus altramentarius (BULL.: FR.) FR.   V–X   ◻◻ / ◼◻

Cap 3–8 cm, at first ovoid, soon bell-shaped with involuted margin, longitudinally grooved, grey and granular. Gills are free, grey-whitish when young, later brownish, finally black and soon, together with the cap, decomposing. Stipe is erect, 7–18 cm long, 1–1.5 cm thick, hollow, smooth and white. Flesh is white, without smell and taste. Spore powder is black. Spores 8–11 × 5–6 μm, ellipsoid, at first brown, soon black, opaque and smooth. It grows on waste land, near roads, by tree stumps. Inedible.

Glistening Ink Cap
Coprinus micaceus (BULL.: FR.) FR.   VI–IX   ◻◻ / ◻◼

Cap at first cylindrical or ovoid, 1–2.5 cm wide, then bell-shaped, with raised to rolled up margin; cuticle is ochre brown to rusty with numerous glistening granules when young. Gills are free, at first whitish and white on the edges, soon turning black and decomposing together with the cap's margin. Stipe is slender 4–10 cm long, 2–5 mm thick, hollow and white, fusing at the base with other fruit-bodies. Flesh is thin, whitish, without smell and taste. Spore powder is black. Spores 7–10 × 5–7 μm, pear-shaped, dark brown. It grows in clusters on the ground around trees and stumps or on them. Inedible.

Coprinaceae

Psathyrella groegeri G. HIRSCH

Syn.: *P. vernalis* (J. LGE.) MOSER (non *P. vernalis* VELEN.)   IV–VI

Cap 2–5 cm wide, deep ochre brown when damp, smooth, bald, cream ochre when dry, with tiny remnants of veil at the margin when young, semi-globular, later shallowly convex. Gills are rather dense, beige-brown, later dark brown, with white edges. Stipe 3–6 cm long, 2–4 mm thick, white, turning yellow with age, smooth. Flesh without specific taste and smell. Spores 7–10 × 4–5 μm, ellipsoid, brown. It has conspicuous broad bladder-shaped cheilocystidia. It grows on the ground between rotting twigs, leaves, humus and grass, in light places in deciduous and mixed woods. Inedible.

Psathyrella candolleana (FR.) R. MAIRE   V–X

Cap 3–10 cm wide, ovoid, bell-shaped to expanded, radially wrinkled, white to pale yellowish, at first pruinose, with disappearing remnants of the white veil along the margin. Gills are adnexed, dense, narrow, at first white, later grey-pink to purple-brown, white tomentose along the edges. Stipe 2–5 cm long, brittle, hollow, white, finely pruinose, grooved at top. Flesh is white, very fragile. Spore powder is purple-brown. Spores 7–8 × 3–4 μm, ellipsoid, smooth, with germinating pore, brown. It grows in clusters or individually on the stumps of deciduous trees, especially on false acacia, in or outside of forests. Edible.

Moist Brittle Cap

Psathyrella hydrophila (BULL.: MÉRAT) R. MAIRE   IX–XII

Cap 2–5 cm wide, bell-shaped, later expanded, membranous, very fragile and strongly hygrophanous; chstnut or date brown in damp conditions, with a transparent, grooved margin, pale coffee brown or buff when dry. Radiating wrinkled, sometimes uneven; young fruit-bodies have loose remnants of veil. Gills are adnexed, at first whitish, later dirty brown to chocolate, white along the edges. Stipe 5–12 cm long, 3–6 mm thick, brittle, white, smooth. Spore powder is dark purple-brown. Spores 5–7 × 3–4 μm, cylindrically ellipsoid, smooth and brown. It grows in large and dense clusters on stumps and roots of deciduous trees. Edible.

Psathyrella prona (FR.) GILLET f. *cana* KITS VAN WAVEREN   VI–X

Cap 1.5–2.5 cm wide, semi-globular, light grey, often with a brown tinge in the centre, with transparent gills when damp, pale grey to whitish when dry, finely wrinkled, with inconspicuous velum. Gills dark grey, later blackish, with edges of the same colour. Stipe 6–7 cm long, 1 mm thick, pale buff or white, forming a tiny bulb, non-rooted in the ground. Flesh without smell and taste. Spores 12–16 × 7–7.5 μm, cylindrically ellipsoid, dark brown to black-brown, spore powder almost black. It grows in grass, along paths, rarely also on horse manure. Inedible.

Coprinaceae

The Weeping Widow
Lacrymaria velutina (PERS.: S. F. GRAY) KONR. et MAUBL. VII–IX ■□ □□

Syn. *Hypholoma lacrymabundum* (BULL.: FR.) QUÉL. s. RICKEN

Cap 3–10 cm wide, semi-globular or bell-shaped, later expanded, buff brown or red-brown, entirely felt-like smooth; margin fringed with remnants of veil. Gills are dense, abnexed, swollen, at first grey-reddish, later black-brown with white edges, when fresh the edges are covered with drops of milky liquid which leave black stains when they dry out. Stipe 8–12 cm long, 0.5–1 cm thick, broadened at the base, whitish, covered with brown fibrillose scales; white pruinose at the top. Spore powder is black. Spores 9–12 × 5–7 µm, lemon yellow, warty, deep black. It grows most frequently in clusters in parks, gardens, fields and along the edges of the roads. Inedible.

Panaeolus sphinctrinus (FR.) QUÉL. VII–X □■ □□

Syn. *Panaeolus campanulatus* (BULL.: FR.) QUÉL. ss. RICKEN, J. LANGE

Cap 2–4 cm wide, permanently bell-shaped, margin white dentate, skin dark grey with brown, leathery and reddish tones, smooth. Gills are adnate, swollen, grey, soon speckled in black, edges are white pruinose. Stipe is very long, slender (1–2 mm), and erect, white pruinose, reddish brown. Flesh is grey and brittle, without smell and taste. Spore powder is black. Spores 14–18 × 9–12 µm, lemon yellow, thick-walled, black and nonamyloid. It grows in groups on cattle and horse manure and on well-manured ground. Inedible.

Bolbitiaceae

Conocybe rickenii (J. SCHAEFF.) KÜHNER V–IX □□ ■□

Cap 1–4 cm wide, ovoid to bell-shaped, thinly membranous, brittle, ochre or cream yellow, during drought almost white; bare. Gills are adnexed fairly dense, ochre yellow. Stipe 3–10 cm long, 1–3 mm thick, sometimes swollen at the base, whitish to light ochre, slightly pruinose. Flesh is yellowish. Spore powder is rusty brown. Basidia usually have two spores. Spores 10–17 × 6–12 µm, ellipsoid, rusty brown, smooth with a wide germaniting pore. Cheilocystidia are club-shaped. It grows in manured soil in gardens, fields, along roads and also directly on old dung. Inedible.

Agrocybe praecox (PERS.: FR.) SING. V–VII □□ □■

Cap 2–8 cm wide, semi-globular to expanded with thin flesh; pale yellowish to brownish, almost white during drought, smooth, joined to the stipe with a membranous velum, which leaves white, disappearing remnants on the cap's margin. Gills are adnate, whitish to grey-rusty. Stipe 4–5 mm thick, whitish, finely fibrillose, with a narrow, white, loose, membranous ring. Flesh is white, strongly mealy in scent and taste. Spore powder is tobacco brown. Spores 9–12 × 5–6 µm, grey-yellowish, smooth, with a germaniting pore. It grows abundantly in grassy patches in the gardens, meadows and light woods. Edible.

Bolbitiaceae

Agrocybe semiorbicularis (BULL.: ST.-AM.) SING.   V–X

Cap 1–4 cm wide, semi-globular, later expanded, slimy, glossy when dry, felt-like at the margin, buff yellow. Gills are rounded, almost adnate, at first greyish, soon light coffee brown. Stipe is slender, 3–6 cm long, 1.5–3 mm thick, slightly broadened at the base, hollow, pale yellow. Flesh is whitish, smell and taste lightly aniseed. Spore powder is dirty rusty brown. Spores 10–14 × 8–10 μm, ellipsoid, smooth, copper brown, nonamyloid. It grows after rain among grass along roadsides, in pastures and fields. Inedible.

The Yellow Cow-pat Toadstool
Bolbitius vitellinus (PERS.: FR.) FR.   V–IX

Cap 2–6 cm wide, ovoid, bell-shaped to expanded, very thinly membranous, vivid yolk yellow or lemon yellow, later growing pale to whitish; radially grooved to the centre, slimy and sticky, quickly fading and partly decomposing. Gills are sparse, pale clay in colour, later light rusty yellow. Stipe is cylindrical, 2–5 mm thick, hollow, brittle, white, entirely pruinose. Spore powder is rusty brown. Spores 12–13 × 6–7 μm, ellipsoid and smooth, with a germ pore, rusty brown. It grows in grass along roadside and on rotting vegetable remnants. Inedible.

Stropharia coronilla (BULL.: FR.) QUÉL.   VII–IX

Cap 2–5 cm wide, stout, fleshy, semi-globular, later shallowly convex, ochre or lemon yellow, sticky when damp, smooth, its margin carries remnants of white velum. Gills are dense, violet-grey, later chocolate brown to purple brown, white at the edges. Stipe 3–5 cm long, 3–6 mm thick, pure white, with a membranous striated ring. Flesh is white and has a sweetish smell. Spore powder is violet brown. Spores 7–9 × 4–5 μm, ellipsoid, violet brown. It grows on lawns, along paths, along the edges of fields. Inedible.

Strophariaceae

Stropharia albocyanea (DESM.) QUÉL.   VII–IX

Cap 1–3 cm wide, convex, later flat, whitish with a bluish or greenish tinge, slimy when damp, smooth and bare. Gills adnexed, fairly deep, whitish, later dark grey-brown. Stipe 5–8 cm long, 6–8 mm thick, cylindrical, straight or crooked, whitish or with a green tinge, with narrow membranous ring in the upper part; smooth, pruinose above the ring. Flesh is white, watery, without specific smell. Spore powder is purple-brown. Spores 8–9 × 4–5 μm, ellipsoid, smooth, with a germ pore, purple-brown. It grows in damp meadows. Inedible.

Strophariaceae

Verdigris Agaric
Stropharia aeruginosa (CURT.: FR.) QUÉL.   VII–XI

Cap 3–8 cm wide, rounded to expanded and convex, cuticle peels off easily; it is slimy with whitish scales, verdigris green, turning ochre when old. Gills are adnexed, whitish, later grey-purple. Stipe is erect, 4–8 cm long, 3–6 mm thick, hollow, bluish green, with a small ring, white squamose underneath. Flesh is whitish, greenish in the stipe, without smell. Spore powder is purple-brown, spores 7–8 × 4–5 μm, ellipsoid, black-brown. It grows on rotten wood in woods, often seemingly from the ground. Edible. Similar to *Stropharia cyanea* (BOLT.: SECR.) TUOMIKOSKI, syn. *Stropharia caerulea* KREISEL.

Stropharia semiglobata (BATSCH.: FR.) QUÉL.   VI–IX

Cap 1–4 cm wide, semi-globular, thinly fleshed, ochre or light lemon yellow, very slimy, smooth and glossy when dry. Gills very broad, adnate, sparse, dark grey, later almost black, whitish along the edges. Stipe 5–10 cm long, 2–3 mm thick, straight, tough, yellowish, slimy, shiny when dry, connected with the cap margin by a thin membranous velum when young which disappears with age. Spore powder is blackish. Spores 15–19 × 8–10 μm, lemon-shaped, violet-brown. It grows on cattle and horse manure on pastures and grassy paths in woods. Inedible.

Hypholoma capnoides (F.) KUMM.   III–XII

Cap 3–8 cm wide, convex, later expanded with firm flesh, yellow-orange ochre, darker in the centre, smooth and glossy, margin with remnants of the white veil which disappear later. Gills are sinuate, crowded, pale, greyish, later bluish-grey or sooty in colour. Stipe 8–10 cm long, 6–8 mm thick, often crooked; base is rusty, top whitish and silky shiny. Flesh is whitish and has no smell. Spore powder is black-purple. Spores 7–8 × 4–5 μm, ellipsoid, smooth, purple-violet with a conspicuous germ pore. It grows in clusters on stumps and roots of coniferous trees, usually on spruce. Edible.

Sulphur Tuft
Hypholoma fasciaculare (HUDS.: FR.) KUMM.   I–XII

Cap 2–8 cm wide, flatly convex, with fine veins at the margin; sulphur yellow, red-brown in the centre. Gills are adnexed, sulphur yellow when young, soon yellowish, finally purple black. Stipe is 5–10 cm long, 3–8 mm thick, tough, hollow, rooting, often fusing together with other fruit-bodies; sulphur yellow, brownish at the base. Flesh is sulphur yellow without smell. Spore powder is brown-purple. Spores 6–8 × 4–5 μm, smooth, dirty yellow-brown. It grows in clusters on stumps and timber of various trees. Slightly poisonous.

Strophariaceae

Psilocybe crobula (FR.) M. LGE. ex SING. VI–XI ■□ □□

Cap 0.5–2 cm wide, shallowly convex, leathery brown to olive-brown, slimy, with detachable skin, without transparent gills, with numerous loose white scales on the surface and margin, light leathery when dry. Gills adnate, shortly decurrent, pale, later dirty brown. Stipe 2–6 cm long, 1.5–2 mm thick, tough, crooked, light buff to rusty brown. Spores 6–9 × 4–5.5 μm, ellipsoid. It grows on rotting remnants of plants, twigs, grass and plant stalks. The cap of the similar species *P. inquilina* (FR.) BRES. has transparent gills and its thin velum soon dispappers. It grows in similar substrates as *P. crobula*. Inedible.

Cortinariaceae

Crepidotus variabilis (PERS.: FR.) KUMM. VI–X □■ ■□

Fruit-body has no stipe, the cap is laterally or with its upper surface attached to the substrate; 0.5–3 cm wide, roundish, reniform or shell-shaped. White, woolly felt-like margin is later lobed, flesh thin, relatively clastic. Gills are radially decurrent and meet in one point on the margin of the cap; fairly dense, white to pinkish brown. Spore powder is pinkish brown. Spores 5.5–7 × 3–4 μm, shortly cylindrical and ellipsoid, finely squamulose and tuberculate, pale brownish. It grows profusely on fallen branches of deciduous trees and occasionally on rotting foliage. Inedible.

Hypholoma marginatum (PERS.: FR.) SCHROET. VII–X □□ □■

Cap 1–4 cm wide, bell-shaped, later shallow and convex, with an umbo in the centre; thin flesh, lemon yellowish to pale brown, margin fibrous and fringed with remnants of veil. Gills are sinuate, dense, coloured pale clay to grey-brown. Stipe 5–10 cm long, 2–3 mm thick, rusty brown to red-brown, yellowish at the top, with longitudinal silvery fibres. Flesh smells of iodoform. Spore powder is purplish-brown. Spores 7–9.5 × 4–5 μm, ellipsoid, light purple-brown. It grows individually on remnants of rotting wood, particularly in spruce wood. Sometimes referred to the genera *Pholiota, Galera* or *Galerina*. Inedible.

Strophariaceae

Hypholoma subericaeum (FR.) KÜHNER   VI–VIII

Cap 1–3 cm wide, bell-shaped, convex to expanded with an umbo in the centre, pale to date brown in damp conditions, turning paler when dry. Young cap shows remnants of veil in the margin. Gills are deeply sinuate, attached by a small tooth; pale, later dark brown. Stipe 3–10 cm long, 2–4 mm thick, yellowish, later rusty to brownish from the base, silky fibrillose. Flesh is yellowish, smells strongly of iodoform. Spore powder is purple-brown. Spores 8–10 × 4–5 μm, ellipsoid, smooth, light brown. It grows individually or gregariously in damp places and swamps among the grass and moss. Inedible.

Psilocybe montana (PERS.: FR.) KUMMER   IV–V

Cap 0.5–1.5 cm wide, semi-globular, then shallowly convex to flat, with transparent gills when damp, dark red-brown, leathery brown when dry, slightly sticky. Gills are sparse, adnate, dark brown. Stipe 1–2 cm long, 1–2 mm thick, tough, lighter than the cap. Flesh has no smell. Spores 6–8 × 4–5 μm, ellipsoid, violetish-brown. It grows in acid and sandy soils in low moss, in heaths, and sunlit hills, on edges of woods in early spring. Inedible.

Psilocybe semilanceata (FR.) QUÉL.   VIII–X

Cap 1.5–2 cm high, 0.5–1 cm wide, conical, lanceolately pointed, very slimy, brown-yellow, olive-yellow, leathery yellowish when dry, slimy, smooth. Gills are adnate, olive-grey, blackish brown when old, white along the edges. Stipe is tall and thin (2–3 mm), tough, crooked, light brown, shiny, sometimes turning blue-green or blue at the base (var. *coerulescens* COOKE). Spores 12–16 × 6–8 μm, ellipsoid, brown. It grows in grass of pastureland and wood meadows often in grass tufts (*Nardus stricta*). Inedible, hallucinogenic species.

Brick Red Hypholoma

Hypholoma sublateritium (FR.) QUÉL.   V–XI

Cap 3–8 cm wide, convex, later expanded, with tough flesh, pale (in the centre vivid) brick red, smooth; margin at first paler, with whitish sulphur yellow, felt-like fibrous or scaly remnants of the veil, smooth. Gills are sinuate, pale yellow, later dirty olive green, finally chocolate brown with whitish edges. Stipe 7–12 cm long, 7–12 mm thick, rusty and scaly and fibrillose below and white-yellowish above; often crooked, with a ring-like remnant of the veil. Flesh is dirty whitish to rusty, rust-brown in the lower part of the stipe. Spore powder is black-purple. Spores 6–8 × 3–4 μm, ellipsoid, smooth, with a small germ pore, dark brown. It grows in clusters, sometimes individually, on stumps of deciduous and less frequently of coniferous trees. Inedible. *Hypholoma capnoides, H. fasciculare,* and *H. sublateritium* are often referred to the genus *Naematoloma* in modern U.S. texts.

Cortinariaceae

Hebeloma mesophaeum (PERS.: FR.) QUÉL. IX–XII

Cap 3–4 cm wide, conically bell-shaped, with a low umbo, later flat and expanded, deep red-brown in the middle, smooth, with a conspicuous wide, filamentous felt-like stripe of the velum along the margin. Gills white, later turning clay ochre, finely serrated along the edges. Stipe 5–8 cm long, 3–5 mm thick, cylindrical, top has a ring-shaped felt-like stripe of velum, whitish filamentous, felt-like under it, turning brown from below. Flesh has almost not smell. Spores 8–10 × 5–6 μm, ellipsoid, smooth. It grows in coniferous woods, especially under spruce and pine. Inedible.

Fairy Cake Hebeloma
Hebeloma crustuliniforme (BULL.: FR.) QUÉL. VIII–XI

Cap 8 cm wide, flat and convex to wavy, often uneven with deeply involuted margin; slimy in damp conditions, brownish or whitish-greyish. Gills are rounded, light grey-brown with bitter tasting, brownish droplets. Stipe is cylindrical, 5–10 cm long, 4–8 mm thick, soonn hollow, whitish, white granular at the top. Flesh is whitish, smells of radish. Spore powder is clay brown. Spores 10–12 × 5.5–6.5 μm, almond-shaped, tuberculate, ochre. It grows in small groups in woods and under the trees outside woods. Slightly poisonous.

Hebeloma sinapizans (PAULET: FR.) GILL. IX– XI

Cap 4–12 cm wide, convex, later flat, ochre-brown, brick-reddish, but also rusty yellow to dirty brown, smooth, bald, slightly slimy, without a velum, fleshy. Gills are coffee brown, then cinnamon brown, sinuate, whitish along the edges. Stipe 5–10 cm long, 15–25 mm thick, with firm flesh, cylindrical to slightly swollen into a bulb, pale, filamentous and striped to scaly. Flesh is white and smells strongly of radish. Spores 10–12 × 6–7 μm, almond-shaped, brown, smooth. It grows in deciduous woods, especially beech, but also in coniferous woods. Inedible.

Inocybe cervicolor (PERS.: PERS.) QUÉL. VII–IX

Cap 4–7 cm wide, bluntly bell-shaped, has a pale surface with dark fibrils; the centre is often cracked into adpressed scales. Gills are dense, at first white, later dirty grey or grey-brown; edges are white tomentose, turning brown when bruised. Stipe 3–10 mm thick, cylindrical, rarely broadened at the base, rather tough, smooth white pruinose at the top, turns brown from the base when bruised. Flesh is whitish, reddish-brown in the stipe, smells very intensively of musty old wine barrels. Spore powder is brown. Spores 12–15 × 7–8.5 μm, reniform and ellipsoid, light brownish. It grows in deciduous woods on limestone. There are several species resembling this one. All inedible, rather poisonous.

Cortinariaceae

 Inocybe patouillardii BRES.
Syn. *Inocybe lateraria* RICKEN   V–VIII
Syn. *Inocybe erubescens* BLYTT

Entire mushroom is white or whitish when young, silky glossy, turning red when touched or in old age. Cap 3–8 cm wide, bell-shaped, soon irregularly expanded, smooth, radiylly cracked. Gills are sinuate, white, soon grey-olive to dark ochre. Stipe is cylindrical, 5–10 cm long, up to 2 cm thick, fleshy. Flesh is white, turning red with age; smell is unpleasant. Spore powder is olive brown, spores 9–14 × 5–8 μm, bean-shaped, light ochre. It grows under deciduous trees in woods and parks, especially in soils with a high content of lime. Very poisonous.

 Inocybe fastigiata (SCHAEFF.: FR.) QUÉL.
Syn. *Inocybe rimosa* (BULL.: FR.) KUMM. ss. AUCT.   VII–IX

Cap 3–9 cm wide, pointed and cone-shaped, soon expanded with a sharp umbo, cracked, radially fibrillose, ochre to dark brown. Gills are free, olive green with whitish edges, later brown. Stipe is cylindrical, up to 1 cm thick, rounded at the base, has no bulb, coloured white to ochre. Flesh is white, has a spermatic smell. Spore powder is brown. Spores 10–18 × 5–8 μm, cylindrical, smooth, yellowish; gill edges display colourless cheilocystidia. It grows commonly in woods, parks, along roadsides and in tree lines. Very poisonous.

 Inocybe geophylla (SOW.: FR.) KUMM.
Syn. *Inocybe argillacea* (PERS.: FR.) FAYOD   VII–IX

Cap is 1–4 cm wide, cone-shaped, soon expanded and convex with a shallow umbo, radially cracking. Silky, lilac or blue-purple, turning yellow, margin of young fruit bodies is joined to the stipe with a purple cobweb. Gills are free, whitish, turning brown. Stipe is 2–5 cm long, 1.5–5 mm thick, blue-purple. Flesh is white, smell spermatic. Spore powder is brown. Spores 7.5–11 × 4.5–6 μm, ellipsoid, smooth, yellowish. Gill edges carry bottle-shaped cystidia with crystals at the top. It grows mostly under deciduous trees, but also under conifers. Very poisonous.

 Inocybe geophylla var. *lilacina* (PECK) GILLET   VII–IX
Different colouring from above species: Cap is purple (at the top yellowish) at first, later loses colour, gills from pale purple to grey-yellowish, stipe purplish, at the bottom ochre. Poisonous.

Cortinariaceae

Inocybe lacera (Fr.) Kumm.   V–XI

Cap 1–4 cm wide, soon broadly expanded and convex, with a small boss; dry, scaly filamentous, grey-brown to brown. Gills are adnexed, whitish when young, later grey-brown with whitish edges. Stipe is 3–11 cm long, 1–6 mm thick, cylindrical, entirely filamentous, light grey, later brown. Flesh is whitish, reddish in the spite; it has a spermatic smell. Spore powder is brownish. Spores 10–15 × 4–6 μm, long and cylindrical, smooth, grey-yellow, cystidia are bottle-shaped with a cap on the side and the edge. It grows in acid soil, particularly on bare slopes and on sandy tracks. Very poisonous. May be confused with the Fairy Ring Champignon (*Marasmius oreades*).

Inocybe jurana (Pat.) Sacc.   VII–IX

Cap 2–8 cm wide, conically bell-shaped, with an umbo, radially broken, its skin is cracked into radial filaments of violet brown to wine-red colour on white, later light pink or wine-reddish flesh of the cap. Gills are dense, greyish yellow, brown-ochre, later violet brown. Stipe 4–7 cm long, 0.5–2 cm thick, swollen into a tuber at the base, whitish in the upper part, downwards grey-violet or brown-red, with a carmine or brown-violet tinge at the base, pruinose. Flesh is white, later pinkish, wine-red at the base, smell and taste are sweetish fruity. Spores 9–12 × 6–8 μm, ellipsoid kindey- to bean-shaped, ochre yellow, smooth. It grows in deciduous, rarely in coniferous woods, especially in limestone substrates. Inedible.

Inocybe pseudodestricta Stangl et Veselský   VII–IX

Cap 2–6 cm wide, bluntly conical, dark brown, with a slightly greasy gloss, radially cracked into dense filaments on whitish surface, without scales. Gills are ochre with an olive tinge. Stipe 2.5–6.5 cm long, 5–12 mm thick, base is slightly swollen into a bulb, white or brownish, finely powdered in the upper part. Spores 8.5–11 × 5–6 μm, ellipsoid, smooth, brown. It grows in the ground in light woods, especially under birch and pine. Inedible.

Inocybe bongardii (Weinm.) Quél.   VIII–IX

Cap 1–5 cm wide, bell-shaped to convex, fibrilose, finely scaly; whitish when young, later yellow, ochre or reddish-brown. Gills are free, whitish, later grey-reddish, finally brown. Stipe is erect, 3–10 cm long, 3–9 mm thick, white, later brownish wine red, longitudinally filamentous. Flesh is whitish, turning red in the stipe, smells of pears or plums. Spore powder is cinnamon in colour. Spores 11–16 × 6–9 μm, reniform, smooth, yellowish. It grows on limestone under deciduous trees, less frequently under conifers. Inedible.

Cortinariaceae

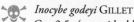

Inocybe godeyi GILLET   VI–X

Cap 2.5–4 cm wide, bluntly bell-shaped, soon expanded with an umbo; silky, white, slightly ochre, turns red when bruised. Gills are rounded, clay yellow with an olive tinge, later grey-brown, turning red. Stipe is erect, 4–8 cm long, 3–8 mm thick, with a flat bulb at the base, whitish, reddish. Flesh is white, turning red; it has an unpleasant earthy smell. Spore powder is brown. Spores 8.5–12 × 5.5–7 μm, almond-shaped, brown, smooth, cystidia are swollen. It grows in limestone soil under beech, hazel and pine trees. Rare in Great Britain. Poisonous.

Cortinarius orellanus (FR.)
Syn. *Dermocybe orellana* (FR.) RICKEN   VII–IX

Cap 3–7 cm wide, soon convex and broadly umbonate, often irregularly wavy, fleshy, felt-like to finely scaly, moulting when older, brown-orange. Stipe is 5–8 cm long, 9–15 mm thick, cylindrical, slightly arched, tapering downwards, pointed at the base, filamentous, golden yellow, turning brown. Flesh is yellow, smells slightly of radish. Spore powder is rusty. Spores 8–12 × 5–7 μm, almond-shaped, dotted, brown. It grows in warm deciduous woods, particularly under oak. Rare or absent in Great Britain. Very poisonous.

Cortinarius armeniacus (SCHAEFF.: FR.) FR.   IX–XI

Cap 4–7 cm wide, bell-shaped, later convex with an umbo, apricot yellow to orange-brown or rusty to cinnamon brown, silky whitish filamentous along the margin when young, dry. Gills are wide, yellowish and creamy ochre, later brightly yellowish ochre to cinnamon rusty. Stipe 5–8 cm long, 1–2 cm thick, often club-shaped at the base, white, later light orange-rusty, filamentous. Cortina is white, and leaves a disappearing ring-like stripe on the stipe. Flesh is whitish, with an ochre or orange tinge. It smells slightly of iodophorm or radish, taste is mild. Spores 8–9.5 × 4.5–5.5 μm, ellipsoid, finely warty, yellow-rusty. It grows in coniferous woods. Inedible.

Cortinarius varius (SCHAEFF.: FR.) FR.   VIII–X

Cap 3–10 cm wide, semi-globular, later shallow and convex, umbonate, with involuted margin; yellow-brown or rusty orange, slimy when damp, glossy during drought. In young fruit-bodies it is connected to the stipe by a white, glossy veil. Gills are sinuate, attached with a small tooth, at first lilac blue, later cinnamon rusty. Stipe is stout and club-shaped, usually shortish, white or lilac. Flesh is white, thick, yellowish in the stipe. Spore powder is rusty brown. Spores 10–12 × 5–6 μm, almond-shaped, finely tuberculate, rusty brown. It grows in coniferous, especially spruce woods on limestone. May be confused with other *Cortinarius* species.

Cortinariaceae

Cortinarius alboviolaceus (PERS.: FR.) FR.   IX–X

Cap 3–8 cm wide, shallow and convex, with an umbo; relatively thin flesh, white-purple, silky filamentous, dry and smooth. Gills are attached by a small tooth, grey-purple, later cinnamon brown. Stipe is cylindrical, 5–12 cm long, 8–15 mm thick, club-shaped at the base, white-purple, half-way down the length with a narrow, filamentous ring and several disjointed fibrous strips below. Flesh is white-purple. Spore powder is rusty brown. Spores 8–10 × 5–6 μm, ellipsoid, finely tuberculate, rusty brown. It grows in coniferous and deciduous woods, especially uner oak. Inedible.

Cortinarius traganus (FR.) FR.   VIII–X

Cap 5–14 cm wide, at first globular, soon expanded and convex, fleshy, felt-like to scaly, lilac when young, then turning pale ochre; margin fringed with a blue, later rusty cobweb, which connects it with the stipe. Gills are free, yellow, turning rusty. Stipe is short, up to 5 cm thick, club-shaped at the base, lilac, later turning pale. Flesh is yellow-brown and smells unpleasantly of acetylene. Spore powder is brown. Spores 8–10 × 5–6 μm, almond-shaped, yellowish. It grows in small groups under coniferous and deciduous trees. Inedible.

Cortinarius caninus (FR.) FR.   VIII–X

Cap 5–10 cm wide, convex, later expanded, broadly umbonate, at first purplish orange-brown, later buff or rusty clay, finely fibrillose, dry. Gills are sparse, sinuate, at first pale lilac, later rusty brown. Stipe is rather long, club-shaped, clay brown with a purple tinge and a ring-like remnant of *velum universale*, with remnants of *velum partiale* at the top. Flesh is at first pale lilac, later whitish. Spore powder is rusty brown. Spores 8–10 × 7–8 μm, almost globular, scaly, rusty brown. It grows in moss and grass in all forests, particularly in mixed woods. There are several similar species. Inedible.

Cortinarius armillatus (FR.: FR.) FR.   VIII–X

Cap 5–10 cm wide, bell-shaped, later broadly convex, in the centre bluntly umbonate, as if broken at the margin and connected to the stipe by a light red veil; entirely brick to brown-red, dry, finely fibrillose. Gills are sinuate, attached with a small tooth, yellowish, later cinnamon rusty. Stipe 10–15 cm long, robust, club-shaped to bulbous, pale brown, usually with several brick red, disjointed bands. Flesh is brownish. Spore powder is rusty brown. Spores 10–12 × 5–6.5 μm, ellipsoid, finely tuberculate, rusty brown. It grows in moss and foliage under birch in damp coniferous woods on acid soil. Inedible.

Cortinariaceae

Cortinarius mucosus (BULL.: ST.-AM.) KICKX   VIII–X

Cap 5–12 cm wide, shallow and convex, later expanded, slightly umbonate, fleshy, yellow-brown, honey to chestnut brown; during damp weather covered with a thick layer of slime, glossy and smooth during drought. Gills are sinuate, pale clay brown, later cinnamon, edges are serrated. Stipe is shortly tapering at the base, white and slimy, with an elevated slimy ring under the gills. Flesh is white. Spore powder is rusty brown. Spores 12–14 × 5.5–6.5 μm, almond-shaped, finely tuberculate, rusty yellow. It grows abundantly in pine woods. Edible.

Cortinarius hinnuleus (WITH.: HOOK.) FR.   VIII–X

Cap 3–8 cm wide, margin bent down as if broken, bluntly umbonate in the centre, bell-shaped, hygrophanous, ochre brown when damp, ochre yellow when dry. Gills are broadly adnate with a shortly decurrent tooth, very deep and sparse, pale cinnamon yellow, later rusty. Stipe 5–12 cm long, 5–10 mm thick, rusty brown, with a white silky cuticle at the top. Flesh is yellow-brown, with a gassy smell. Spore powder is rusty brown. Spores 7.5–9 × 5.5–6.5 μm, almond-shaped, finely tuberculate, rusty brown. It grows in deciduous and coniferous woods, particularly in moss and grass. Inedible.

Cortinarius bicolor COOKE   VIII–X

Cap 2–5 cm wide, shallowly convex, with an umbo, violet to chestnut-brown, light brownish when dry, bald, smooth. Gills are sparse, thick, often wrinkled, violet, turning rusty-brown with age. Stipe 5–8 cm long, 1–1.5 cm thick, cylindrical, tapering off towards the base, violet with white stripes of cortina. Flesh smells of radish when cut and has a mild taste. Spores 8–10 × 4–6 μm, ellipsoid, almond-shaped, finely warty, rusty-brown. It grows in coniferous and deciduous woods. Inedible.

Cortinarius caesiocyaneus BRITZ.   IX–X

Cap 6–12 cm wide, shallowly convex, later flat, with inrolled margin, fleshy, light grey-blue, bluish violet, turning pale, slimy, dull when dry, with ingrown filaments. Gills rather dense, whitish blue or grey-violet, later rusty-brown with blue edges. Stipe 5–8 cm long, 1–2 cm thick, with a conspicuous truncated bulb at the base (3–4 cm thick), of the same colour as the cap, filamentous. Cortina is pale violet. Flesh is light blue-violet, with an unpleasant smell, its taste is mild. Spore powder is rusty brown. Spores 8–10 × 5–5.5 μm, ellipsoid and almond-shaped, finely warty, buff ochre. It grows in deciduous woods in limestone substrates. Inedible.

Cortinariaceae

Cortinarius delibutus FR.   IX–X

Cap 4–8 cm wide, bell-shaped, convex, later almost flat, straw yellow or pale yellow, rather slimy, silky filamentous when dry. Gills are bluish to azure lilac, later of cinnamon colour. Stipe 5–10 cm long, 8–10 mm thick, downwards enlarged into a club (up to 2 cm thick), bluish in the upper part, later completely white or slightly yellowish, smooth, slimy, shiny, cortina forms a ring-like stripe in the upper part. Flesh is white, later yellow, taste is mild or slightly bitter and has almost no smell. Spore powder is ochre-rusty. Spores 7–8 × 6–6.5 μm, globularly ovoid, finely warty, light rusty. It grows in mixed and deciduous woods, mainly under birch and asp. Inedible.

Cortinarius trivialis LANGE   VIII–X

Cap 5–12 cm wide, bell-shaped, later expanded with an umbo, olive greenish or ochre brown, very slimy in damp, pale yellow and glossy during dry weather. Gills are sinuate, attached by a small tooth, distant, at first light purple, later clay to rusty brown. Stipe is cylindrical, tapering at the base, covered with slime; blue under this layer, cracked into transverse, disjointed, scaly stripes. Flesh is whitish or yellowish, the top of the stipe is bluish. Spore powder is rusty brown. Spores 10–15 × 7–8 μm, ellipsoid, tuberculate, rusty brown. It grows in coniferous and deciduous woods, mostly under aspen. Inedible.

Cortinarius duracinus FR.   IX–XI

Cap 3–10 cm wide, bell-shaped with a fleshy blunt umbo, with strongly inrolled margin, light chestnut brown to bright bay, sometimes with a violet tinge, ochre to leathery brownish when dry, with white felt-like margin, turning bald with age. Gills are sparse, broad, pale meat ochre, with whitish edges. Stipe 5–15 cm long, 10–15 mm thick, cylindrical, tapering into a spindle-shaped base rooted deeply (up to 6 cm) in the ground, bald, white. Flesh is white, with mild taste and slight smell. The whole fruit-body is firm, elastic, almost cartilaginous. Spores 7–11 × 4–6 μm, almond-shaped, coarsely warty, brown-rusty. It grows in coniferous and deciduous woods. Inedible.

Cortinarius bolaris (PERS.: FR.) FR.   VIII–IX

Cap 2–6 cm wide, convex, with an umbo in the centre, whitish or reddish, surface displays adpressed, vermilion or wine red granular scales; margin is connected with the stipe by a white cortina when young. Turns pale and dry during dry weather. Gills are sinuate, pale clay or light brown. Stipe 5–8 cm high, 0.5–1.2 cm thick, white pruinose and granulas at the top with vermilion red filaments at the base. Flesh is white, turning slightly yellow when bruised. Spore powder is rusty yellow. Spores 6–7 × 5–6 μm, globularly ellipsoid, finely tuberculate, rusty brown. It is rare and grows in deciduous woods. Inedible.

Cortinariaceae

Cortinarius fulgens (ALB. et SCHW.: FR.) FR.   IX–X   ◼◻◻◻

Cap 6–10 cm wide, convex, later flat and expanded, fleshy, orange yellow-ochre to orange bay, slimy, with dark ingrown filaments when dry. Gills bright bay, later cinnamon rusty. Stipe 5–20 cm long, 1–2 mm thick, with a huge heart-shaped bulb at the bottom (3–4 cm thick), yellow or pale sulphur-yellow, later bright bay to almost rusty, lighter than the cap. Cortina is light sulphur yellow and covers the stipe with filaments. Flesh is pale yellow, later turning rusty, with a slight smell and mild taste. Spores 8–10 × 4.5–5 μm, almond-ellipsoid, yellow-brown, warty. It grows in deciduous and coniferous woods, especially in limestone substrates. Inedible.

Cortinarius helvolus FR.   VIII–X   ◻◼◻◻

Cap 4–8 cm wide, soon expanded, with a blunt umbo, red-brown, rusty-yellow or ochre-yellow when dry, with filaments. Gills are sparse, rusty brown. Stipe 7–10 cm long, 10–15 mm thick, of the same colour as the cap, cortina forms a white stripe. Flesh is rusty-brown, with no smell and taste. Spores 7–9 × 5–6 μm, almond-shaped, warty, rusty brown. It grows in coniferous and mixed woods. It resembles *C. hinnuleus* (WITH.: HOOK.) FR. but it lacks the typical earthy smell. Inedible.

Cortinarius paleaceus FR.   VIII–X   ◻◻◼◻

Cap 1–3 cm wide, bell-shaped, grey-brown, covered densely with grey-white scales, without transparent gills. Gills are grey or grey-brown, rather dense. Stipe 5–7 cm long, 1–3 mm thick, of similar colour as the cap with a white cortina stripe, silky filamentous. Flesh smells of geranium leaves when rubbed. Spores 7–9 × 4–6 μm, ellipsoid, slightly warty, rusty-brown. It grows in damp places in coniferous and mixed woods. Inedible.

Cortinarius triformis FR.   VIII–IX   ◻◻◻◼

Cap 4–8 cm wide, with thick flesh in the centre, shallowly convex, often with irregular folds, covered with white hairs when young, which remain along the margin only in mature specimen, smooth, bald, dirty brown when damp, dirty leathery and yellowish when dry. Gills are rather dense, whitish, later pale brownish-yellow to honey-yellow. Stipe 4–8 cm long, 1–1.5 cm thick, enlarged into a spindle-shaped paunchy base, white, with well developed stripe, cortina is white and leaves a filamentous ring on the stipe. Flesh is white with a violet tinge, it has no taste and smell. Spores 8–10 × 5–6 μm, ellipsoid, finely warty, light rusty-yellow. It grows in coniferous and deciduous woods. Inedible.

Cortinariaceae

Cortinarius bulliardii (PERS.: FR.) FR.   VIII–X

Cap 4–8 cm wide, with a low blunt umbo, slightly fleshy, red-brown in the centre, brown with a violet tinge towards the margin when damp, light brown or buff when dry, smooth, silky shiny. Gills are broad, sparse, cloudy violet-purplish, turning brown to brown-rusty with age, whitish at the edges. Stipe 6–8 cm long, 1–2 cm thick, usually club-shaped or swollen to a bulb, often curved, tough, whitish or light lilac at the top, downwards red-orange and of lively, conspicuous vermilion-red colour in the lower part. Flesh is whitish with a lilac tinge, without specific smell and taste. Spores 8–11 × 4.5–6 μm, ellipsoid, almond-shaped, finely warty, yellow-brown. It grows in deciduous and mixed woods in damp places, especially in limestone substrates. Inedible.

 Cortinarius evernius FR.   VIII–IX

Cap 5–9 cm wide, bell-shaped, with a conspicuous umbo, violet, brownish-yellow when dry, smooth, bald. Gills are broad, thick, sparse, violet, later brown-cinnamon. Stipe 6–10 cm long, 1–2 cm thick, violet, tapering off towards the base, filamentous, with a thin stripe of cortina in the middle. Flesh of the cap is brownish, violet in the stipe and smells strongly of radish. Spores 10–12 × 5–6 μm, ellipsoid, almond-shaped, rich yellow, finely warty. It grows in coniferous and deciduous woods in moist places and in peat-moss. Inedible.

Sheathed Cortinarius
Cortinarius torvus (FR.: FR.) FR.   VIII–X

Cap 4–10 cm wide, semi-globular to expanded, chestnut or clay brown with a purple tinge,, later dirty yellow-brown or red-brown, dry, finely silky fibrillose; margin is connected with the stipe by a whitish cortina. Gills are sparse, deep, sinuate with a decurrent tooth, brownish lilac, later cinnamon brown. Stipe 5–10 cm high, 1–2 cm thick, in the lower half covered with a white sheath which terminates at the top in a narrow ring; sheath later breaks into scales and strips. Flesh is purplish, later grey-brown, smells of camphor. Spore powder is yellow-rusty. Spores 8–10 × 5–6 μm, ovoid ellipsoid, finely tuberculate. It grows in deciduous forests, especially in oak woods. Inedible.

Cortinariaceae

☓ *Cortinarius semisanguineus* Fr.: Fr.   VII–X   ■□
                                                                                      □□

Cap 2–6 cm wide, shallowly convex to flat and expanded, bluntly umbonate, glabrous or finely scally; dry, dark olive brown, when young its margin is connected with the stipe by a yellowish velum. Gills are sinuate, rather dense, purple or blood red, later brown-red. Stipe is 3–10 cm long, 4–6 mm thick, vivid chrome or olive yellow. Flesh is yellowish, smells faintly of iodoform. Spore powder is rusty. Spores 6–8 × 4–6 μm, ellipsoid ovoid, very finely tuberculate. It grows in damp coniferous woods and under birch. Inedible.

☓ *Cortinarius cinnamomeoluteus* P. D. Orton   □■
Syn.: *Dermocybe cinnamomeolutea* (P. D. Orton) Moser   VIII–IX   ■□

Cap 1–4.5 cm wide, bluntly conical, with an umbo, yellowish-olive, later olive or brown in colour, finely filamentous, dry, smooth. Gills are sparse, light yellow, later turn rusty yellow. Stipe 3–10 cm long, 2–5 mm thick, cylindrical, light yellow, then turning brown with a red tinge, mycellium is olive at the base. Spores 7–10 × 4.2–5.2 μm, ellipsoid, finely warty, rusty-brown. Flesh is yellow, smells slightly of iodoform, tasteless. It grows in deciduous woods, particularly under willows (*S. aurita, S. cinerea*) on moors. Inedible.

☓ *Leucocortinarius bulbiger* (Alb. et Schw.: Fr.) Sing.   VIII–IX   □□
                                                                                      □■

Cap 5–10 cm wide, semi-globular, later convex, in the centre slightly umbonate, fairly fleshy; when young it is connected to the stipe by a white cobweb. Gills are sinuate, attached by a small tooth, rather dense; at first white, later dirty brownish. Stipe is cylindrical, with a large, sharply defined bulb at the base; white, finely brownish at the base. Flesh is white. Spore powder is white. Spores 7–8 × 4–5 μm, ellipsoid, smooth and colourless. It grows rarely in dry coniferous woods in warm areas. Edible.

Cortinariaceae

Rozites caperata (PERS.: FR.) P. KARST. VIII–X

Cap 4–10 cm wide, at first pestle-shaped, later bell-shaped to expanded, umbonate in the centre, margin folded downwards; clay yellow and white-bluish pruinose (which makes it tinged in purple), later radially wrinkled during drought, margin cracked, ochre yellowish. Gills are sinuate, attached with a small tooth, dense, pale, later clay yellowish, edges are serrate. Stipe 7–10 cm long, 1–2 cm thick, whitish, tough, full, at the top with a membranous ring which has a double edge; stipe is finely scaly above it. The inconspicuous, thinly membranous volva under the ring is firmly attached to the surface of the stipe. Flesh is white and has a mushroom smell. Spore powder is rusty brown. Spores 11–14 × 7–9 μm, almond-shaped, finely tuberculate, with a germ pore, yellow. It grows usually gregariously in coniferous (less frequently deciduous) woods in subalpine areas with acid soil. Edible, tasty.

Gymnopilus penetrans (FR.: FR.) MUSS. VIII–IX

Cap 4–8 cm wide, shallowly convex, later expanded, involute at the margin, rusty to orange-yellow, connected to the stipe by sparse and disappearing filaments of the cortina; dry, almost smooth and bare. Gills are sinuate, attached by a small tooth, rather dense, yellow, later with rusty patches. Stipe 4–7 cm long, 5–10 mm thick, pale yellow, longitudinally and delicately filamentous. Flesh is pale yellow, almost without a smell, slightly bitter in taste. Spore powder is rusty brown. Spores 8–9 × 4–5 μm, ellipsoid almond-shaped, scaly, yellow. It grows individually or in small clusters on stumps of coniferous trees, especially pine. Inedible.

Gymnopilus hybridus (FR.) SING. VIII–X

Cap 3–6 cm wide, semi-globular, later shallowly convex, thinly fleshed, rusty-orange, smooth, bald. Gills are rather dense, yellow, later rusty-yellow. Stipe 3–6 cm long, 2–5 mm thick, light ochre, yellowish at the top, later rusty, with white filaments, sometimes with filamentous ring, white felted at the base. Flesh of the cap is pale yellowish to whitish, with a rusty tinge in the stipe and has a bitter taste. Spores 7–9 × 3.5–4.5 μm, ovoid, almond-shaped, finely warty. It grows on stumps of coniferous trees. Inedible.

Cortinariaceae

Galerina marginata (BATSCH: FR.) SING.   VII–X

Cap 2–4 cm wide, rounded and convex, soon expanded, hygrophanous, grooved when damp, glossy when dry, sticky, ochre to yellow-brown. Gills are ochre brown, adnexed and slightly decurrent. Stipe is 2–6 cm long, 2–6 mm thick, tube-like, ochre brown with a loose ring. Flesh is thin and brittle. Spores 8–12 × 5–7 μm, ovoid, finely tuberculate, yellowish. It grows individually or in clusters on stumps and timber of coniferous trees. May be confused with *Kuehneromyces mutabilis*. Deadly poisonous.

Galerina unicolor (FR.) SING.   VII–X

Cap 0.5–2.5 cm wide, cone-shaped, slightly umbonate, hydrophanous, somewhat sticky when damp, transparent at the margin, reddish to orange-brown, in dry conditions clay ochre. Gills are adnate, deep, sparse, cinnamon brown. Stipe 2–8 cm long, 1–2.5 mm thick, little lighter than the cap, the base is brownish; the top part bears a narrow, loose ring. Spore powder is rusty brown. Flesh is yellowish and has a mealy smell. Spores 7–12 × 5–7.5 μm, ellipsoid ovoid, very finely tuberculate, rusty yellow. It grows on rotting stumps and branches. Sometimes regarded as a small variety of *G. marginata*. Inedible.

Kuehneromyces mutabilis (FR.) SING. et SMITH   V–XI

Cap 3–6 cm wide, bell-shaped, later broadly convex with an umbo, narrowing towards the margin, strongly hygrophanous; in damp conditions cinnamon or honey brown, partly translucent, smooth and bare, during dry weather paler, ochre in colour. Gills are adnate, shortly decurrent, dense, coloured pale to rusty brown. Stipe 5–7 cm long, 5–7 mm thick, usually curved, with a whitish, later brownish ring which is rusty brown underneath. The base is black-brown, scaly, stipe above the ring is pale and glabrous. Flesh is whitish. Spore powder is rusty brown. Spores 6–7 × 3.5–4.5 μm, shortly ovoid, smooth and rusty with a broad germ pore. It grows in clusters on stumps of deciduous trees. Edible, tasty.

Shaggy Pholiota
Pholiota squarrosa (BATSCH: FR.) KUMM.   VIII–X

Cap 4–10 cm wide, semi-globular to shallowly convex, dry; lemon to straw yellow, entirely covered with rusty brown, erect to back-curved scales. Light yellow, later rusty brown gills are attached by a small tooth. Stipe is tough and full, pale yellow, entirely brown scaly with a scaly ring. Flesh is pale yellowish, smells of raddish; it is slightly bitter in taste. Spore powder is rusty brown. Spores 6–8 × 3.5–4 μm, rusty brown, ovoid and smooth, with a germ pore. It grows in dense clusters on stumps and at the base of deciduous (less frequently coniferous) trees. Edible.

Cortinariaceae

Pholiota flammans (FR.) KUMM.   VIII–X

Cap 2–7 cm wide, semi-globular, later broadly expanded, deep orange-yellow, covered with sulphur or lemon yellow scales, partly loose to erect; later turns bare. Gills are dense, bright yellow, later rusty brown and are attached with a small tooth. Stipe is cylindrical, later hollow, bright to lemon yellow with loose scales and a scaly ring at the top. Flesh is vivid yellow, gradually turning rusty; smells of tan. Spore powder is rusty brown. Spores 4–4.5×2–3 μm, rusty brown, ellipsoid, smooth with a germ pore. It grows in small clusters or individually on stumps of coniferous trees, particularly in subalpine woods. Inedible.

Pholiota aurivella (BATSCH: FR.) KUMM.   VII–IX

Cap 5–10 cm wide, shallowly convex, deep to rusty yellow, with sparse, slimy, appressed yellow-brown scales; glossy when dry. Gills are attached by a small tooth, at first yellow to olive yellow, later chestnut brown. Stipe is usually bulbous, yellow, brown scaly at the base, tough and full; when young it is connected with the cap's margin by a veil which later leaves a yellow ring on the stipe. Flesh is light yellow, taste is bitter. Spore powder is rusty brown. Spores 8–9×5–6 μm, ellipsoid brown and smooth, with a germ pore. It grows in clusters, usually on stumps of deciduous trees. Edible.

Gymnopilus junonius (FR.) P. D. ORTON   VIII–X

Stout, fleshy mushroom. Cap 10–20 cm wide, shallowly convex, rounded, golden yellow, silky, with fine scales and filaments, dry. Gills are adnate and shortly decurrent, yellow, light yellow-rusty, later rusty-brown. Stipe 8–15 cm long, 2–3 cm thick, yellow with a disappearing leathery ring, filamentous, smooth, thickened in the lower part and sometimes rooted. Flesh is yellow and has a strong bitter taste. Spores 8–10×5–6 μm, ovoid-ellipsoid, finely warty, light yellow. It grows on bases and roots of stems of deciduous trees (especially oak), singly or in clusters. Inedible.

Cortinariaceae

Pholiota carbonaria (FR.) SING.
Syn. *Flammula carbonaria* (FR.) KUMM.   V–X

Cap 1.5–6 cm wide, semi-globular, later expanded with involuted margin; brown-yellow or rusty yellow with lighter margin, slimy in damp conditions. Gills are rather dense, sinuate, attached by a short touth, light to ochre yellow, later olive brown with white edges. Stipe 2–6 cm long, 2–5 mm thick, pale yellow, whitish at the top, whole finely scaly, with the disappearing whitish filaments of the cortina. Flesh is yellow, bitter in taste. Spore powder is rusty. Spores 6–7 × 3–4 μm, ellipsoid, smooth, pale yellow. It grows only on old burnt ground in fir forests and is one of the most abundant anthracophilous fungi. Inedible.

Pholiota astragalina (FR.) SING.   VIII–X

Cap 3–6 cm wide, broadly convex, in the centre blood red or saffron yellow, lighter to almost pallid towards the margin; damp, bare, silky remnants of the pale veil on the margin soon disappear. Gills are sinuate, attached by a small tooth, rather dense, pale yellowish, later rusty brown. Stipe 5–10 cm long, 4–7 mm thick, pale yellow, covered with fibrillose scales, crooked, later hollow. Flesh has a rhubarb colouring, gradually turns red when bruised; the smell is indistinct. Spore powder is rusty yellow. Spores 6–7 × 3–4 μm, ellipsoid, smooth and pale yellow. It grows singly or in small clusters on coniferous stumps, particularly in mountainous woods. Rare. Inedible.

Pholiota lenta (PERS.: FR.) FR.   IX–XI

Cap 5–8 cm wide, shallowly convex, later expanded, whitish or pale clay brown, covered with a thick layer of slime with embedded scales. Gills are adnate to shortly decurrent, pale, later light clay brown with a yellow tinge. Stipe 5–8 cm long, 7–12 mm thick, bulbous at the base, whitish, brown and scaly at the base. Flesh is pale and tough, smells faintly of radish. Spore powder is rusty brown. Spores 6–7.5 × 3.5–4 μm, cylindrical ellipsoid, smooth, ochre rusty. It grows in fallen foliage, on heaps of fallen branches or directly on branches of all trees. Inedible.

Entolomataceae

The Miller
Clitopilus prunulus (SCOP.: FR.) KUMM.   VI–XI

Cap 3–12 cm wide, semi-globular, with deeply involuted margin soon expanded, concave, white or greyish, velvety, later bare. Gills are dense, shallow and deeply decurrent, whitish, later flesh pink. Stipe 3–6 cm long, 7–12 mm thick, sometimes eccentric, tough, white, filamentous and grooved, pruinose at the top, white felt-like at the base. Flesh is white, soft and has a strong smell of new meal. Spore powder is pink. Spores 8–14 × 5–6 μm, pale pink, spindle-shaped, longitudinally ribbed (with 6–8 sides). It grows most frequently in grass along forest tracks, especially in spruce forests or in forest meadows. Edible. May be confused with *Clitocybe dealbata*.

Entolomataceae

Nolanea staurospora BRES.   VI–IX ◨

Cap 2–5 cm wide, bell-shaped, later expanded, sometimes with a shallow umbo or a central wart, hygrophanous, dark brown-grey when damp, translucent; pale to whitish grey during dry weather, silky glossy. Gills are deeply sinuate, deep, greyish, later pinkish grey. Stipe 2–4 mm thick, fragile, grey-brown, longitudinally covered with glossy, silky filaments; the base is white felt-like. Flesh is whitish to greyish and has a strong smell of new meal. Spore powder is pink. Spores 7–10 × 6.5–9 μm, squarely indented, pale pink. It grows profusely in grass along woodland tracks, in meadows and pastures. Inedible.

Nolanea verna (LUNDELL) KOTL. et POUZ.
Syn. *Rhodophyllus vernus* (LUNDELL) ROMAGN.   V–VI ◨

Cap 3–5 cm wide, soon broadly convex, rounded at top, fragile, hygrophanous; dark brown in damp conditions, light grey-brown during dry weather, silky glossy. Gills are sinuate, sparse, deep, grey when young, pink when mature. Stipe is laterally depressed, with a longitudinal groove, hollow, grey, white at the base. Flesh is thin, fragile and greyish. Spore powder is pink, spores 8–11 × 7–8 μm, angular, pink. It grows in groups among grass in meadows and light woods. Very poisonous. May be confused with the Fairy Ring Champignon (*Marasmius oreades*).

Roman Shield Entoloma
Entoloma clypeatum (L.: FR.) KUMMER   V–VI ◨

Cap 2–12 cm wide, bell-shaped, later expanded, with a umbo in the centre and an involuted margin which is often wavy to lobed. Dark buff, brown to sooty brown when damp; pale buff, brownish, greyish to whitish when dry, streaked with dark, ingrown filaments, bald, silky and greasily glossy, often cracked when mature. Gills are deeply sinuate, deep, separable from the flesh of the cap, whitish, soon flesh pink, dusted with spores when old. Stipe 5–10 cm long, 7–20 mm thick, often curved at the base, firm, white, fibrillose, often with uneven surface. Flesh is white, has a conspicuous smell of new meal. Spore powder is pink. Spores 9.5–12.5 × 8.5–10 μm, squarely globular, 6- to 7-sided, distinctly apiculate, pale flesh pink. It usually grows in clusters outside woods in bushes, gardens, along forest edges and in ditches but most frequently under fruit trees of the genus *Prunus*. Inedible.

Entolomataceae

 Entoloma rhodopolium (FR.) KUMM.   VII–IX

Cap 5–10 cm wide, cone-shaped, soon expanded with a convex umbo, often irregularly undulate, slimy when damp, glossy and smooth when dry, pale ochre grey. Gills are rounded at the stipe, glossy and white. Stipe is 5–10 cm long, 1–2 cm thick, oval, white. Flesh is white and has a mealy smell. Spore powder is flesh pink; spores 8–10 × 7–8 μm, hexagonal, pinkish. It grows under deciduous trees in forests and also in gardens. Poisonous. May be confused with *Entoloma clypeatum*.

 Leptonia chalybaea (PERS.) QUÉL.   VII–IX

Cap 2–4 cm wide, convex, later flat with a blunt umbo, sometimes slightly depressed, dark-violet to black-violet, black-blue to almost black, later grey-brown blackish, with silky flakes, later slightly scaly. Gills are attached, sinuate to shortly decurrent, bluish, later light reddish, white along the edges. Stipe 2–5 cm long, 2–3 mm thick, light steel-blue to black-violet, smooth, bald, white felted in the lower part. Flesh has no smell and a mild taste. Spore powder is flesh pink. Spores 9–12 × 6–7.5 μm, elongated, angular, light brown-pink. It grows in grass, rarely in woods. Inedible.

Paxillaceae

 False Chanterelle
Hygrophoropsis aurantiaca (WULF.: FR.) R. MAIRE   VII–XII

Cap 2–6 cm wide, flat, soon concave, lightly undulated, leathery, dry, yellow-orange, soon pallid to almost white. Gills are deeply decurrent, shallow, branched, orange. Stipe is 3–4 cm long, 4–6 mm thick, cylindrical, elastic, orange, soon brownish at the base. Flesh is thin, pale orange, brownish in the stipe, of inconspicuous smell and an unpleasant sweet taste. Spore powder is whitish, spores ellipsoid, 4–7 × 2–4 μm, colourless. It grows in coniferous and deciduous woods, often gregariously. Distinguished from the Chanterelle (*Cantharellus cibarius*) by its thin gills which are not vein-like. In small amount edible.

Paxillaceae

Paxillus involutus (BATSCH: FR.) FR.   V–XI

Cap 5–15 cm wide, expanded to slightly concave with deeply involuted margin, felt-like; cuticle red-brown or olive ochre. Gills are decurrent, joined together, yellow turning brown. Stipe is 4–5 cm long, 1–2 cm thick, cylindrical, dirty yellow-brown. Flesh is yellowish, brownish, turns black when boiled; smells acid. Spore powder is rusty brown. Spores 8–10 × 4–6 μm, ovoid, smooth, yellow-brown. It grows in all types of forest, often in large groups. Poisonous. Causes serious allergic reaction, including fatal kidney damage.

Paxillus atrotomentosus (BATSCH: FR.) FR.   VII–X

Cap 6–25 cm wide, eccentric, convex with an involuted margin; thick flesh, velvety, olive or rusty brown, smooth. Gills are rusty yellow, decurrent, easily separate from the stipe, joined together. Stipe is eccentric or lateral, short, broadly cylindrical, black-brown, velvety felted. Flesh is creamy, watery; smells acid, similar to ink. Spore powder is brown. Spores 5–6 × 3–4 μm, shortly ovoid, light yellow-brown. It grows individually or in clusters on stumps of pine and spruce trees. Inedible.

Paxillus panuoides (FR.) FR.
Syn. *Paxillus acheruntius* (HUMB.: STEUDEL) SCHROET.   VI–X (I–XII)

Cap 2–12 cm wide, laterally or with a small stipe attached to the substrate, shell-shaped or spoon-like; velvety to finely scaly, at first white, soon ochre, yellow, olive to purplish-brown. Gills are yellowish, olive yellow, finally cinnamon. Brownish stipe is usually missing or very short. Flesh is yellow, smells lightly of aniseed. Spore powder is brown. Spores 4–6 × 3–4 μ, almost globular, yellowish. It grows in small numbers on coniferous timber in open country but also on wood in cellars, mines etc. *P. a.* var. *ionipus* QUÉL. is very interesting. Inedible.

Gomphidiaceae

Gomphidius roseus (FR.) KARST.
Syn. *Leucogomphidius roseus* (FR.) KOTL. et POUZ.   VIII–XI

Cap 3–6 cm wide, convex, later expanded, covered with a layer of slime, glossy and dry during drought, pink. Gills are decurrent, covered with a membranous veil when young, white, smoky grey, later turning black. Stipe is white, short, tapering downwards, with a delicate ring remaining from the veil. Flesh is white, pink in the stipe. Spore powder is dark red-brown. Spores 18–20 × 5–5.5 μm, spindle-shaped, dark olive. It is rather rare and grows with *Suillus bovinus* in pine woods. Fruit-bodies of these two species often fuse together. Edible.

Gomphidiaceae

Gomphidius glutinosus (SCHAEFF.: FR.) FR.   VIII–X ⬛⬜⬜⬜

Cap 5–13 com wide, convex, later expanded, covered with a colourless, detachable slimy cuticle; grey-brown, with black patches when old. Gills are decurrent, sparse, whitish, turning grey. Stipe tapers downwards, is coloured, white, greyish, yellow at the base and is covered by a slimy veil with a ring. Flesh is white, yellow in the stipe. Spore powder is brown-black. Spores 16–23 × 5–7 μm, spindle-shaped, smooth and dark brown. It grows in small groups particularly under spruce. Edible.

Gomphidius rutilus (SCHAEFF.: FR.) LUND. et NANNF.   VIII–X ⬜⬛⬜⬜

Cap 3–10 cm wide, cone-shaped, soon expanded with a rounded umbo, slimy, smooth when dry; orange-yellow, wine red when old. Gills are decurrent, sparse, yellow-orange turning red. Stipe is 5–8 cm long, 1–1.5 cm thick, orange yellow-brown, cylindrical, tapering downwards, with a disappearing ring. Flesh is orange yellow, later pink; it turns purple when boiles and has a pleasant smell but an insipid taste. Spore powder is olive black. Spores 17–20 × 6–8 μm, spindle-shaped, brownish. It grows abundantly in coniferous woods, mainly under pine trees, even high in the mountains. Edible.

Boletaceae

Phylloporus pelletieri (LÉV. in CROUAN) QUÉL.   VII–X ⬜⬜⬛⬜

Cap 3–8 cm wide, irregularly convex, cuticle is velvety, smooth, soon cracks into a reticulate pattern; red or olive brown. Gills are sparse, joined together, slightly decurrent, golden yellow. Stipe is red-brown, cylindrical, tapering at the base. Flesh is yellow, red-brown, under the cap's skin. Spore powder is pale ochre. Spores 10–14 × 3–5 μm, spindle-shaped, pale yellow. It grows individually in small numbers in coniferous and deciduous woods. Rare in Great Britain. Edible.

Boletinus cavipes (KLOTZSCH in FR.) KALCHBR.   VII–X ⬜⬜⬜⬛

Cap 4–10 cm wide, woon broadly expanded, umbonate, soft, felt-like, finely scaly, rusty brown or lemon yellow. Pores are covered by the veil when young; large, irregular, radially arranged, decurrent to the stipe, pale yellow, olive when old. Stipe is short, hollow, red-brown with brownish ring. Flesh is invariably yellowish, soon becoming very soft. Spore powder is olive yellow; spores 8–10 × 3–4 μm, spindle-shaped, yellowish, smooth. It grows in coniferous forests under larch, often gregariously. Edible.

Boletaceae

🍴 *Suillus aeruginascens* (SECR.) SNELL in SLIPP et SNELL
Syn. *Boletus viscidus* FR.   VI–X ■■
                                                                          □□

Cap 4–12 cm wide, soon convex and expanded, thin; cuticle is detachable, whitish, light brownish to greenish, slimy. Pores are angular, broad, dirty grey, and turn darker when bruised; when young they are covered with a veil. Stipe is 4–10 cm long, 8–25 mm thick, grey-yellow, with a fleshy, white, later brownish ring. Flesh is soft, whitish, greyish, sometimes blue-green and it smells faintly of fruit. Spore powder is light brown. Spores 10–14 × 4–5 μm, spindle-shaped, pale yellow. It grows in small numbers and almost exclusively under larch. Edible.

🍴 *Suillus grevillei* (KLOTZSCH) SING.
Syn. *Boletus elegans* SCHUM: FR.   VI–XI □■
Syn. *Suillus elegans* (SCHUM.: FR.) SNELL in SLIPP et SNELL   □□

Cap 4–15 cm wide, semi-globular when young, later broadly convex to involuted, orange-yellow, later pallid; cuticle is slimy and easily detachable when damp. Pores are dense, covered by the veil when young; lemon yellow, watery when old. Stipe is 1–2.5 cm thick, full, yellow at the top, with a ring, brown striated underneath. Flesh is yellow, sometimes greenish, watery in old specimens. Spore powder is dark brown; spores 7–11 × 3–4 μm, yellow. It grows gregariously, exclusively under larch. Edible.

🍴 *Suillus luteus* (L.: FR.) S. F. GRAY
Syn. *Boletus luteus* L.: FR.   V–XI □□
                                                                         ■□

Cap 5–12 cm wide, rounded and convex, chocolate brown, cuticle peels off easily; it is slimy when damp, glossy when dry. Tubes are slightly decurrent; their pores are yellow, covered with a white to pale purple veil when young. Stipe is 3–10 cm long, 1–2.5 cm thick, full, short, yellow and granular above the ring, brownish underneath. Flesh is white. Spore powder is ochre brown; spores 7–10 × 3–4 μm, spindle-shaped, pale yellow. It grows profusely under pine trees. Edible.

🍴 *Suillus bovinus* (L.: FR.) O. KUNTZE
Syn. *Boletus bovinus* L.: FR.   VII–X □□
                                                                          □■

Cap 4–12 cm wide, expanded and convex, light ochre-brown; cuticle is slippery when damp, glossy when dry. Tubes are short, pores large and angular, ochre, soon greenish. Stipe is 1–20 cm long, 5–10 cm thick, the same colour as the cap. Flesh is very elastic; if squashed the fruit-body immediately regains its shape. Pale ochre, slightly bluish or pinkish and smells faintly of fruit. It turns purple in vinegar and black when boiled. Spore powder is olive brownish. Spores 6–10 × 3–4 μm, spindle-shaped, yellowish. It grows gregariously in sandy pine woods, along their edges and along woodland tracks. Edible.

Boletaceae

Suillus granulatus (L.: FR.) O. KUNTZE
Sy. *Boletus granulatus* L.: FR.   VI–XI

Cap 5–10 cm wide, broadly convex, bare, red-brown, ochre yellow when dry; detachable cuticle is slimy when damp, smooth when dry. Tubes are slightly decurrent, pores very small, pale sulphur yellow with drops of white milky liquid when young; these turn brown and dry out into small grains when old. Stipe is full, 4–6 cm long, 8–20 mm thick, yellowish, with drops of liquid when young, later transforming into yellow and finally brown grains; old specimens are brown at the base and have no ring. Flesh is whitish to yellowish. Spore powder is whitish to yellow-brown. Spores 8–10 × 3–4 μm, spindle-shaped, yellowish. It is locally abundant in coniferous forests, where it grows under spruce and pine, along grassy edges and forest tracks and in pastures. Edible.

Suillus variegatus (SWARTZ: FR.) KARST.
Syn. *Boletus variegatus* SWARTZ: FR.   VII–IX

Cap 5–14 cm wide, broadly convex, brownyellow cuticle cannot be peeled off; slimy when damp but it dries out quickly and is then felt-like to scaly. Pores are greyish olive brown, large, angular, turning blue when bruised. Stipe is 3–9 cm long, 2.5–4 cm thick, slightly swollen at the base, yellow-brown. Flesh is pale ochre, turning slightly bluish and smells sharply of *Scleroderma*. Spore powder is light brown. Spores 8–11 × 3–4 μm, spindle-shaped, pale green-yellow. It grows gregariously in coniferous woods, particularly under pine. Edible.

Peppery Boletus
Chalciporus piperatus (BULL.: FR.) BAT.   VIII–X
Syn. *Boletus piperatus* BULL.: FR.
Syn. *Suillus piperatus* (BULL.: FR.) O. KUNTZE

Cap 2–6 cm wide, broadly convex, red-brown; cuticle is underachable, sticky when damp, glossy when dry. Tubes are slightly decurrent, pores broad and rusty. Stipe is 3–6 cm long, 4–10 cm thick, full; ochre, saffron yellow at the base. Flesh is bright yellow, smells faintly of fruit. Spore powder is yellow-brown. Spores 7–12 × 3–5 μm, spindle-shaped, pale yellowish. It often grows in groups in coniferous woods, especially in pine woods, along woodland tracks, in sparse moss and in ditches. Edible.

Boletaceae

Bay Boletus
Xerocomus badius (FR.) KÜHN.: GILB.   VII–X

Cap 4–15 cm wide, rounded and convex, sometimes concave when old; slimy during damp wheather, dark brown. Tubes are sinuate, pores whitish when young, soon yellowish, then olive green; they turn blue, green and then brown when bruised. Stipe is 4–12 cm long, 1–4 cm thick, cylindrical, yellowish-brown. Flesh is yellowish, bluish, has a pleasant smell and taste, but is often attacked by larvae and rot. Spore powder is olive brown. Spores 12–16 × 4–6 μm, spindle-shaped, pale yellow. It grows profusely under spruce and pine, less frequently under beech and oak, and sometimes on wood and cones. Edible.

Xerocomus subtomentosus (L.: FR.) QUÉL.   VI–X

Cap 3–10 cm wide, broadly conves, velvety, olive brown or yellow-olive; cuticle is not detachable and does not crack. Pores are golden yellow, faintly bluish, angular. Stipe is cylindrical, 6–10 cm long, 1.5–2 cm thick, firm to hard, with coarse veining, yellow-brown. Flesh is whitish, sometimes slightly bluish, smells faintly of fruit and of iodoform when young. Spore powder is light ochre to olive-brown; spores 12–14 × 5–6 μm, spindle-shaped, yellow. It usually grows individually in deciduous and coniferous woods. One of the commonest British boleti in towns. Edible.

Xerocomus rubellus (KROMBH.) QUÉL.   VI–X

Cap 3–6 cm wide, cushion-like, velvety, vermilion to blood red, becoming paler when old; in dry weather cracks into irregular patches. Tubes golden yellow, have broad openings, when bruised or mature becoming blue-green. Stipe is 3–10 cm long, 4–25 mm thick, fibrillose, yolk yellow, turning red when old, brown when bruised. Flesh is soft, yellow, turning blue-greenish; taste is acid and becomes soft when old. Spore powder is olive. Spores 9–14 × 5–6 μm, long ellipsoid, brown. It often grows in fgroups under oaks and limes in woods and parks. Edible.

Boletus radicans PERS.: FR.   VII–X

Cap 5–20 cm wide, convex, fleshy, tough, whitish, ochre, with a grey tinge, later yellow-brownish, with fine felt-like surface and silky shine, often with shallow depressions. Tubes are light, later rich lemon-yellow, then olive, becoming blue-green when bruised; pores are tiny. Stipe is 4–12 cm long, 3–8 cm thick, swollen at the base, bulbous or club-shaped, tapering and spindle-shaped in the lower part, yellow with a fine veil above, pale below, later with a brown tinge. Flesh is pale yellow, often turning blue in the cap, ochre yellow in the stipe, slightly bitter in taste, with an unpleasant smell of phenol. Spore powder is olive. Spores 10–16 × 4–6 μm, ellipsoid, spindle-shaped, light yellow-green. It grows in deciduous and mixed woods and parks, especially under old beech, oak and lime trees in limestone substrates in lowlands. Inedible.

Boletaceae

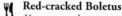

Red-cracked Boletus

Xerocomus chrysenteron (BULL.: ST. AMANS) QUÉL.   VII–XI

Syn. *Boletus chrysenteron* BULL.: ST. AMANS

Cap 3–10 cm wide, semi-globular when young, soon broadly convex and slightly irregular, almost concave when old. Cuticle is thin, dull, pruinose when young, later bare and velvety. Cuticle stores two pigments which respond according to temperature, lighting and age of the fruit-body. Fruit-bodies which grow in summer are grey, yellow or red-brown, grey or ochre grey and some parts of the cap can also be pinkish in a mature fruit-body. Specimens grown in cold and damp weather, in partial or complete shade are lmost black-brown and the red pigment appears only as a narrow stripe on the cap's cross-section. Cap's surface of these fruit-bodies is not deeply cracked but forms small patches with cracks in the cuticle which reveal red pigment. Fruit-bodies growing in the sunshine have deeper cracks which reach the flesh and are therefore white. If the surface of the cap is bitten off by wild animals or slugs, the rest turns vermilion red. The red pigment is most visible in the variety with an entirely vermilion red cap, but it has become an independent species names *B. rubellus*. Tubes 7–10 mm high, attached to the cap's flesh; pale yellow, greenish when old. Pores are rather large, angular, pale yellow, soon green-yellow, turning blue-green to brown when bruised. Stipe 2–8 cm long and 0.7–2 cm wide, erect or slightly crooked, often pointed and tapering at the base, cylindrical, most slender at top. When young it is canary yellow, later brownish, brown-yellow, reddish at the base; when mature it is always vermilion or wine red, brownish at the base and white close to the mycelium. Old fruit-bodies are fibrillose but fragile. Flesh is soft, spongy, yellow except for the narrow red stripe under the cap's skin; depending on the weather it turns stronger or weaker blue when cut and it is reddish when dry. Flesh of the stipe is yellow when young, soon becomes red (this colour can be seen on the entire cross-section of an old fruit-body) and brownish at the base. Flesh rots easily and is often attacked by insect larvae. It grows in deciduous and coniferous woods up to 1,000-m altitudes , often even in winter; sometimes its fruit-bodies can be found under snow in December.

Similar species:

Xerocomus porosporus IMLER (syn. *Xerocomus truncatus* SING., SNELL et DICK ss. auct. europ.) – picture opposite above left, and *Xerocomus fragilipes* (C. MARTIN) POUZ. – picture opposite above right.

Boletaceae

Red-stalked Boletus
Boletus erythropus (FR.) KROMBH.   V–X

Cap 5–20 cm wide, semi-globular when young, later broadly convex, fleshy, velvety and smooth, dark brown, black-brown when old. Tubes are sinuate, pores minute, at first yellow, later greyish vermilion to blood red; turn deep b lue when touched. Stipe is cylindrical to club-shaped, 2–4 cm wide; the basic yellow colouring is densely covered by fine red scales in the upper part. Olive at the base, turning blue when bruised. Flesh is deep yellow, becoming immediately dark indigo blue when cut; smell and taste is pleasant. Spore powder is dark olive. Spores 13–18 × 5–7 μm, spindle-shaped, olive yellow. It grows individually and in small groups in deciduous woods, particularly under beech trees but also in coniferous woods, often in mountainous areas. Similar species in North America. Inedible.

Devil's Boletus
Boletus satanas LENZ   VIII–IX

Cap 6–25 cm wide, semi-globular, expanded when mature, bare, white to faintly olive. Tubes do not reach the stipe, pores are yellow at first, soon carmine red. Stipe 8–15 cm long and 3–10 cm wide, swollen at the base, yellow under the cap, in the middle with reddish or scarlet red tetragonal network of veins; olive brown at the base. Flesh is pulpy, yellowish, only slightly turning blue; when young it smells like *Scleroderma*, when old it has an unpleasant smell of rotten meat or onions. Taste is pleasant at first, but repulsive in old fruit-bodies. Spore powder is olive yellow. Spores 10–15 × 5–7 μm, spindle-shaped, smooth, olive yellow. It usually grows individually on limestone in warm deciduous woods under hazel, oak, hornbeam and hawthorn trees. An uncommon species. Poisonous.

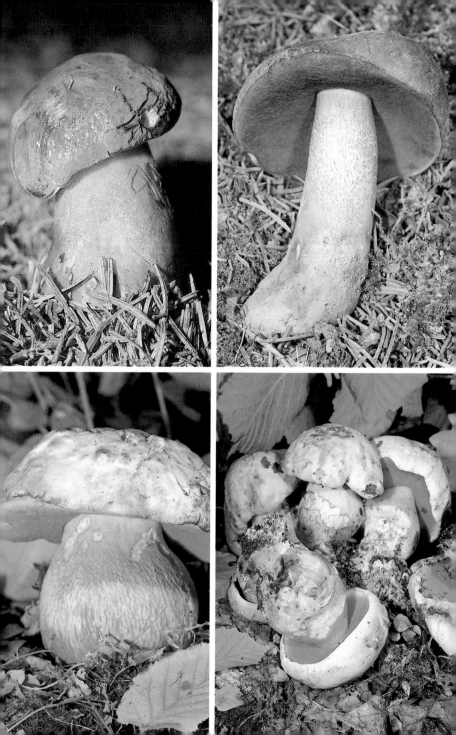

Boletaceae

Boletus calopus FR.   VI–X

Cap 8–15 cm wide, semi-globular, with an undulated margin; buff brown or faintly olive. Pores are lemon yellow, turning blue to green when touched. Stipe is clavate, swollen, with network of white veins on yellow surface at the top, brown at the base with scarlet red network; the size of mesh increases towards the base. Flesh is pale, turning blue when cut, smells acidic; repulsively bitter in taste. Spore powder is olive brown. Spores 10–14 × 4–6 μm, spindle-shaped, pale olive. It grows particularly in coniferous, but also deciduous woods in mountainous areas. Inedible.

Boletus pinophilus PIL. et DERMEK   V–XI

Cap 6–25 cm wide, semi-globular, later convex and expanded, often with uneven surface; fleshy, dark red-brown, pruinose when young. Tubes are deep, do not reach the stipe; pores are creamy, later yellow-green. Stipe is swollen, broadened at the base, red-brown, with a dense network of veins. Flesh is firm, white, red-brown under the cap, smell and taste is mushroom-like. Spore powder is olive brown. Spores 14–20 × 4–6 μm, spindle-shaped, pale honey in colour. It is not very abundant, growing early in spring in sandy pine woods and also under beech. Rare or absent in Great Britain. Edible, tasty.

Cep
Boletus edulis BULL.: FR.   VIII–XI
Syn. *Boletus bulbosus* SCHAEFF.: SCHROET.

Cap 5–20 cm wide, at first semi-globular with margin adpressed to the stipe, soon broadly convex, smooth or slightly uneven; fleshy, light or dark chestnut brown. Skin is detachable only in old specimens, slightly sticky when damp, mat when dry. Tubes are slightly sinuate, pores are minute, rounded, white, soon becoming creamy, yellow-green when old. Stipe is up to 20 cm long, 15–70 mm thick, clavate, later cylindrical, white, turning brown when old, with a network of white veins at the top. Flesh is firm, brownish under the cap's cuticle, otherwise white; has a pleasant mushroom smell and a specific taste. Spore poweder is olive brown. Spores 14–20 × 3.5–6 μm, spindle-shaped, olive brown. It grows in spruce forests in summer; in beech, oak and pine woods in autumn. Edible, very tasty.

Boletaceae

Boletus appendiculatus (SCHAEFF.: FR.) SECR.   VII–IX

Cap 6–20 cm wide, semi-globular, soon cushion-like, smooth with ingrown filaments; red-brown. Tubes are yellow in cross-section, openings are very small, golden
yellow, greenish, turning green-blue when bruised. Stipe is 5–15 cm long, 1.5–5 cm
thick, cylindrical, protruding into a radicle at the base, golden yellow, with a network of veins at the top. Flesh is yellow, bluish above the tubes, brownish at the base
of the stipe; it has a characteristic smell and sweet taste. Spore powder is olive-brown.
Spores 11–15 × 4–5.5 μm, spindle-shaped, copper yellow. It grows even in pro-
longed drought under deciduous, less frequently under coniferous, trees. Edible.

Boletus pulverulentus OPAT.   VI–IX

Cap 4–8 cm wide, convex, later cushion-like, sticky, deep brown, with fine cracks
during drought. Tubes are waxy yellow, with angular openings of the same colour,
turning deep blue when bruised. Stipe is 4–5 cm long, 0.5–2 cm thick, cylindrical,
rather slender, delicately granular; yellow at the top, brown at the base. Flesh is yellow, reddish at the base of the stipe, soon turning deep blue to black-blue. Spore
powder is olive. Spores 11–15 × 4–7 μm, spindle-shaped, copper-coloured. It grows
under deciduous, less frequently coniferous, trees in woods and parks. Edible.

Lecccinum aurantiacum (BULL.) S. F. GRAY (ss. auct.)
Syn. *Boletus aurantiacus* BULL.   VI–X
Syn. *Leccinum rufum* (SCHAEFF.) KREISEL

Cap 4–15 cm wide, regularly expanded and convex, with cuticle reaching over the
margin, red or brown-orange, matt, delicately felt-like. Tubes are deeply sinuate,
pores whitish, turning grey. Stipe, 5–15 cm long, 1–5 cm thick, soon becomes tough,
is white with whitish, later brick red scales. Flesh is white, lilac grey when exposed
to the air, becoming black, gree-bluish at the base of the stipe. Spore powder is olive
brown. Spores 13–17 × 4–5 μm, spindle-shaped, ochre brown. It grows only under
aspen, sometimes very abundantly. Rare or absent in Great Britain. Edible.

Leccinum vulpinum WATL.   VII–X

Cap 3–10 cm wide, soon cushion-like, orange-red when damp, soon becoming
brown to grey-rusty. Tubes and openings are whitish, soon greyish-creamy. Stipe is
5–15 cm long, 1–5 cm thick, white, scaly; scales are brick red, brownish or almost
black. Flesh is whitish, pink in the stipe, later grey-purple. Spore powder is olive
brown. Spores 13–16 × 4–5 μm, spindle-shaped, honey yellow-brown. It grows in
acid soil mainly under pine, but also under spruce.
Similar species:
Leccinum piceinum PILÁT et DERMEK.

Boletaceae

🍴 **Brown Birch Boletus**
Leccinum scabrum (BULL.: FR.) S. F. GRAY   VI–X ▪▪

Syn. *Boletus scaber* BULL.: FR.
Syn. *Krombholzia scabra* (BULL.: FR.) KARST.
Syn. *Krombholziella scabra* (BULL.: FR.) R. MAIRE

Cap 5–15 cm wide, convexly expanded, smooth, sometimes even delicately wrinkled, with soft flesh (particularly when old); grey, grey to reddish-brown, sometimes greenish and rarely pure white. Cuticle is not detachable but in old fruit-bodies it becomes slightly loose; in damp weather sticky and slightly slimy, dull and delicately felt-like during drought. Tubes are sinuate, soon soft and watery, swollen downwards, easily separable from cap's flesh. Pores are small and rounded, white, soon greyish, and do not change colour when bruised. Stipe is 8–20 cm long, 1–3 cm thick, cylindrical, compact when young, soon becoming tough and fibrillose; light greyish, covered with fine, loose, dark grey to black-grey scales which form longitudinal stripes under the cap. Flesh is compact when young, but soon becomes soft, watery and spongy in the cap; easily bruises. Stipe's flesh is fibrillose and tough, almost woody when old. Smell and taste is pleasant; colour white to white-grey or faintly pinkish. Spore powder is brown. Spores 14–20 × 5–6 μm, cylindrical, smooth, pale brownish. It is restricted to birch growths, where it grows individually or in groups, in or outside woods, in parks, hedgerows, and clearings.

Many varied form of *Leccinum scabrum* can be found growing in Europe and North America and it is sometimes very difficult to distinguish them from each other, in fact some authors have started recently to regard them as independent species. Easily distinguishable is *Leccinum nigrescens* (RICHON et ROZE) SING., syn. *Leccinum crocipodium* (LET. ex GILB.) WATL. with chrome yellow pores and pink flesh, which turns brownish and charcoal black when cut. It is rare and grows in warm areas under oak, beech and hornbeam. *Leccinum griseum* (QUÉL.) SING., syn. *Leccinum carpini* (R. SCHULZ.) MOSER grows only under hornbeam. Its cap is wrinkled and pitted, black-brown, hard; the whitish flesh does not change its colour. Similar *Leccinum duriusculum* (SCHULZER in FR.) SING. grows mainly under white poplar. Its flesh is white, salmon pink at the top of the stipe, later becoming grey-purple.

Several remarkable *Leccinum scabrum* forms grow only under birch trees. These include *Leccinum oxydabile* (SING.) SING., syn. *Leccinum variicolor* WATL. with pinkish to reddish flesh in the stipe which is blue-greenish at the base. *Leccinum thalassinum* PIL. et DERM., in which the surface of the stipe is green scaly at the base and the flesh is also green, *Leccinum subcinnamomeum* PIL. et DERM. with cinnamon brown cap, and *Leccinumm melaneum* (SMOTL.) PIL. et DERM. which is brown-black to black. Another form has a pure white cap; *Leccinum holopus* (ROSTK.) WATL., syn. *Leccinum scabrum* subsp. *niveum* (FR.) SING. ss. SING., growing on peat under birch trees, with blue-greenish base.

Boletaceae

Leccinum versipelle (FR.) SNELL
Syn. *Leccinum testaceoscabrum* (SECR.) SING. VII–X

Cap 4–20 cm wide, up to 1.5 kg weight, broadly convex, fleshy, yellow-brown to orange-yellow, sometimes even brick red, dry; skin of young fruit-bodies reaches over the cap's margin. Tubes are sinuate, pores grey-brownish with an olive tinge, black-brown, when old. Stipe is club-shaped, usually swollen at the base, rarely cylindrical, 8–22 cm long and up to 7 cm wide, tough, white or greyish, covered with sooty black scales. Flesh is compact, tough in the stipe, white, pink-purple when cut; blue-greenish at the base of the stipe, later turning entirely dark grey. Inconspicuous smell, pleasant taste, usually not attacked by insect larvae; turns black when dry. Spore powder is brown. Spores 13–16 × 4–5 μm, spindle-shaped, yellow-brown. It grows under birch trees in mixed woods. Edible.

Bitter Boletus

Tylopilus felleus (BULL.: FR.) KARST. VII–XI

Cap 4–12 cm wide, broadly convex, later flat, dry, coloured honey yellow, grey to grey-brown. Tubes do not reach the stipe, are swollen when old; pores are white at first, soon pink, rusty when old or bruised. Stipe is 4–12 cm long, 1–5 cm thick, slightly swollen at the base, brownish with olive tones and with a coarse and conspicuous network or yellowish veins. Flesh is white, the smell inconspicuous. Spore powder is pink. Spores 12–16 × 3–5 μm, spindle-shaped, colourless. It grows only in acid soil under coniferous, less frequently deciduous, trees, sometimes together with *Boletus edulis*, with which it can be easily confused, especially in its early stages of development. Poisonous but readily distinguished from *B. edulis* by its bitter taste.

Porphyrellus pseudoscaber (SECR.) SING. VII–X

Cap 5–15 cm wide, rounded and convex, smooth, finely velvety, brownish to faintly olive. Pores do not reach the stipe, are angular, grey, reddish when old, turning blue when touched. Stipe 4–16 cm long, 1–4 cm thick, slightly swollen at the base, smoky grey to black-brown, white at the base. Flesh is white at first, turning pink to blue when cut, black when old or dried; taste is mild, but smell acidic. Spore powder is grey-brown, pinkish. Spores 13–16 × 5–6 μm, spindle-shaped, dark. It grows most frequently in alpine or subalpine spruce forests. Rare or absent in Great Britain.

Boletaceae

Strobilomyces floccopus (VAHL: FR.) KARST.   VII–X   ■□
                                                                         □□

Cap 5–12 cm, broadly globular and convex, felt-like, skin is cracked into black, pointed and loose scales. Pores are angular, large, white, turning red to black when bruised, covered with veil when young. Stipe is 6–10 cm long, 1–1.5 cm thick, cylindrical, full, scaly, with a ring. Flesh is soft, whitish, soon becoming orange to red or black. Spore powder is black-brown. Spores 10–15 × 9–12 μm, almost globular. The only European species whose spores have a conspicuous network of veins on the spore surface. It grows mainly in spruce and fir woods, less frequently in deciduous woods. Edible, not first-rate.

Russulaceae

Fleecy Milk Cap   □■
Lactarius vellereus (FR.) FR.   VII–IX   □□

Large white mushroom with hard flesh. Cap 8–20 cm wide, in the centre depressed to funnel-shaped, depressed with involuted margin; soft, felt-like and velvety. Gills are sparse, depressed white, later ochre. Stipe is shortly cylindrical firm, full, finely felt-like. Flesh is hard, white, sometimes becoming faintly yellow or rusty; when broken it releases white, milky and very astringent liquid which turns pink-purple in the air. Spore powder is white. Spores 9–12 × 7.5–10 μm, broadly ellipsoid, partly covered with incomplete network of veins, amyloid. It is very abundant in deciduous, especially beech woods, but it also grows under coniferous trees. Inedible.

Lactarius pergamenus (SOW.: FR.) FR.   □□
Syn. *Lactarius piperatus* (FR.) S. F. GRAY auct.   VII–IX   ■□

Large white mushroom with hard flesh. Cap 6–18 cm wide, depressed in the centre, later funnel-shaped, bare, dry, slightly wrinkled, later with ochre patches. Gills are very dense, narrow, creamy yellowish. Stipe is smooth, bare and tough. Flesh is hard; when broken it invariably release white, very astringent milk. Spore powder is white. Spores 8–9.5 × 5.5–7 μm, broadly ellipsoid, covered with an incomplete network of veins. It grows abundantly, especially in mixed woods even during dry spells. The very similar *L. glaucescens* differs from the former in having milky liquid which becomes grey-greenish and in felt-like apex of the stipe. Inedible. (Edible when specially prepared.)

Lactarius necator (BULL.: FR.) KARST.   □□
Syn. *Lactarius turpis* (WEINM.) FR.   VII–X   □■

Cap 5–15 cm wide with a shallow depression in the centre, bare, slimy, with involuted margin, yellow felt-like; entirely greenish, dark olive brown to olive blackish. Gills are dirty yellow, turn brown when bruised. Stipe is short and tough, greenish to dark dirty olive, glossy. Flesh produces white, very astringent milk when broken. Spore powder is yellowish. Spores 7.5–8.5 × 6–7 μm, globularly ellipsoid with an incomplete network of veins, amyloid. It grows abundantly in spruce woods and under birch trees. Inedible.

Russulaceae

Wooly Milk Cap
Lactarius torminosus (SCHAEFF.: FR.) S. F. GRAY   VII–X   ■□ □□

Large mushroom with hard flesh. Cap 5–15 cm wide, shallowly convex, deeply concave to funnel-shaped, bare, margin strongly involuted and whitish tomentose to woolly; colouration light buff, reddish to red-brown with darker rings. Gills are crowded, cream pinkish. Stipe is short, pale, pinkish, hollow. Flesh produces white, very acrid milk when broken. Spore powder is yellowish. Spores 7–10 × 6–8 μm, amyloid, broadly ellipsoid, with an incomplete network of veins. It grows most frequently among grass under birch trees in and outside woods. Inedible.

Lactarius lignyotus FR.   VII–IX   □■ □□

Cap 3–8 cm wide with a pointed umbo in the centre and vein-like wrinkles, velvety, black-brown, dark sooty brown to almost black. Gills are dense, white, later light ochre, gradually becoming red when bruised. Stipe is long, wrinkled at the top, black-brown, velvety. Flesh, particularly at the base of the stipe turns orange-yellowish to reddish-brown and produces pure white, mild tasting milk when broken. Spore powder is light ochre yellow. Spores 9–10.5 μm in diameter, globular, amyloid, with a network of spikes. It grows profusely in subalpine and alpine conifer woods, especially in mossy spruce growths with acid soil. There are several similar species in Great Britain. Edible.

Saffron Milk Cap
Lactarius deliciosus (L.: FR.) S. F. GRAY   VIII–X   □□ ■□

Cap 3–8 cm wide, depressed in the centre, margin involuted; flesh or orange-red with darker concentric rings, smooth, bare, slimy when damp; old specimens often have greenish patches. Gills are light red-brown, turning green when bruised. Stipe is flesh red or orange, soon hollow. Flesh becomes greenish when bruised and produces orange-red milk; taste is astringent and smell unpleasantly resinous. Spore powder is yellowish. Spores 7–9 × 6–7 μm, ellipsoid, amyloid, with an incomplete network of veins. It grows among grass in low spruce undergrowth and along their edges. Edible, very tasty (especially pickled).

Slimy Milk Cap
Lactarius blennius FR.   VI–XI   □□ □■

Cap 3–9 cm wide. shallowly convex, depressed in the centre, green, grey-green or light olive brown, slimy when damp, smooth, bare, with bands of brownish patches looking like rain drops. Gills are dense, white, later yellowish; when bruised they turn brown, grey to green. Stipe is pale, greyish. Flesh is whitish, producing white milk which becomes grey-green when dry. Spore powder is yellowish. Spores 7–8.5 × 5.5 × 6.5 μm, broadly ellipsoid, ribbed, amyloid. It grows profusely and exclusively under beech trees. Inedible.

Ressulaceae

Grey Milk Cap
Lactarius vietus FR.   VII–X

Cap 3–7 cm wide, with thin flesh, depressed in the centre, light grey with a fleshy or purple tinge, bare, dry, without rings. Gills are yellowish, turning grey or grey-green when bruised. Stipe is creamy yellow or greyish, later hollow. Flesh is white, releases white milk which later turns grey or grey-green. Spore powder is yellowish. Spores 8–9.5 × 6.5–7.5 μm, ellipsoid, with an incomplete network or veins, amyloid. It grows frequently in mixed woods under birch trees in acid soil. Inedible.

Coconut-scented Milk Cap
Lactarius odoratus VELEN.   VII–XI
Syn. *Lactarius glyciosmus* sensu NEUHOFF (et al.)

Cap 2–7 cm wide, umbonate in the centre, later concave to funnel-shaped, its flesh is thin, cuticle buff ochre with a yellow-pink tinge, finely felt-like, dry. Gills are dense, whitish to pale ochre. Stipe is slender, pale ochre. Flesh is pale, producing a small quantity of white, slightly sharp milk. The entire fruit-body smells of coconut, particularly when it is fading. Spore powder is pale yellow. Spores 7–8.5 × 5.5–6.5 μm, globularly ellipsoid, with a network of veins, amyloid. It grows abundantly under birch in mixed woods and along their edges. Can also be found under the name *L. impolitus* FR. Inedible.

Lactarius glyciosmus FR.
Syn. *Lactarius mammosus* (FR.) FR.   VIII–X
Syn. *Lactarius hibbardae* (BURL.) SACC.

Cap 3–8 cm wide, umbonate or convexely rounded, dark brown-grey to black-grey, sometimes with a purple tinge, felt-like, dull. Gills are dense, pale, deep ochre yellow. Stipe is 3–8 cm long, 5–15 mm thick, cylindrical, pale. Flesh is pale, discharges white milk when broken. Fruit-body smells pleasantly of coconut when it is drying. Spore powder is yellowish. Spores 6–10 × 5–8 μm, broadly ellipsoid, amyloid, with a network of veins. It grows abundantly in damp and mossy coniferous woods on acid substrate, especially in submountainous areas. Inedible.

Lactarius mitissimus (FR.) FR.   VII–XI

Cap 3–7 cm wide, depressed and umbonate in the centre, entirely vivid orange or red-orange, without rings, smooth, bare and dry. Gills are dense, yellowish, later pale ochre. Stipe is slender and cylindrical, concolorous with the cap or slightly paler. Flesh is yellowish, produces an abundance of white milk, which is sweet at first, but later becomes slightly sharp. Spore powder is yellowish. Spores 8–9.5 × 6.5–7.5 μm, broadly ellipsoid, with a network of veins, amyloid. It grows abundantly coniferous woods. Edible.

Ressulaceae

Lactarius volemus (Fr.) Fr.   VII–IX

Cap 5–15 cm wide, convex, later depressed in the centre, with hard and thick flesh, brittle, vivid red-brown to orange, smooth, dry and finely pruinose. Gills are sparse, whitish, later yellowish, becoming rusty brown when bruised. Stipe is longish, cylindrical, hard and firm, pale reddish and white pruinose. Flesh is pale, releases an abundance of white, sweet milk which turn brown and leaves persistent brown flecks on clothes. Young fruit-bodies have a pleasant smell, but fading and old fruit-bodies have an unpleasant herring-like smell (trimethylamin). Spore powder is yellowish. Spores 7.5–10 μm, globular, finely tuberculate amyloid. It grows in all types of woods, especially in pine woods in dry and sunny places. Edible.

Rufus Milk Cap
Lactarius rufus (Scop.: Fr.) Fr.   V–XI

Cap 5–11 cm wide, shallowly convex in the centre with a conspicuous, pointed wart, later shallowly concave, entirely cloudy red-brown, with a faint silvery shine; smooth, bare and dry. Gills are dense, white-yellowish, later ochre. Stipe is reddish, white-felted at the base. Flesh is yellowish, discharging an abundance of white milk. Spore poweder is pale ochre. Spores 8–9.5 × 6.5–7.5 μm, almost globular, with a network of veins, amyloid. It grows very abundantly and gregariously in coniferous and mixed woods, even during dry spells. Inedible.

Curry-scented Milk Cap
Lactarius camphoratus (Bull.: Fr.) Fr.   VI–X

Cap 3–5 cm wide, concave with an umbo in the centre; it is cloudy brown-red when damp, flesh red when dry. Young fruit-bodies have a purple tinge, later becoming ochre-pinkish, smooth, bare and mat. Gills are pale reddish, later deep scarlet-brown and white pruinose. Stipe is slender, rather long, dark buff to red-brown, pruinose. Flesh is yellowish, produces watery, invariable, sweet milk which smells of camphor or chicory especially when it is drying out. Spore powder is yellowish. Spores 8–8.5 × 7–7.5 μm, globularly ellipsoid, covered with lines of tubercles and amyloid. It grows quite often in deciduous and coniferous woods. Edible.

Russulaceae

Lactarius pubescens FR.　　　　　　　　　　　　　　　　　　　　VII–XIII

Cap 4–9 cm wide, shallow and depressed in the centre, with tough flesh, coloured whitish with a creamy or pale fleshy shade; dry, ringless, smooth, bare in the centre and tomentose on the margin. Gills are narrow, dense, pale fleshy. Stipe is short, pale reddish, tapers downwards. Flesh is pale, cream red under the cap's cuticle; when broken it releases white milk. Spore poweder is white. Spores 6.5–8.5 × 5.5–6,5 μm, broadly ellipsoid with an incomplete network of veins. It grows under birch in damp woods and in mossy woodland meadows. Rare or absent in Great Britain. Inedible.

Lactarius hysginus (FR.: FR.) FR.　　　　　　　　　　　　　　　VII–X

Cap 4–12 cm wide, often with a deep depression in the centre, with tough flesh and undulated margin; slimy, but glossy during drought, smooth, bare, grey with a lilac tinge. Gills are very sparse, shallow, ochre to rusty yellowish. Stipe is shortly cylindrical, a little paler than the cap, with a yellowish shade; slimy, later hollow inside. Flesh turns rusty when cut, has an acid smell and produces white milk. Spores 6.5–7.5 × 5.5–6.5 μm, broadly ellipsoid, with a comb-like network of veins. It grows in coniferous woods on acid soil, especially in grass along woodland tracks. Inedible.

Lactarius chrysorrheus FR.　　　　　　　　　　　　　　　　　　VII–IX

Cap 4–7 cm wide, deressed in the centre, at first pink, later pale orange with several darker rings; sticky when young, then dry, mat, smooth and bare. Gills are dense, creamy to ochre with rusty patches. Stipe later hollow, yellowish with an orange tinge. Flesh releases an abundance of white milk which quickly turns sulphur yellow when exposed to the air. Spore powder is light yellow. Spores 7–8.5 × 6–6.5 μm, broadly ellipsoid, tuberculate and spiky with an incomplete network of veins, amyloid. It grows in oak or mixed woods under oak. Rare in Great Britain. Inedible.

Lactarius lilacinus (LASCH) FR.　　　　　　　　　　　　　　　　VII–IX

Cap 3–5 cm wide, in the centre depressed or sometimes umbonate with involuted margin, dry, without rings; it is felt-like scaly when young, later smooth, bare, dark granular, lilac, dark pink or greyish-lilac. Gills are sparse, pale ochre, later fleshy yellowish. Stipe is grey to fleshy ochre, paler at the top, smooth, bare and slender. Flesh produces white milk when broken which dries out into grey droplets. Spore powder is whitish. Spores 6–8 μm in diameter, globular, spiky and amyloid. It grows in small numbers in damp soil in alder groves. Inedible.

Russulaceae

Lactarius lacunarum ROMAGN. ex HORA   VII–VIII   ⬛⬛⬜⬜

Cap 2–5 cm wide, shallowly convex, later expanded with a shallow depression in the centre; at first vivid red-brown, later rusty orange, dry, pale ochre yellow, smooth and bare. Gills are shortly decurrent, pale buff, later almost orange. Stipe 2–5 cm long, 3–5 mm thick, rusty orange, darker at the base. Flesh produces white milk when cut which turns yellow in the air. Spore powder is white. Spores $7–9 \times 5.5–7$ μm, broadly ellipsoid, comb-like or broken network of veins, amyloid. It grows in damp, boggy soil, sometimes even peat, under alder or willow, along the edges of ponds and marches. Inedible.

Russula adusta (PERS.: FR.) FR.   VI–X   ⬜⬛⬜⬜

Cap 5–12 cm wide, hard, depressed in the centre, whitish, soon as if burnt, smoky brown to brownish. Cuticle is slightly slimy when damp, glossy, undetachable, often covered with soil and needles. Gills are dirty whitish, medium dense. Stipe is short, whitish, turning brown from the base, full and hard. Flesh is white, hard, gradually turning grey when bruised; solution of $FeSO_4$ colours it grey-pink. Taste is mild, smell acid and musty. Spore powder is white. Spores $7–10 \times 6–8$ μm, with a very delicate ornamental pattern, ellipsoid. It grows profusely in coniferous woods in lime-free soil.

Russula decolorans (FR.) FR.   VII–IX   ⬜⬜⬛⬜

Cap 5–12 cm wide, almost globular, later flat, fleshy, orange-red, apricot to pale ochre, with narrow and smooth margin. Cuticle is smooth and bare, mat, detachable midway across the cap. Gills are creamy, turning grey along the edges when old. Stipe is long and cylindrical, stout, white, turning grey from the base when old; this is best visible on the cross-section of the stipe. Taste is mild, slightly sharp when young. Spore powder is light butter yellow. Spores $10–14 \times 9–12$ μm, widely ellipsoid, spiky. Grows fairly abundantly in damp pine woods, particularly at higher altitudes. Edible, tasty.

Russula pectinata (BULL.: ST.-AM.) FR.   VII–IX   ⬜⬜⬜⬛

Cap 3–7 cm wide, depressed in the centre, dull buff to clay-coloured, in the centre usually brownish with grooved and notched margin; cuticle is bare, sticky, detachable almost to the centre of the cap. Gills are narrow, pale, later straw yellow, brittle. Stipe tapers downwards, is soon hollow, pale at the base with copper patches. Flesh is pale with rusty patches when mature; smells unpleasantly of fish. Spore powder is creamy to light ochre yellow. Spores $7–9 \times 6–7$ μm, almost globular, coarsely tuberculate, amyloid. It grows in all types of woods, most often under limes in parks and avenues. Inedible.

Russulaceae

🍴 *Russula laurocerasi* MELZER   VII–IX ⬛⬜/⬜⬜

Similar to the Stinking Russula (*R. foetens*) but smaller, more slender and has a conspicuous bitter-almond smell. Cap 5–10 cm wide, depressed in the centre, brown-yellow or cloudy ochre; margin is sharp and deeply grooved, cuticle is slimy and detachable. Gills are dense, straw yellow, with rusty patches along the edges. Stipe is slender, as if tied up, white, later with rusty patches and hollows. Flesh is whitish, has a pleasant bitter-almond smell. Spore powder is pale cream-yellow. Spores 10–14 × 9–12 μm, globular, comb-like, amyloid. It grows in deciduous and pine woods, particularly in limy soil in warm areas. There are several similar species. Inedible.

🍴 **Geranium-scented Russula**
Russula fellea (FR.) FR.   VII–IX ⬜⬛/⬜⬜

Cap 4–7 cm wide, buff or straw yellow, margin is smooth for a long time, rounded, later shortly grooved; cuticle is dull, slimy when damp, peels off in short stripes. Gills are pale, soon buff straw yellow, not too dense. Stipe is first white, then pale ochre. Flesh is white at first, later pale yellow; smell resembles that of *Geranium*. Spore powder is whitish. Spores 8–10 × 7–8 μm, almost globular, finely and densely tuberculate. It grows profusely in all woods, especially in beech woods. Inedible.

🍴 **Common Yellow Russula**
Russula ochroleuca (PERS.) ex FR.   VIII–X ⬜⬜/⬛⬜

Cap 5–10 cm wide, le,on yellow, golden yellow, ochre or even greenish yellow, margin is blunt and smooth, cuticle is slimy when damp and easily detachable. Gills are broad, white, later yellowish-grey. Stipe is almost cylindrical, white, seldom yellowish, turns grey when old. Flesh is white, greyish when old; smell is inconspicuous. Spore powder is whitish. Spores 8–11 × 8–9 μm, broadly ellipsoid, almost globular, with coarsely tuberculate network of veins, amyloid. It grows abundantly mainly in spruce woods. Inedible.

🍴 **Cracked Green Russula**
Russula virescens (SCHAEFF.: ZANTED.) FR.   VII–IX ⬜⬜/⬜⬛

Cap 5–15 cm wide, semi-globular convex, very hard, with thick flesh, verdigris or greyish green, turning paler with age; margin is granular and grooved, cuticle is dry, velvety, soon cracked into irregular patches, undetachable. Gills are white, later creamy, edges are rusty brown. Stipe is stout, hard, white and wrinkled. Flesh is hard, white, susceptible to turning rusty; solution of $FeSO_4$ colours it immediately deep red. It tastes of nuts. Spore powder is white. Spores 8–10 × 7–8 μm, ellipsoid with delicate ornamental pattern. It grows in light, dry forests and along their margins, especially under oak and pine. Edible, tasty.

Russulaceae

Bare-toothed Russula
Russula vesca FR.   VI–IX

Cap 5–10 cm wide, semi-globular, hard, cloudy fleshy or pinkish red, with grey pallid patches, cuticle often falls short of margin of cap, often radially wrinkled in the centre. Gills are white, low and dense, turning rusty with age. Stipe is short, white and hard, narrowed at the base. Flesh gradually turns rusty when damaged; solution of $FeSO_4$ colours it orange-red. It tastes of sweet almonds. Spore powder is white. Spores $6–7 \times 5–6$ μm, ellipsoid, finely tuberculate, amyloid. It grows abundantly in dry woods. Edible, tasty.

Russula cyanoxantha (SCHAEFF.: SCHW.) FR.   VI–X

Cap 5–15 cm wide, slate black-grey or greenish with an olive shade; margin is often scarlet, the centre grows pale to yellowish. Cuticle has fine radiating veins and it is detachable along the margin. Gills are white, flexible and as if greasy when touched. Stipe is white, rarely partly blue. Flesh is white, does not change colour in the solution of $FeSO_4$ and usually has a mild taste. Spore powder is white. Spores $8–9 \times 7–8$ μm, ellipsoid, very finely tuberculate, amyloid. It grows profusely in all types of woods, particularly under oak and beech. Edible, tasty.

Grass Green Russula
Russula aeruginea LINDBL. in FR.   VI–X

Cap 5–10 cm wide, semi-globular, later expanded and broadly concave, olive to grass green with ochre, brown and whitish patches; margin is sharp, later grooved, cuticle glossy, bare and detachable almost to the centre. Gills are white, later creamy, often turning rusty along the edges. Stipe is white, becoming rusty from the base, later hollow. Flesh is white, turns pink iun the solution of $FeSO_4$; taste is mild but sometimes acrid to sharp. Spore powder is pale yellow. Spores $7–10 \times 6–8$ μm, longitudinally ellipsoid, tuberculate, amyloid. It grows in forests and parks, especially under birch and spruce. Edible.

Russulaceae

Ψ *Russula xerampelina* (SCHAEFF.: SECR.) FR.   VII–X ■□ / □■

Cap 5–12 cm wide, at first globular, later expanded, with a shallow depression in the centre; its colouring is greatly variable, e.g. scarlet pink, wine or brown-red, purple and often patched; centre is usually pallid. Cuticle is finely velvety, slightly slimy when damp; it is detachable halfway across the cap. Gills are rounded to free, deep, fairly dense, fragile; coloured creamy ochre and turning brown when bruised. Stipe is slightly clavate, white or partly purple reddish, pruinose, later smooth, turning yellow when touched. Flesh is pale, turning brown when damaged or old; its taste is mild but when it is drying out it smells of crab or lobster. Spore powder is ochre yellow. Spores 8–13 × 8–12 μm, almost globular, tuberculate to spiky. It grows in all types of forest. It forms several varieties of different colour, for example var. *linnaei*, var. *olivascens* (with an oliver green cap) and var. *fusca* (with a brown or yellow-brown cap). Edible.

Ψ *Russula erythropoda* PELTERAU   VII–X □■ / □□

Cap 6–10 cm wide, globular, later convex to expanded, depressed in the centre, deep scarlet or blood red, centre almost black. Cuticle is velvety, slightly slimy when damp, detachable to halfway across the cap. Gills are rounded, at first pale, later creamy, edges are often purple. Stipe 5–8 cm long, 10–15 mm thick, slightly clavate, entirely or at least on one side purple-red, gradually turning brown when bruised or growing old. Flesh is pale, turns brown and smells of kippers when fading; taste is mild. Spore powder is ochre yellow. Spores 8–10 × 7.5–9 μm, almost globular, tuberculate and spiky, light yellow, amyloid. It grows in coniferous, particularly spruce woods.

Ψ **Golden Russula**
Russula paurata (WITH.) ex FR.   VII–IX □□ / □■

Cap 5–9 cm wide, firm, vermilion-red, orange to golden yellow with bare cuticle which is slimy during damp weather and detachable only at the margin; the lower surface is chrome yellow. Gills are pale yellow, edges usually strikingly golden yellow. Stipe is white and partly yellow. Flesh is white, chrome yellow under the cap's skin; taste is mild or slightly bitter. Spores 8–10 × 8–9 μm, almost globular, densely and coarsely spiky, amyloid. It grows mainly in deciduous woods in warmer areas. Edible.

Russulaceae

Russula puellaris FR.   V–X ▪▪▫▫

Cap 3–7 cm wide, expanded, depressed in the centre, dark flesh red or cloudy purple, centre is darker, usually with shades of ochre, yellow-green or lilac, grooved along the thin margin; cuticle is slimy, detachable to halfway across the cap. Gills are white, later light yellow, brittle. Stipe is white, fragile, often swollen at the base. Whole mushroom becomes ochre yellow when old. Flesh is mild, smells like that of *Boletus variegatus*. Spore powder is deep ceramy. Spores 8–10 × 7–9 μm, broadly ellipsoid, almost globular, spiky. It grows in all types of woods in damp places. Edible.

Russula paludosa BRITZ.   VII–IX ▫▪▫▫

Cap 6–15 cm wide, semi-globular, later flat, strawberry or rosehip red, g rowing pale to orange or creamy; cuticle is bare, detachable. Gills are dense, white, later butter yellow, sometimes red along the edges. Stipe is long and strong, white, partly reddish. Flesh is white, mild or slightly sharp in taste; it turns faint grey pink in the solution of $FeSO_4$. Spore powder is pale ochre. Spores 9–12 × 8–10 μm, broadly ellipsoid, coarsely spiky, amyloid. It grows in moss, bilberry and heather growths in damp coniferous woods in acid soil. Edible, tasty.

Russula lepida FR.   VII–IX ▫▫▪▫

Cap 5–10 cm wide, convex, very hard and firm, vivid vermilion-red, in the centre growing pale to whitish or yellowish;margin is rounded and smooth, cuticle dry, not peeling, cracked in dry weather. Gills are white, later yellowish, edges often red. Stipe is very hard, white and flushed pinkish. Flesh is brittle and dry. Spore powder is light yellow. Spores 8–10 × 7–8 μm, broadly ellipsoid, with a dense tuberculate network. It grows abundantly in dry, warm woods. Inedible.

Russula velenovskyi MELZER et ZVÁRA   VII–X ▫▫▫▪

Cap 5–10 cm wide, soon saucer-shaped, often with a blunt wart in the centre, pink or brick red, turning pale to yellowish, usually with a darker zone around the centre; cuticle slimy, mat when dry, often dotted in white. Gills are white to light ochre, edges sometimes red. Stipe is stout, longitudinally wrinkled, firm, white, sometimes pinkish at the base. Flesh is white, turns deep grey-pinkish in the solution of $FeSO_4$. Spore powder is light yellow. Spores 8–10 × 7–9 μm, a ellipsoid and spiky. It grows in deciduous, less frequently in coniferous woods. Edible. May be confused with *R. emetica*.

Russulaceae

 The Sickener
Russula emetica (SCHAEFF.: FR.) S. F. GRAY VII–X

Cap 4–10 cm wide, flat and convex, brittle, cuticle is easily detached, vivid red, glossy. Gills are white, velvety when old, acrid. Stipe is white, sharply contrasting with the red skin of the cap. Flesh is white. Spore powder is white. Spores 8–12 × 6–8 μm, elongated and oval, with warts and combs, colourless. The ornamentation can be revealed by using iodine. It grows in coniferous woods. Lightly poisonous.

 The Fragile Russula
Russula gracilis (PERS.: FR.) FR. (ss. J. SCHAEFFER) VIII–XI

Cap 2–6 cm wide, soon flat and expanded to concave, flesh red with pink, purple, grey and greenish tones, soon becoming pallid, furrowed at the margin. Gills are white. Stipe is cylindrical, brittle, wrinkled and white. Flesh is white, faint fruity smell. Spore powder is white, spores 7–9 × 6–8 μm, broadly oval, colourless with ornamentation. It grows particularly in damp spruce woods. Lightly poisonous.

 Russula firmula J. SCHAEFF. VII–X

Cap 4–7 cm wide, shallowly depressed in the centre, convex, brittle, cloudy purple or brown-red, usually turning pallid in the centre; margin is grooved, cuticle is easily detachable. Gills are brittle, pale, later deep golden yellow. Stipe is 4–7 cm long, 0.8–1.5 cm thick, wrinkled, white, sometimes grey. Flesh is pale, smell acid and resinous. Spore powder is light yolk yellow. Spores 8–9 × 7–8 μm, broadly ellipsoid, coarsely tuberculate to comb-like, amyloid. It grows gregariously in coniferous and deciduous woods, especially in limy soil. Rare or absent in Great Britain. Inedible.

 Russula badia QUÉL. VIII–XI

Cap 5–12 cm wide, with firm flesh, smooth, later shortly grooved, depressed in the centre, blood-red or red-brown, purple-red, almost black in the centre or yellowish, violet, with ochre-brown patches, cuticle is smooth and bald, detachable only on the margin. Gills are white, later butter-yellowish, turning straw-yellow or light-ochre, often with pink edges. Stipe 4–10 cm long, 1–2.5 cm thick, white or partly pink, turning yellow to brown from the base, hard. Flesh is white and has a pleasant cedar-like scent when fading and in warm weather. Its taste is mild at first, but leaves a sharp long-lasting burning sensation. Spore powder is light yellow to dark ochre. Spores 8–10 × 6–8 μm, broadly ellipsoid, with rather coarse warts and incomplete network of veins. It grows in coniferous woods, especially pine. Inedible.

Russulaceae

Russula amoenolens ROMAGN.
Syn. *Russula consobrina* auct.   VII–X

Cap 4–8 cm wide, fleshy, depressed in the centre, grey-brown, in the centre sepia brown to reddish, often wrinkled, margin grooved and nodulose; cuticle is sticky when damp, detachable to the middle of the cap. Gills are white, later greyish. Stipe tapers downwards; is white, later greyish, longitudinally wrinkled, hollow and brittle. Flesh is pale, greyish under the cap's skin, greyish, smelling of fish or Camembert cheese. Spore powder is pale yellowish. Spores 7.5–10 × 6.5–8 μm, ellipsoid, coarsely tuberculate, amyloid. It grows in small numbers in deciduous woods, mainly under oak. Inedible.

Stinking Russula
Russula foetens (PERS.: FR.) FR.   VI–IX

Cap 5–15 cm wide, enclosed globular, later expanded, with firm, thick flesh; margin undulated and grooved, light ochre, cloudy ochre to dirty honey brown, with rusty-brown patches, cuticle rather gelatinous when damp, slimy to sticky, shiny when dry, detachable almost to the centre. Gills are straw-yellow, with edges of the same colour, they produce drops of yellowish liquid which leave rusty-brown spots. Stipe 6–12 cm long, 1.5–3 cm thick, hard, later hollow, white, with rusty-brown patches in the lower part. Flesh is yellowish, firm, it has unpleasant to distateful smell and strong burning taste (var. *grata* [BRITZ].) ROMAGN. has an exceptionally mild taste). Spore powder is cream. Spores 7.5–10 × 6.5–9 μm, almost globular, with sparse coarse warts and spikes. It grows in all types of woods. Inedible.

Russula parazurea J. SCHAEFF.   VI–IX

Cap 3–6 cm wide, dark or light blue, grey-blue or grey-purple, sometimes dark olive in the centre; mat, thickly pruinose, cuticle is detachable to the middle of the cap. Gills are white, later yellowish, with rusty patches. Stipe is white, later yellowish, brownish at the base. Flesh is white, mild in taste. It turns pink in the solution of $FeSO_4$. Spore powder is pale yellow. Spores 6–8 × 6–7 μm, almost globular, linked and tuberculate, amyloid. It grows in sunny places of deciduous and pine woods in small numbers.

Russula pseudointegra ARNOULD et GORIS   VIII–IX

Cap 4–12 cm wide, later flat, with firm flesh and rounded margin, smooth, often lobed, vermilion-red or pink red, with pale yellow or pink and whitish or yellowish spots; cuticle detachable to halfway or up to two thirds across the cap, finely cream, whitish pruinose along the margin when young. Gills are whitish, later yellowish, turning light ochre with age. Stipe 5–8 cm long, 2–3 cm thick, pure white, turning grey with age. Flesh is white; the lower surface of the cap is pink, it smells of fruit and menthol, its taste is mild but soon bitterish to slightly burning. Spore powder is light yellow. Spores 7–8 × 6.5-8 μm, almost globular, with low warts. It grows in deciduous woods, mainly under oak, beech and hazel, it prefers moist substrates. Inedible.

Russulaceae

Russula sardonia Fr. em. Romell.
Syn. *Russula chrysodacryon* Sing.   VII–X
Syn. *Russula drimeia* Cooke

Cap 5–10 cm wide, convex, with a small umbo, hard, cuticle hardly, detachable, purple-red patched with yellow and green, often flecked. Gills are adnate, lemon yellow. Stipe is slightly clavate, hard in some sections, lemon yellow and partly purple. Flesh is lemon, later turning saffron red. Spore powder is creamy, spores 7–9 × 7–8 μm, almost globular, ornamented, colourless. It grows in acid coniferous woods under pine trees. Poisonous.

Russula mustelina Fr.   VIII–X

Cap 6–12 cm wide, semi-globular, later convex, depressed in the centre, ochre to ochre brown, dark in the centre; cuticle is bare, slimy when damp, detachable at the margin, thick. Gills taper towards the stipe, creamy. Stipe is 4–7 cm long, 15–25 mm thick, white, patched ochre, smooth, hard, turning rusty when old. Flesh is pale, turning rusty when bruised or old, mild in taste; it turns orange to red in the solution of $FeSO_4$. Spore powder is pale ochre. Spores 7–9 × 6–7.5 μm, ellipsoid, with a dense network of shallow veins, amyloid, pale yellow. It grows mainly in sub-alpine spruce woods. Edible, tasty.

Blackening Russula
Russula nigricans (Bull.: Mérat) Fr.   VII–X

Cap 8–20 cm wide, hard, depressed in the centre, white, soon with grey and brown patches, later black-brown; cuticle is bare and undetachable. Gills are pale, greyish when mature, with a pink reflex inside, turning red when bruised, thick, brittle, rather sparse. Stipe is short and stout, white, later grey-brown, full and very hard. Flesh is hard, white; when bruised it turns pink to red at first, later gradually becomes black; solution $FeSO_4$ colours it pink at first, cloudy green later. Taste is mild, smell earthy. Spore powder is white. Spores 7–9 × 6–8 μm, ellipsoid, with very delicate ornamentation. It is profuse in all woods. Edible, not very tasty.

Russula densifolia (Secr.) Gill.   VII–IX

Cap 5–10 cm wide, shallowly convex with involuted margin, flesh rather firm, at first white, later brown to blackish, with smooth, undetachable cuticle. Gills are very dense, whitish, turning red to brown when bruised. Stipe is short and stout, firm, white. Flesh is white, when broken turns red at first, later becomes gradually black. Solution $FeSO_4$ colours it dark green. Spore powder is white. Spores 7–8 μm, somewhat smooth and bare, very finely tuberculate, colourless. It grows in limy soil in coniferous woods. Inedible.

Russulaceae

Black Purple Russula
Russula undulata VELEN.   VIII–X

Syn. *Russula atropurpurea* (KROMBH.) BRITZ. (non *R. atropurpurea* PECK)

Cap 6–12 cm wide, shallowly convex, later broadly concave, often with deeply undulated margin; flesh in firm, cuticle smooth, bare and slightly slimy, detachable to
the middle of the cap; purple lilac or cloudy red to wine red, with pale patches in
the centre, soon pallid to ochre, or sometimes almost black. Gills are pale, later greyish or with rusty patches. Stipe is 4–8 cm long, 1.5–3 cm thick, white, rusty at the
base, turning grey when old. Flesh is white, later greyish, with an acid smell. Spore
powder is white. Spores 8–10 × 7–8 μm, broadly ellipsoid, delicately tuberculate.
It grows under oak and pine trees. Inedible.

Russula olivacea (SCHAEFF.: SECR.) FR.   VII–X

Cap 10–20 cm wide, broadly convex, later with a shallow depression, thick fleshed,
mostly purple to violet with olive green or ochre patches, velvety, margin has wavy
stripes; cuticle is detachable only at the margin. Gills are sparse, thick, deep, yellow,
edges often tinged in red. Stipe is robust, white, usually purple red along one side.
Flesh is white, mild in taste, turns violet red in phenol. Spore powder is yolk yellow. Spores 8–13 × 7–12 μm, broadly ellipsoid, with long spikes, amyloid. It grows
in dry woods along their sunny edges. Edible.

Russula sororia (FR.) ROMELL   VI–IX

Cap 4–8 cm wide, at first semi-globular, later broadly convex, depressed in the centre, margin is smooth to finely grooved, ash grey-brown, almost black in the centre,
cuticle detachable almost to the middle of the cap. Gills are white, later greyish.
Stipe is 4–6 cm long, 1–2.5 cm thick, white, later greyish, with delicate wrinkles,
brittle. Flesh is white, greyish under the skin, very acrid, smelling of old oil. Spore
powder is pale yellowish. Spores 9–11 × 8–9 μm, broadly ellipsoid, with delicate
incomplete network of veins, pale yellowish. It grows most frequently in parks and
along roads, especially under oak trees. Inedible.

Russula amara KUČERA
Syn. *Russula caerulea* (PERS.: FR.) ss. COOKE   VII–X

Cap 5–7 cm wide, shallowly convex, usually with a small wart and often depressed
in the centre, brown violet or lilac, smooth at the margin, cuticle is bare, detachable
only at the margin. Gills are rather dense, white, later light yellowish, fragile. Stipe
is 4–6 cm long, 1–1.5 cm thick, white, finely pruinose, later smooth, bare and
slightly grey. Flesh is white, turning greyish when old. Spore powder is light yellowish. Spores 7–9 × 7–8 μm, broadly ellipsoid to globular, sparsely tuberculate, amyloid. It grows in damp pine woods, also under birch and aspen. Inedible.

Russulaceae

Milk-white Russula
Russula brevipes PECK   VII–IX
Syn. *Russula delica* auct.

Cap 6–15 cm wide, shallowly convex, later expanded, depressed in the centre, deeply involuted margin, with thick and hard flesh, white or whitish, also pale yellowish, with dull, coarsely filamentous and undetachable cuticle. Gills are dense, rather thin, white, sometimes with blue-green reflex. Stipe 2–6 cm long, 1.5–3 cm thick, usually tapering at the base; hard, white with a bluish ring at the top. Smell is slightly spicy and taste mildly sharp. Spore powder is whitish. Spores 8–11 × 6.5–9 μm, broadly ellipsoid, bluntly spiky, with an incomplete network of veins, colourless and amyloid. It grows in all types of woods. There are several closely related species. Edible, though not first-rate.

Russula nauseosa (PERS.: SCHW.) FR.   V–X

Cap 2–6 cm wide, semi-globular, later expanded, slightly depressed in the centre, in various shades of cloudy red, violet and yellow, sometimes also green; cuticle is smooth, bare, sticky when damp, almost entirely detachable. Gills are sparse, pale, later yellowish, very fragile. Stipe 3–5 cm long, 0.5–1 cm thick, very fragile, soon hollow. Flesh is white, has an acid, resinous smell and a mild taste what is sometimes sharp when young. Spore powder is ochre yellow. Spores 8–11 × 7–9 μm, almost globular, sparsely spiky, amyloid. It grows mainly in cool coniferous woods, especially in grassy and mossy places. Edible.

Russula chamaeleotina (FR.) FR.   V–IX

Cap 3–6 cm wide, soon expanded, with a shallow depression in the centre, supple and fragile, vermilion or pink red with orange patches, margin is delicately grooved, cuticle is dull, detachable to the middle of the cap. Hills are deep, brittle, thin, at first pale, later deep orange-yellow. Stipe 3–6 cm long, 1–1.5 cm thick, white, pruinose, soft. Flesh is white, sweet in taste. Spore powder is yolk yellow. Spores 7–9 × 7–8 μm, globularly ellipsoid, coarsely tuberculate, yellow, amyloid. It grows in all types of woods but is less frequent than similar *R. lutea*, which has a pure yellow cap. Edible.

Russula heterophylla (FR.) FR.   VI–IX

Cap 6–12 cm wide, at first semi-globular, later expanded, depressed in the centre, ash grey, greish olive, brown-greenish, yellow-greenish, with pale fleshy patches; cuticle detachable at the margin. Gills are shallow, shortly decurrent, uneven, fragile, pale, then straw yellow, later with rusty patches. Stipe is 3–7 cm long, 1–2.5 cm thick, tapering at the base, hard, smooth, bare, white, turning rusty when old. Flesh is white, tending to turn rusty, mild in taste; it turns immediately orange in the solution of $FeSO_4$. Spore powder is white. Spores 6–7 × 5–6 μm, sub-globose, faintly tuberculate, colourless, amyloid. It grows in deciduous woods. Edible, tasty.

Russulaceae

Russula nitida (PERS.: FR.) FR. ss J. SCHAEF.   VII–IX

Cap 2–6 cm wide, soon flat expanded, with grooves at the margin, red, violet-red or ochre-red, sometimes with brownish or cloudy green patches, or flesh-red, brown-red, rarely bright-red or pink, turning pale, cuticle detachable the halfway across the cap, dull when dry. Gills are yellowish, later rich cream yellow. Stipe 3–7 cm long, 8–10 mm thick, sometimes club-shaped, white, mostly with a violetish-pink to purple tinge, rather shiny, ochre brownish when fading. Flesh is white, very brittle with a slightly fruity or inconspicuous smell and sweet taste. Spore powder is of rich ochre colour. Spores 8–10 × 7–8 (10) μm, almost globular, rather coarse with blunt spikes. It grows under birch in damp grassy places; it prefers acid soils. Edible.

Russula polychroma SING. ex HORA
Syn. *Russula integra* (L.: HOOK.) FR. s. MLZ. et ZV.   VII–IX

Cap 6–12 cm wide, semi-globular, later shallowly convex, broadly depressed in the centre, with tough flesh, copper red-brown, cloudy red or violet, with ochre or brown patches, pallid; cuticle is detachable to the centre of the cap, glabrous, glossy when dry. Gills are white, later pale ochre with reflex on the edges. Stipe is 4–7 cm long, 2–3 cm thick, hard. Flesh is white, inconspicuous in smell, mild in taste. Spore powder is deep ochre. Spores 9–12 × 8–10 μm, almost globular, densely spiky. It grows abundantly in groups in coniferous, particularly spruce woods. Edible.

Russula persicina KROMBH. em. MELZER et ZVÁRA   VII–IX

Cap 3–8 cm wide, shallowly convex, depressed in the centre, flesh is firm, margin smooth, later shortly grooved; it is coloured pink or vivid blood red, pale pink with yellow patches. Cuticle is full, detachable only at the margin. Gills are pale yellowish. Stipe is 3–6 cm long, 1–2 cm thick, white or partly pinkish. Flesh is white, turning yellow with age, smell is acid and resinous. Spore powder is creamy yellow. Spores 7–9 × 6–7 μm, broadly ellipsoid, tuberculate and spiky with an incomplete network of veins, amyloid. It grows in deciduous, especially oak, hornbeam and lime woods. Inedible.

Phallaceae

Phallus impudicus L.: PERS.   VI–IX

Young fruit-body is globular or ovoid, elastic, up to 6 cm wide, white, with a tough, white mycelial cord at the base. When ripe, peridium bursts and release 10–20 cm long and 3–5 cm thick, hollow and porous stipe carrying thimble-shaped or bell-shaped cap. The surface of the cap is hirsute and ribbed, covered with dark green, unpleasantly smelling slime; when it dries out, it smells of honey. Spores 3.5–5 × 1.5–2 μm, longish ellipsoid, yellowish. It grows profusely in humus in deciduous woods. *P. ravenelii* is more common in North America. Edible when young.

Melanogastraceae

Melanogaster variegatus (VITT.) TUL.   VI–X

Fruit-body 1.5–4 cm wide, tuber-like, with uneven surface, at first yellow, rusty ochre, brownish when bruised, later dark brown to blackish, with sparse, dark mycelial cords at the base; toughly gelatinous, gleba in cross-section is yellowish brown, black when mature, glossy, juicy, filled with numerous chambers which are bordered in yellow and white. Ripe fruit-bodies smell of fermenting fruit. Spores 6–8 × 3.5–5.5 μm, ellipsoid, blunt at the base, with remnants of sterigmata, brown. It grows in humus of deciduous or mixed woods.

Sclerodermataceae

Scleroderma citrinum PERS.   VI–X

Fruit-body 3–10 cm in diameter, longish globular or tuber-like, sessile and tough, straw yellow or pale ochre, tuberculate and cracked. Gleba is white and firm at first, cross-section shows minute, rounded chambers; later it is pinkish, bluish and finally black and disintegrating into green spore powder. It has a strong, aromatic smell. Spores 7–15 μm wide, globular, with net-like ornamentations and cospicuous spines, black-brown. It grows in all types of woods, most abundant in sandy pine woods on bare ground and along forest tracks. There are several similar specis common in Europe. Poisonous. (In small amount used as herbs.)

Pisolithus arrhizus (PERS.) RAUSCHERT   VI–IX

Fruit-body 3–11 cm wide, clavate to club-shaped, at the base tapering into a divided, deeply rooting part up to 30 cm long. Peridium is smooth, ochre yellowish, later dark brown, fragile. Gleba is tough when young, juicy, composed of minute, white to yellow peridioles. It ripens from the top and transforms into chocolate brown spore powder. Spores 9–12 μm in diameter, globular, spiky, brown. It grows in sandy soil at light places, e.g. along tracks or in pine forests. *P. tinctorius* is a rare species in Britain and North America. Edible when young.

Lycoperdaceae

Common Puff-ball
Lycoperdon perlatum PERS.   VI–X

Fruit-body 1.5–8 cm tall, 2–5 cm wide, most frequently pear-shaped or pestle-like; it is white when young, densely covered with spines or loose, cone-shaped warts, which leave angular areoles on the surface of the peridium. Gleba of young fruit-bodies is white, porose, turning grey, grey-green to brown when mature and changing into brown spore powder. Ripe fruit-bodies are brown and open through a small apical pore. Spores 3.5–4.5 μm in diameter, globular, yellowish. It grows very fusely in all types of woods. Edible and tasty when young.

Lycoperdaceae

🍴 *Lycoperdon umbrinum* PERS.   VII–IX   ■□
                                                                                □□

Fruit-body 1.5–3.5 cm wide, 2–5 cm tall, shortly pear-shaped, pestle-like, globular, shortly drawn base with a shallow, blunt boss at the top. The outer peridium
consists of tomentose spines up to 1 mm long, which are usually clustered together,
brown or black-brown; the inner peridium is smooth, glossy, brass yellow, without
markings left by spines. Gleba is amber brown, sterile base is coarsely porous in the
cross-section, grey-olive or olive brown. Spore powder is amber brown. Spores 4–4.5
μm wide, globular, finely spiny, light brown. It grows most frequently in spruce
woods. Also known as *L. molle.* Edible when young.

🍴 *Calvatia excipuliformis* (SCOP.: PERS.) PERD.   VII–IX   □■
                                                                                ■□

Fruit-body 5–15 cm tall, 3–8 cm wide, pestle-like or clavate, tapering downwards
into sterile cylindrical stem, entirely white when young covered with minute granules and spines, turning smooth, bare and brown when ripe. Fertile upper part of
the fruit-body is not separated from the remaining infertile section by a membrane
(diaphragm). Gleba is white at first, later dark brown. Spore 5–6 μm, globular, spiky,
with sterigmata up to 16 mm long, brownish. It is fairly abundant in woodland
meadows and in woods. Edible when young.

🍴 *Geastrum sessile* (SOW.) POUZ.   IX–X   □□
                                                                                □■

Fruit-body 1.5–3 cm tall, 2–7 cm wide, ochre or ochre-brown, internal peridium
which encloses the gleba is sessile, paper-thin, with tomentose pore without a ring;
external peridium bursts into 5, 10, but most frequently 8 pointed sections which
curl downwards. Spores 3–4 μm in diameter, globular, almost smooth, light brown.
It grows profusely and often gregariously on the ground in coniferous, particularly
spruce woods. Dry fruit-bodies remain in their places several years. Inedible.

Lycoperdaceae

Gaestrum rufescens PERS. IX–XI

Fruit-body 2.5–5 cm wide, globular, at first hidden in soil, whitish, later reddish; when ripe, outer peridium bursts into 5–8 thick, tough and fleshy, pale pink pointed sections, which when expanded are 10 cm wide, later brown-red and transversely cracked. Gleba is flat and globular, sessile, with a tomentose pore without a sharply-defined target. Spores 4–5 μm in diameter, globular, brownish, with fine spines. It grows in small numbers in coniferous and less frequently in deciduous woods. Inedible.

Geastrum quadrifidum PERS. VIII–X

Fruit-body 2–5 cm tall, 1.5–3 cm wide, inner peridium is globular or elongated, grey-blue, whitish pruinose with a pointed pore in the centre of the circular disc; outer peridium bursts usually into 4 yellowish or yellow-brown pointed sections joined together at the base into membranous saucer which is set deeply into the ground and later disappears. Spores 4–6 μm in diameter, globular, tuberculate and brown. It often grows in large groups in coniferous, mainly spruce forests. Together with *G. sessile* it is the most frequent representative of the genus *Geastrum* in European forests. Inedible.

Geastrum pectinatum PERS. VIII–XI

Fruit-body 2–5 cm tall, 3–9 cm wide, with the external peridium bursting into 5–8 grey-brown, pointed sections; it has no membranous saucer at the base. Gleba is on a long stem, black-brown, pruinose, with a beak-like, longitudinally deeply grooved or frilled pore, without circular disc. Spores 6–7.5 μm in diameter, globular, tuberculate, brown. It grows abundantly on the ground in coniferous, mainly spruce, woods. Dry fruit-bodies remain in their place for several years. Inedible.

Clathraceae

Anthurus archeri (BERK.) E. FISCHER VII–IX

Fruit-body is ovoid when young, up to 4 cm tall, whitish; it bursts into a white stipe up to 5 cm long, and 5–8 simple arms, which are at first joined together at the top, later arched back to form a star, 3–7 cm long, fragile, orange-red and transversely wrinkled on the inner surface. Gleba is slimy on the inner surface of its arms, olive green, smelling of carrion. Spores 6–7.5 × 2–2.5 μm, ellipsoid, smooth and colourless. It grows in humus, rotting wood, in and outside forests. Originally a tropical and subtropical mushroom, probably introduced to Europe from Australia. A few recorded in Great Britain. Inedible.

BIBLIOGRAPHY

AINSWORTH, G. C. and BISBY, G. R., *Dictionary of the Fungi,* 8th edition, London 1995

BRIGHTMAN, F. H., *The Oxford Book of Flowerless Plants,* Oxford University Press, 1966

FINDLAY, W. P. K., *Wayside and Woodland Fungi,* Warne, 1967

GREGORY, O., *Mushrooms and Toadstools,* Muller, 1972

HVASS, E. and H., *Mushrooms and Toadstools,* Blandford, 1961

LANGE, M. and HORA, F. H., *Collins Guide to Mushrooms and Toadstools,* Collins, 1967

MAJOR, A., *Collecting and Studying Mushrooms, Toadstools and Fungi,* Bartholomew, 1975

NEUNER, A., *British and European Mushrooms and Fungi,* Chatto and Windus, 1978

NILSSON, S. and PERSSON, O., *Fungi of Northern Europe* (2 vols), Penguin, 1978

Observer's Book of Fungi, Warne, 1977

RAMSBOTTOM, J., *Mushrooms and Toadstools,* Collins, 1970

RINALDI, A. and TYNDALE, V., *Mushrooms and Other Fungi,* Hamlyn, 1974

SAVONIUS, M., *Colour Guide to Familiar Mushrooms,* Octopus, 1974

SOOTHILL, F. E. and FAIRHURST, A., *New Field Guide to Fungi,* Michael Joseph, 1978

TRIBE, I. (ed.), *World of Mushrooms,* Orbis, 1974

INDEX